EX LIBRIS

VINTAGE **CLASSICS**

PATRICIA HIGHSMITH

Patricia Highsmith was born in Fort Worth, Texas in 1921 but moved to New York when she was six. In her senior year she edited the college magazine, having decided to become a writer at the age of sixteen. Her first novel, *Strangers on a Train*, was made into a famous film by Alfred Hitchcock in 1951. Patricia Highsmith died in Locarno, Switzerland in 1995. Her last novel, *Small g: a Summer Idyll*, was published posthumously just over a month later.

PATRICIA HIGHSMITH

Strangers on a Train

WITH AN INTRODUCTION BY
Paula Hawkins

VINTAGE

1 3 5 7 9 10 8 6 4 2

Vintage Classics is part of the Penguin Random House
group of companies whose addresses can be found at
global.penguinrandomhouse.com

Penguin
Random House
UK

Copyright © Patricia Highsmith 1950

Patricia Highsmith has asserted her right to be identified as
the author of this Work in accordance with the Copyright,
Designs and Patents Act 1988

Introduction copyright © Paula Hawkins 2021

'Leaden-Eyed' from *The Congo and Other Poems* by Vachel Lindsay,
copyright 1914, 1942, by The Macmillan Company and used with
their permission

First published in Great Britain in 1950 by The Cresset Press
Copyright © 1993 by Diogenes Verlag AG, Zurich
This edition first published in Great Britain by
William Heinemann in 1966
First published by Vintage in 1999
This edition published in Vintage Classics in 2021

penguin.co.uk/vintage-classics

A CIP catalogue record for this book is available from the
British Library

ISBN 9781784876777

Printed and bound in Great Britain by Clays Ltd, Elcograf S.p.A.

The authorised representative in the EEA is Penguin Random House
Ireland, Morrison Chambers, 32 Nassau Street, Dublin DO2 YH68.

Penguin Random House is committed to a sustainable future for our
business, our readers and our planet. This book is made from Forest
Stewardship Council® certified paper.

INTRODUCTION

Paula Hawkins

What is it about trains? What is it about them that fires the imagination, that suggests to those of a certain disposition the possibility of danger lurking behind every seat and in every carriage? There
is something in the collective experience of a journey that lends
itself to storytelling, and then of course the tantalising proximity
to strangers of every stripe. The chance meeting, whether fleeting
or prolonged, the accidental brush of hands as the train hurtles
around a sharp bend, a casual conversation in the dining car taking an unexpected turn.

In a letter she wrote to her friend Marc Brandel in 1985, Patricia
Highsmith confessed to thrilling to the idea that anyone – the most
ordinary neighbour, the dullest of co-workers, that unexceptional
girl you see every day on the train – might be hiding a terrible secret or harbouring some sordid proclivity: 'I can't think of anything
more apt to set the imagination stirring, drifting, creating, than the
idea – the fact – that anyone you walk past on the pavement anywhere might be a sadist, a compulsive thief, or even a murderer.'

In *Strangers on a Train*, Highsmith's exceptionally accomplished debut published when the writer was just twenty-nine
years old, she explored this very idea. The novel begins with a
chance meeting between two young men, and this fleeting encounter sets in motion a terrible chain of events: their drunken
conversation leads to a macabre *folie à deux*, a good man turned
murderous, utterly corrupted by guilt.

The fact that, more than seventy years after its publication,
Strangers on a Train has lost none of its power to disturb is evidence of Highsmith's extraordinary talent. Her novels, of which
she wrote twenty-two over the course of her career, feel disarming-
ly fresh and modern, from their high concepts and economic style
to her groundbreaking and frequently shocking device of allowing

the reader to occupy the mind of a killer. Decades before we rooted for Villanelle and Amy Dunne, Tony Soprano and Walter White, we were rooting for Highsmith's Guy Haines.

Highsmith wrote a draft of *Strangers on a Train* in 1948, during an apparently frenzied two-month period of creativity while she was staying at Yaddo, the artist's retreat in upstate New York. It is a sign of how important this period was to her that on her death, she left her entire $3 million estate to Yaddo; however, the idea for the book had been percolating for many years. Indeed, she had met her villain – the inspiration for the despicable Charles Bruno – more than a decade earlier, when on a trip back to her hometown of Fort Worth. 'When I was seventeen, in Texas,' Highsmith told a BBC interviewer, 'I met briefly a very spoiled boy who was very much like Bruno, completely dissolute . . . completely worthless, and he was sort of the genesis of Bruno.'

Highsmith – who had an unhappy childhood, who suffered, as an adult, from depression, anorexia and alcoholism, who was deeply misanthropic – was not as a writer particularly interested in happiness. Contentment, she suspected, was often a sign of stupidity; well-balanced people must be, at best, mediocre. Nor was she interested in the simplicity of popular morality, but she was fascinated by the idea that all of us carried within the capacity for good and ill, that identity was not fixed but shifting, that a sort of dualism existed in all of us. 'There are always two,' she wrote in her notebook in 1947. 'One can love two people, the sexes are within all of us, emotions directly contrary do exist side by side.'

This idea, frequently expressed by the author, is a central theme of *Strangers on a Train*. A good man – kind, responsible, loving, conscientious Guy Haines – corrupted by fear and guilt, suffers a split in his personality; over the course of the novel he becomes someone he barely recognises, someone he refers to in the third person, as though he were talking about a stranger. 'What was he doing here at 1.15 in the afternoon,' Guy asks himself, 'growing swimmy on this third martini, making himself incapable of work, assuming he had any? Guy Haines who loved Anne, who had built the Palmyra?'

As Highsmith ratchets up the tension, as Guy's fear and guilt bloom, so too does his conviction that he is 'two people, one of whom could create and feel in harmony with God . . . and the other who could murder'. He sees this other self as 'a secret brother', a discrete part of his identity which he longs to crush.

Ultimately, however, Guy comes to express the view that Highsmith held, that the murdering part of himself is not something externally produced but something that was always inside him. In the end he believes that he had committed a terrible crime 'because there had been that measure of perversity within him sufficient to do it, that he had done it because of the worm in the wood'.

This dualism, this push and pull between essential goodness and darker impulses, is mirrored in another of Highsmith's favourite themes, the relationship of love to hate, the proximity that loathing has to desire. In one of her notebooks, writing about a woman she has met and 'almost' fallen in love with, she confesses to murderous feelings about her, fantasises about putting her hands around the throat she longs to kiss, writing that 'murder is a kind of making love, a way of possessing'.

In *Strangers on a Train*, we see Guy's feelings for Bruno veer wildly from virulent dislike to affection and even identification with him. At the opening of the book, Guy finds Bruno brash and physically repulsive, and he immediately suspects this man is dangerous: 'Bruno could be violent,' he thinks during their first meeting, no ordinary stranger on a train but someone 'cruel and corrupt'. And yet during the encounter he describes a 'rush of affection for Bruno', he feels 'a burst of companionship'. Later, although he is sick of Bruno, positively loathes Bruno, he suspects that 'Bruno had always been able to read him', and later still Guy muses: 'And Bruno, he and Bruno. Each was what the other had not chosen to be, the cast-off self, what he thought he hated but perhaps in reality loved.'

A large part of Highsmith's talent for getting under the reader's skin comes from her creation of psychologically believable – if frequently monstrous – characters, whom she then entices us to embrace. However, she has many other tricks up her sleeve, not least the way in which she tells her stories, her pared-back, laconic style, the deceptive one-note pitch at which she recounts the horrifying and the banal alike.

It is uniquely disturbing, as evidenced by one of the book's most memorable scenes, in which Bruno stalks Guy's wife, poor ill-fated Miriam, through a carnival. As we follow the hunt, it is through the cat's eyes that we see the mouse, and we are party to all Bruno's observations: 'The roller coaster made a *tat-tat-tat-tat-tat* like a machine-gun over their heads. There was a clang and a roar as someone sent the red arrow all the way to the top with a sledge hammer. He wouldn't mind killing Miriam with a sledge hammer.'

In one breath Bruno observes Miriam looking ugly and stupid with her mouth open, 'as if she were being strangled', while in the next he is musing that 'the prospect of a cool row was delightful'.

When it is Guy's turn to take up the mantle of murderer, there is a similar effect given by his prevaricating over which gun to take with him to do the killing: 'The gloves were purple and the flannel bag of his revolver was lavender. Suddenly it seemed fitting he should take the smaller revolver, because of the similar colours.' Such odd and inappropriate thoughts give the killings a sort of dreamlike irrationality, nightmarish and unsettling, the images staying in the mind long after the reader has closed the book.

This propensity to affect and disturb was noted by critics as unusual in a lowly crime writer: the critic Terrence Rafferty, writing in the *New Yorker*, observed that 'popular fiction isn't supposed to work on us this way'. Rafferty's comment is rather typical of the reception meted out to Highsmith by literary critics and novelists alike, those eager to stress that she cannot be a crime writer – she's too good for that. And while it is true that Highsmith herself disdained the traditional whodunnit ('puzzles do not interest me,' she said), she did place her writing within the scope of popular fiction, stressing that she was 'an entertainer' who liked 'to tell a fascinating story'.

From a crime writer's perspective, all talk of Highsmith's work being 'relegated' to the classifications of crime and suspense is irritating in the extreme. The notion that her books do not belong on those shelves, because of the complexity of their characters or the acuity with which they interrogate social mores, is laughable – for this is exactly what the very best crime novels do.

It is why they endure. It is why we find them irresistible.

And it is why we will likely be reading Patricia Highsmith for the next one hundred years, too.

To all the Virginias

1

The train tore along with an angry, irregular rhythm. It was having to stop at smaller and more frequent stations, where it would wait impatiently for a moment, then attack the prairie again. But progress was imperceptible. The prairie only undulated, like a vast, pink-tan blanket being casually shaken. The faster the train went, the more buoyant and taunting the undulations.

Guy took his eyes from the window and hitched himself back against the seat.

Miriam would delay the divorce at best, he thought. She might not even want a divorce, only money. Would there really ever be a divorce from her?

Hate had begun to paralyse his thinking, he realized, to make little blind alleys of the roads that logic had pointed out to him in New York. He could sense Miriam ahead of him, not much farther now, pink and tan-freckled, and radiating a kind of unhealthful heat, like the prairie out the window. Sullen and cruel.

Automatically, he reached for a cigarette, remembered for the tenth time that he couldn't smoke in the Pullman car, then took one anyway. He tapped it twice on the face of his wristwatch, read the time, 5.12, as if it meant anything today, and fitted the cigarette into the corner of his mouth before he brought the cupped match up. The cigarette replaced the match inside his hand, and he smoked in slow, steady pulls. Again and again his brown eyes dropped to the stubborn, fascinating ground out the window. A tab of his soft shirt collar began to ride up. In the reflection the dusk had started to create in the window's glass, the peak of white collar along his jaw suggested a style of the last century, like his black hair that grew high and loose on top and lay close in back. The rise of hair and the slope of his long nose gave him a look of intense purpose and somehow of forward motion, though from the front, his heavy, horizontal brows and mouth imposed a stillness and reserve. He wore flannel trousers that needed pressing, a dark jacket that slacked over his slight body and showed faintly purple where the light struck it, and a tomato-coloured woollen tie, carelessly knotted.

He did not think Miriam would be having a child unless she wanted it. Which should mean the lover intended to marry her. But why had she sent for him? She didn't need him to get a divorce. And why did he go over the same dull ground he had four days ago when he had got her letter? The five or six lines in Miriam's round handwriting had said only that she was going to have a child and wanted to see him. That she was pregnant guaranteed the divorce, he reasoned, so why was he nervous? A suspicion that he might, in some unreachable depth of himself, be jealous because she was going to bear another man's child and had once aborted his own tormented him above all. No, it was nothing but shame that nettled him, he told himself, shame that he had once loved such a person as Miriam. He mashed his cigarette on the heater's grilled cover. The stub rolled out at his feet, and he kicked it back under the heater.

There was so much to look forward to now. His divorce, the work in Florida – it was practically certain the board would pass on his drawings, and he would learn this week – and Anne. He and Anne could begin to plan now. For over a year he had been waiting, fretting, for something – *this* – to happen so he would be free. He felt a pleasant explosion of happiness inside him, and relaxed in the corner of the plush seat. For the last three years, really, he had been waiting for this to happen. He could have bought a divorce, of course, but he hadn't ever amassed that much spare money. Starting a career as an architect, without benefit of a job with a firm, had not been easy and still wasn't. Miriam had never asked for an income, but she plagued him in other ways, by talking of him in Metcalf as if they were still on the best of terms, as if he were up in New York only to establish himself and eventually send for her. Occasionally she wrote him for money, small but irritating amounts which he let her have because it would be so easy for her, so natural to her, to start a campaign in Metcalf against him, and his mother was in Metcalf.

A tall blond young man in a rust-brown suit dropped into the empty seat opposite Guy and, smiling with a vague friendliness, slid over into the corner. Guy glanced at his pallid, undersized face. There was a huge pimple in the exact centre of his forehead. Guy looked out the window again.

The young man opposite him seemed to debate whether to start a conversation or take a nap. His elbow kept sliding along the window-sill, and whenever the stubby lashes came open, the grey bloodshot eyes were looking at him and the soft smile came back. He might have been slightly drunk.

Guy opened his book, but his mind wandered after half a page. He looked up as the row of white fluorescent lights flickered on down the ceiling of the car, let his eyes wander to the unlighted cigar that still gyrated conversationally in a bony hand behind one of the seat backs, and to the monogram that trembled on a thin gold chain across the tie of the young man opposite him. The monogram was CAB, and the tie was of green silk, hand-painted with offensively orange-coloured palm trees. The long rust-brown body was sprawled vulnerably now, the head thrown back so that the big pimple or boil on the forehead might have been a topmost point that had erupted. It was an interesting face, though Guy did not know why. It looked neither young nor old, neither intelligent nor entirely stupid. Between the narrow bulging forehead and the lantern jaw, it scooped degenerately, deep where the mouth lay in a fine line, deepest in the blue hollows that held the small scallops of the lids. The skin was smooth as a girl's, even waxenly clear, as if all its impurities had been drained to feed the pimple's outburst.

For a few moments, Guy read again. The words made sense to him and began to lift his anxiety. But what good will Plato do you with Miriam, an inner voice asked him. It had asked him that in New York, but he had brought the book anyway, an old text from a high-school philosophy course, an indulgence to compensate him, perhaps, for having to make the trip to Miriam.

He looked out the window and, seeing his own image, straightened his curling collar. Anne was always doing that for him. Suddenly he felt helpless without her. He shifted his position, accidentally touched the outstretched foot of the young man asleep, and watched fascinatedly as the lashes twitched and came open. The bloodshot eyes might have been focused on him all the while through the lids.

'Sorry,' Guy murmured.

' 'S all right,' the other said. He sat up and shook his head sharply. 'Where are we?'

'Getting into Texas.'

The blond young man brought a gold flask from his inside pocket, opened it, and extended it amiably.

'No, thanks,' Guy said. The woman across the aisle, Guy noticed, who had not looked up from her knitting since St Louis, glanced over just as the flask upended with a metallic splash.

'Where you bound?' The smile was a thin wet crescent now.

'Metcalf,' Guy said.

'Oh, Nice town, Metcalf. Down on business?' He blinked his sore-looking eyes politely.

'Yes.'

'What business?'

Guy looked up reluctantly from his book. 'Architect.'

'Oh,' with wistful interest. 'Build houses and things?'

'Yes.'

'I don't think I've introduced myself.' He half stood up. 'Bruno. Charles Anthony Bruno.'

Guy shook his hand briefly. 'Guy Haines.'

'Glad to meet you. You live in New York?' The hoarse baritone voice sounded false, as if he were talking to wake himself up.

'Yes.'

'I live in Long Island. Going to Santa Fe for a little vacation. Ever been to Santa Fe?'

Guy shook his head.

'Great town to relax in.' He smiled, showing poor teeth. 'Mostly Indian architecture there, I guess.'

A conductor stopped in the aisle, thumbing through tickets. 'That your seat?' he asked Bruno.

Bruno leaned possessively into his corner. 'Drawing-room next car.'

'Number Three?'

'I guess. Yeah.'

The conductor went on.

'Those guys!' Bruno murmured. He leaned forward and gazed out the window amusedly.

Guy went back to his book, but the other's obtrusive boredom, a feeling he was about to say something in another instant, kept him from concentrating. Guy contemplated going to the diner, but for some reason sat on. The train was slowing again. When Bruno looked as if he were going to speak, Guy got up, retreated into the next car, and leapt the steps to the crunchy ground before the train had quite stopped.

The more organic air, weighted with nightfall, struck him like a smothering pillow. There was a smell of dusty, sun-warm gravel, of oil and hot metal. He was hungry and lingered near the diner, pacing in slow strides with his hands in his pockets, breathing the air deeply, though he disliked it. A constellation of red and green and white lights hummed southward in the sky. Yesterday, Anne might have come this route, he thought, on her way to Mexico. He might have been with her. She had wanted him to come with her as far as Metcalf. He might have asked her to stay over a day and meet his mother, if it had not been for Miriam. Or even regardless of Miriam, if he had been another sort of person, if he could be simply unconcerned. He had told Anne about Miriam, about almost all of it, but he could not bear the thought of their meeting. He had wanted to travel alone on the train in order to think. And what had he thought so far? What good had thinking or logic ever been where Miriam was concerned?

The conductor's voice shouted a warning, but Guy paced till the last moment, then swung himself aboard the car behind the diner.

The waiter had just taken his order when the blond young man appeared in the doorway of the car, swaying, looking a little truculent with a short cigarette in his mouth. Guy had put him quite out of mind and now his tall rust-brown figure was like a vaguely unpleasant memory. Guy saw him smile as he sighted him.

'Thought you might have missed the train,' Bruno said cheerfully, pulling out a chair.

'If you don't mind, Mr Bruno, I'd like privacy for a while. I have some things to think over.'

Bruno stabbed out the cigarette that was burning his fingers and looked at him blankly. He was drunker than before. His face seemed smeared and fuzzy at the edges. 'We could have privacy in my place. We could have dinner there. How about it?'

'Thanks, I'd rather stay here.'

'Oh, but I insist. Waiter!' Bruno clapped his hands. 'Would you have this gentleman's order sent to Drawing-Room Three and bring me a steak medium rare with French fries and apple pie? And two Scotch and sodas fast as you can, huh?' He looked at Guy and smiled, the soft wistful smile. 'Okay?'

Guy debated, then got up and came with him. What did it matter after all? And wasn't he utterly sick of himself?

There was no need of the Scotches except to provide glasses and ice. The four yellow-labelled bottles of Scotch lined up on an alligator suitcase were the one neat unit of the little room. Suitcases and wardrobe trunks blocked passage everywhere except for a small labyrinthine area in the centre of the floor, and on top of them were strewn sports clothes and equipment, tennis rackets, a bag of golf clubs, a couple of cameras, a wicker basket of fruit and wine bedded in fuchsia paper. A splay of current magazines, comic books and novels covered the seat by the window. There was also a box of candy with a red ribbon across the lid.

'Looks kind of athletic, I guess,' Bruno said, suddenly apologetic.

'It's fine.' Guy smiled slowly. The room amused him and gave him a welcome sense of seclusion. With the smile his dark brows relaxed, transforming his whole expression. His eyes looked outward now. He stepped lithely in the alleys between suitcases, examining things like a curious cat.

'Brand-new. Never felt a ball,' Bruno informed him, holding out a tennis racket for him to feel. 'My mother makes me take all this stuff, hoping it'll keep me out of bars. Good to hock if I run out, anyway. I like to drink when I travel. It enhances things, don't you think?' The highballs arrived, and Bruno strengthened them from one of his bottles. 'Sit down. Take off your coat.'

But neither of them sat down or removed his coat. There was an awkward several minutes when they had nothing to say to each other. Guy took a swallow of the highball that seemed to be all Scotch, and looked down at the littered floor. Bruno had odd feet, Guy noticed, or maybe it was the shoes. Small, light tan shoes with a long plain toecap shaped like Bruno's lantern chin. Somehow old-fashioned-looking feet. And Bruno was not so slender as he had thought. His long legs were heavy and his body rounded.

'I hope you weren't annoyed,' Bruno said cautiously, 'when I came in the diner.'

'Oh, no.'

'I felt lonely. You know.'

Guy said something about its being lonely travelling in a drawing-room alone, then nearly tripped on something: the strap of a Rolleiflex camera. There was a new white scratch deep down the side of its leather case. He was conscious of Bruno's shy stare. He was going to be bored, of course. Why had he come? A pang of conscience made him want to return to the diner. Then the waiter arrived with a pewter-covered tray, and snapped up a table. The smell of charcoal-broiled meat cheered him. Bruno insisted so desperately on paying the check that Guy gave it up. Bruno had a big mushroom-covered steak. Guy had hamburger.

'What're you building in Metcalf?'

'Nothing,' Guy said. 'My mother lives there.'

'Oh,' Bruno said interestedly. 'Visiting her? Is that where you're from?'

'Yes. Born there.'

'You don't look much like a Texan.' Bruno shot ketchup all over his steak and French fries, then delicately picked up the parsley and held it poised. 'How long since you been home?'

'About two years.'

'Your father there, too?'

'My father's dead.'

'Oh. Get along with your mother okay?'

Guy said he did. The taste of Scotch, though Guy didn't much care for it, was pleasant because it reminded him of Anne. She drank Scotch, when she drank. It was like her, golden, full of light, made with careful art. 'Where do you live in Long Island?'

'Great Neck.'

Anne lived much farther out on Long Island.

'In a house I call the Doghouse,' Bruno went on. 'There's dogwood all around it and everybody in it's in some kind of doghouse, down to the chauffeur.' He laughed suddenly with real pleasure, and bent again over his food.

Looking at him now, Guy saw only the top of his narrow thin-haired head and the protruding pimple. He had not been conscious of the pimple since he had seen him asleep, but now that he noticed it again, it seemed a monstrous, shocking thing and he saw it alone. 'Why?' Guy asked.

'Account of my father. Bastard. I get on okay with my mother, too. My mother's coming out to Santa Fe in a couple days.'

'That's nice.'

'It is,' Bruno said as if contradicting him. 'We have a lot of fun together – sitting around, playing golf. We even go to parties together.' He laughed, half ashamed, half proud, and suddenly uncertain and young. 'You think that's funny?'

'No,' said Guy.

'I just wish I had my own dough. See, my income was supposed to start this year, only my father won't let me have it. He's deflecting it into his own exchequer. You might not think so, but I haven't got any more money now than I had when I was in school with

8

everything paid for. I have to ask for a hundred dollars now and then from my mother.' He smiled, pluckily.

'I wish you had let me pay the check.'

'A-aw, now!' Bruno protested. 'I just mean it's a hell of a thing, isn't it, when your own father robs you. It isn't even his money, it's my mother's family's money.' He waited for Guy to comment.

'Hasn't your mother any say about it?'

'My father got his name put on it when I was a kid!' Bruno shouted hoarsely.

'Oh.' Guy wondered how many people Bruno had met, bought dinners for, and told the same story about his father. 'Why did he do that?'

Bruno brought his hands up in a hopeless shrug, then hid them fast in his pockets. 'I said he was a bastard, didn't I? He robs everyone he can. Now he says he won't give it to me because I won't work, but that's a lie. He thinks my mother and I have too good a time as it is. He's always scheming up ways to cut in.'

Guy could see him and his mother, a youngish Long Island society woman who used too much mascara and occasionally, like her son, enjoyed tough company. 'Where'd you go to college?'

'Harvard. Busted out sophomore year. Drinking and gambling.' He shrugged with a writhing movement of his narrow shoulders. 'Not like you, huh? Okay, I'm a bum, so what?' He poured more Scotch for both of them.

'Who said you were?'

'My father says so. He should've had a nice quiet son like you, then everybody would've been happy.'

'What makes you think I'm nice and quiet?'

'I mean you're serious and you choose a profession. Like architecture. Me, I don't feel like working. I don't have to work, see? I'm not a writer or a painter or a musician. Is there any reason a person should work if they don't have to? I'll get my ulcers the easy way. My father has ulcers. Hah! He still has hopes I'll enter his hardware business. I tell him his business, all business, is legalized throat-cutting, like marriage is legalized fornication. Am I right?'

Guy looked at him wryly and sprinkled salt on the French fried potato on his fork. He was eating slowly, enjoying his meal, even vaguely enjoying Bruno, as he might have enjoyed an entertainment on a distant stage. Actually, he was thinking of Anne. Sometimes the faint continuous dream he had of her seemed more real than the outside world that penetrated only in sharp fragments, occasional images, like the scratch on the Rolleiflex case, the long cigarette Bruno had plunged into his pat of butter, the shattered glass of the photograph of the father Bruno had thrown out in the hall in the story he was telling now. It had just occurred to Guy he might have time to see Anne in Mexico, between seeing Miriam and going to Florida. If he got through with Miriam quickly, he could fly to Mexico and fly to Palm Beach. It hadn't occurred to him before because he couldn't afford it. But if the Palm Beach contract came through, he could.

'Can you imagine anything more insulting? Locking the garage where my own car is?' Bruno's voice had cracked and was stuck at a shrieking pitch.

'Why?' Guy asked.

'Just because he knew I needed it bad that night! My friends picked me up finally, so what does he get out of it?'

Guy didn't know what to say. 'He keeps the keys?'

'He took *my keys*! Took them out of my room! That's why he was scared of me. He left the house that night, he was so scared.' Bruno was turned in his chair, breathing hard, chewing a fingernail. Some wisps of hair, darkened brown with sweat, bobbed like antennae over his forehead. 'My mother wasn't home, or it never could have happened, of course.'

'Of course,' Guy echoed involuntarily. Their whole conversation had been leading to this story, he supposed, that he had heard only half of. Back of the bloodshot eyes that had opened on him in the Pullman car, back of the wistful smile, another story of hatred and injustice. 'So you threw his picture out in the hall?' Guy asked meaninglessly.

'I threw it out of my mother's room,' Bruno said, emphasizing the last three words. 'My father put it in my mother's room. She doesn't like the Captain any better than I do. The Captain! – *I* don't call him anything, brother!'

'But what's he got against you?'

'Against me and my mother, too! He's different from us or any other *human*! He doesn't like anybody. He doesn't like anything but money. He cut enough throats to make a lot of money, that's all. Sure he's smart! Okay! But his conscience is sure eating him now! That's why he wants me to go into his business, so I'll cut throats and feel as lousy as he does!' Bruno's stiff hand closed, then his mouth, then his eyes.

Guy thought he was about to cry, when the puffy lids lifted and the smile staggered back.

'Boring, huh? I was just explaining why I left town so soon, ahead of my mother. You don't know what a cheerful guy I am really! Honest!'

'Can't you leave home if you want to?'

Bruno didn't seem to understand his question at first, then he answered calmly, 'Sure, only I like to be with my mother.'

And his mother stayed because of the money, Guy supposed. 'Cigarette?'

Bruno took one, smiling. 'You know, the night he left the house was the first time in maybe ten years he'd gone out. I wonder where the hell he even went. I was sore enough that night to kill him and he knew it. Ever feel like murdering somebody?'

'No.'

'I do. I'm sure sometimes I could kill my father.' He looked down at his plate with a bemused smile. 'You know what my father does for a hobby? Guess.'

Guy didn't want to guess. He felt suddenly bored and wanted to be alone.

'He collects cookie cutters!' Bruno exploded with a snickering laugh. 'Cookie cutters, honest! He's got all kinds – Pennsylvania

Dutch, Bavarian, English, French, a lot of Hungarian, all around the room. Animal-cracker cookie cutters framed over his desk – you know, the things kids eat in boxes? He wrote the president of the company and they sent him a whole set. The machine age!' Bruno laughed and ducked his head.

Guy stared at him. Bruno himself was funnier than what he said. 'Does he ever use them?'

'Huh?'

'Does he ever make cookies?'

Bruno whooped. With a wriggle, he removed his jacket and flung it at a suitcase. For a moment he seemed too excited to say anything, then remarked with sudden quiet, 'My mother's always telling him to go back to his cookie cutters.' A film of sweat covered his smooth face like thin oil. He thrust his smile solicitously half across the table. 'Enjoy your dinner?'

'Very much,' Guy said heartily.

'Ever hear of the Bruno Transforming Company of Long Island? Makes AC-DC gadgets?'

'I don't think so.'

'Well, why should you? Makes plenty of dough though. You interested in making money?'

'Not awfully.'

'Mind if I ask how old you are?'

'Twenty-nine.'

'Yeah? I would've said older. How old you think I look?'

Guy studied him politely. 'Maybe twenty-four or five,' he answered, intending to flatter him, for he looked younger.

'Yeah, I am. Twenty-five. You mean I do look twenty-five with this – this *thing* right in the centre of my head?' Bruno caught his underlip between his teeth. A glint of wariness came in his eyes, and suddenly he cupped his hand over his forehead in intense and bitter shame. He sprang up and went to the mirror. 'I meant to put something over it.'

Guy said something reassuring, but Bruno kept looking at himself this way and that in the mirror, in an agony of self-torture. 'It *couldn't* be a pimple,' he said nasally. 'It's a boil. It's everything I *hate* boiling up in me. It's a plague of Job!'

'Oh, now!' Guy laughed.

'It started coming Monday night after that fight. It's getting worse. I bet it leaves a scar.'

'No, it won't.'

'Yes, it will. A fine thing to get to Santa Fe with!' He was sitting in his chair now with his fists clenched and one heavy leg trailing, in a pose of brooding tragedy.

Guy went over and opened one of the books on the seat by the window. It was a detective novel. They were all detective novels. When he tried to read a few lines, the print swam and he closed the book. He must have drunk a lot, he thought. He didn't really care, tonight.

'In Santa Fe,' Bruno said, 'I want everything there is. Wine, women, and song. Hah!'

'What do you want?'

'Something.' Bruno's mouth turned down in an ugly grimace of unconcern. 'Everything. I got a theory a person ought to do everything it's possible to do before he dies, and maybe die trying to do something that's really impossible.'

Something in Guy responded with a leap, then cautiously drew back. He asked softly, 'Like what?'

'Like a trip to the moon in a rocket. Setting a speed record in a car – blindfolded. I did that once. Didn't set a record, but I went up to a hundred sixty.'

'Blindfolded?'

'And I did a robbery.' Bruno stared at Guy rigidly. 'Good one. Out of an apartment.'

An incredulous smile started on Guy's lips, though actually he believed Bruno. Bruno could be violent. He could be insane, too. Despair, Guy thought, not insanity. The desperate boredom of the wealthy, that he often spoke of to Anne. It tended to destroy rather than create. And it could lead to crime as easily as privation.

'Not to get anything,' Bruno went on. 'I didn't want what I took. I especially took what I didn't want.'

'What did you take?'

Bruno shrugged. 'Cigarette lighter. Table model. And a statue off the mantel. Coloured glass. And something else.' Another shrug. 'You're the only one knows about it. I don't talk much. Guess you think I do.' He smiled.

Guy drew on his cigarette. 'How'd you go about it?'

'Watched an apartment house in Astoria till I got the time right, then just walked in the window. Down the fire escape. Sort of easy. One of the things I cross off my list, thinking thank God.'

'Why "thank God"?'

Bruno grinned shyly. 'I don't know why I said that.' He refilled his glass, then Guy's.

Guy looked at the stiff, shaky hands that had stolen, at the nails bitten below the quick. The hands played clumsily with a match cover and dropped it, like a baby's hands, on to the ash-sprinkled steak. How boring it was really, Guy thought, crime. How motiveless often. A certain type turned to crime. And who would know from Bruno's hands, or his room, or his ugly wistful face that he had stolen? Guy dropped into his chair again.

'Tell me about you,' Bruno invited pleasantly.

'Nothing to tell.' Guy took a pipe from his jacket pocket, banged it on his heel, looked down at the ashes on the carpet, and then forgot them. The tingling of the alcohol sank deeper into his flesh. He thought, if the Palm Beach contract came through, the two weeks before work began would pass quickly. A divorce needn't take long. The pattern of the low white buildings on the green lawn in his finished drawing swam familiarly in his mind, in detail, without his trying to evoke them. He felt subtly flattered, immensely secure suddenly, and blessed.

'What kind of houses you build?' Bruno asked.

'Oh – what's known as modern. I've done a couple of stores and a small office building.' Guy smiled, feeling none of the reticence, the faint vexation he generally did when people asked him about his work.

'You married?'

'No. Well, I am, yes. Separated.'

'Oh. Why?'

'Incompatible,' Guy replied.

'How long you been separated?'

'Three years.'

'You don't want a divorce?'

Guy hesitated, frowning.

'Is she in Texas, too?'

'Yes.'

'Going to see her?'

'I'll see her. We're going to arrange the divorce now.' His teeth set. Why had he said it?

Bruno sneered. 'What kind of girls you find to marry down there?'

'Very pretty,' Guy replied. 'Some of them.'

'Mostly dumb though, huh?'

'They can be.' He smiled to himself. Miriam was the kind of Southern girl Bruno probably meant.

'What kind of girl's your wife?'

'Rather pretty,' Guy said cautiously. 'Red hair. A little plump.'

'What's her name?'

'Miriam. Miriam Joyce.'

'Hm-m. Smart or dumb?'

'She's not an intellectual. I didn't want to marry an intellectual.'

'And you loved her like hell, huh?'

Why? Did he show it? Bruno's eyes were fixed on him, missing nothing, unblinking, as if their exhaustion had passed the point where sleep is imperative. Guy had a feeling those grey eyes had been searching him for hours and hours. 'Why do you say that?'

'You're a nice guy. You take everything serious. You take women the hard way, too, don't you?'

'What's the hard way?' he retorted. But he felt a rush of affection for Bruno because Bruno had said what he thought about him. Most people, Guy knew, didn't say what they thought about him.

Bruno made little scallops in the air with his hands, and sighed.

'What's the hard way?' Guy repeated.

'All out, with a lot of high hopes. Then you get kicked in the teeth, right?'

'Not entirely.' A throb of self-pity piqued him, however, and he got up, taking his drink with him. There was no place to move in the room. The swaying of the train made it difficult even to stand upright.

And Bruno kept staring at him, one old-fashioned foot dangling at the end of the crossed leg, flicking his finger again and again on the cigarette he held over his plate. The unfinished pink and black steak was slowly being covered by the rain of ashes. Bruno looked less friendly, Guy suspected, since he had told him he was married. And more curious.

'What happened with your wife? She start sleeping around?'

That irritated him, too, Bruno's accuracy. 'No. That's all past anyway.'

'But you're still married to her. Couldn't you get a divorce before now?'

Guy felt instantaneous shame. 'I haven't been much concerned about a divorce.'

'What's happened now?'

'She just decided she wanted one. I think she's going to have a child.'

'Oh. Fine time to decide, huh? She's been sleeping around for three years and finally landed somebody?'

Just what had happened, of course, and probably it had taken the baby to do it. How did Bruno know? Guy felt that Bruno was superimposing upon Miriam the knowledge and hatred of someone else he knew. Guy turned to the window. The window gave him nothing but his own image. He could feel his heartbeats shaking his body, deeper than the train's vibrations. Perhaps, he thought, his heart was beating because he had never told anyone so much about Miriam. He had never told Anne as much as Bruno knew already. Except that Miriam had once been different – sweet, loyal, lonely, terribly in need of him and of freedom from her family. He would see Miriam tomorrow, be able to touch her by putting out his hand. He could not bear the thought of touching her oversoft flesh that once he had loved. Failure overwhelmed him suddenly.

'What happened with your marriage?' Bruno's voice asked gently, right behind him. 'I'm really very interested, as a friend. How old was she?'

'Eighteen.'

'She start sleeping around right away?'

Guy turned reflexively, as if to shoulder Miriam's guilt. 'That's not the only thing women do, you know.'

'But she did, didn't she?'

Guy looked away, annoyed and fascinated at the same time. 'Yes.' How ugly the little word sounded, hissing in his ears!

'I know that Southern redhead type,' Bruno said, poking at his apple pie.

Guy was conscious again of an acute and absolutely useless shame. Useless, because nothing Miriam had done or said would embarrass or surprise Bruno. Bruno seemed incapable of surprise, only of a whetting of interest.

Bruno looked down at his plate with coy amusement. His eyes widened, bright as they could be with the bloodshot and the blue circles. 'Marriage,' he sighed.

The word 'marriage' lingered in Guy's ears, too. It was a solemn word to him. It had the primordial solemnity of *holy*, *love*, *sin*. It was Miriam's round terracotta-coloured mouth saying, 'Why should I put myself out for *you*?' and it was Anne's eyes as she pushed her hair back and looked up at him on the lawn of her house where she planted crocuses. It was Miriam turning from the tall thin window in the room in Chicago, lifting her freckled, shield-shaped face directly up to his as she always did before she told a lie, and Steve's long dark head, insolently smiling. Memories began to crowd in, and he wanted to put his hands up and push them back. The room in Chicago where it had all happened . . . He could smell the room, Miriam's perfume, and the heat from painted radiators. He stood passively, for the first time in years not thrusting Miriam's face back to a pink blur. What would it do to him if he let it all flood him again, now? Arm him against her or undermine him?

'I mean it,' Bruno's voice said distantly. 'What happened? You don't mind telling me, do you? I'm interested.'

Steve happened. Guy picked up his drink. He saw the afternoon in Chicago, framed by the doorway of the room, the image grey and black now like a photograph. The afternoon he had found them in the apartment, like no other afternoon, with its own colour, taste, and sound, its own world, like a horrible little work of art. Like a date in history fixed in time. Or wasn't it just the opposite, that it travelled with him always? For here it was now, as clear as it had ever been. And, worst of all, he was aware of an impulse to tell Bruno everything, the stranger on the train who would listen, commiserate, and forget. The idea of telling Bruno began to comfort him. Bruno was not the ordinary stranger on the train by any means. He was cruel and corrupt enough himself to appreciate a story like that of his first love. And Steve was only the surprise ending that made the rest fall into place. Steve wasn't the first betrayal. It was only his twenty-six-year-old pride that had exploded in his face that afternoon. He had told the story to himself a thousand times, a classic story, dramatic for all his stupidity. His stupidity only lent it humour.

'I expected too much of her,' Guy said casually, 'without any right to. She happened to like attention. She'll probably flirt all her life, no matter whom she's with.'

'I know, the eternal high-school type.' Bruno waved his hand. 'Can't even pretend to belong to one guy, ever.'

Guy looked at him. Miriam had, of course, once.

Abruptly he abandoned his idea of telling Bruno, ashamed that he had nearly begun. Bruno seemed unconcerned now, in fact, whether he told it or not. Slumped, Bruno was drawing with a match in the gravy of his plate. The down-turned half of his mouth, in profile, was sunken between nose and chin like the mouth of an old man. The mouth seemed to say, whatever the story, it was really beneath his contempt to listen.

'Women like that draw men,' Bruno mumbled, 'like garbage draws flies.'

2

The shock of Bruno's words detached him from himself. 'You must have had some unpleasant experiences yourself,' he remarked. But Bruno troubled by women was hard to imagine.

'Oh, my father had one like that. Redhead, too. Named Carlotta.' He looked up, and the hatred for his father penetrated his fuzziness like a barb. 'Fine, isn't it? It's men like my father keep 'em in business.'

Carlotta. Guy felt he understood now why Bruno loathed Miriam. It seemed the key to Bruno's whole personality, to the hatred of his father and to his retarded adolescence.

'There's two kinds of guys!' Bruno announced in a roaring voice, and stopped.

Guy caught a glimpse of himself in a narrow panel mirror on the wall. His eyes looked frightened, he thought, his mouth grim, and deliberately he relaxed. A golf club nudged him in the back. He ran his fingertips over its cool varnished surface. The inlaid metal in the dark wood recalled the binnacle on Anne's sailboat.

'And essentially one kind of women!' Bruno went on. 'Two-timers. At one end it's two-timing and the other end it's a whore! Take your choice!'

'What about women like your mother?'

'I never seen another woman like my mother,' Bruno declared. 'I never seen a woman take so much. She's good-looking, too, lots of men friends, but she doesn't fool around with them.'

Silence.

Guy tapped another cigarette on his watch and saw it was 10.30. He must go in a moment.

'How'd you find out about your wife?' Bruno peered up at him.

Guy took his time with his cigarette.

'How many'd she have?'

'Quite a few. Before I found out.' And just as he assured himself it made no difference at all now to admit it, a sensation as of a tiny whirlpool inside him began to confuse him. Tiny, but realer than the memories somehow, because he had uttered it. Pride? Hatred? Or merely impatience with himself, because all that he kept feeling now was so useless? He turned the conversation from himself. 'Tell me what else you want to do before you die?'

'Die? Who said anything about dying? I got a few crack-proof rackets doped out. Could start one some day in Chicago or New York, or I might just sell my ideas. And I got a lot of ideas for perfect murders.' Bruno looked up again with that fixity that seemed to invite challenge.

'I hope your asking me here isn't part of one of your plans.' Guy sat down.

'Jesus Christ, I *like* you, Guy! I really do!'

The wistful face pled with Guy to say he liked him, too. The loneliness in those tiny, tortured eyes! Guy looked down embarrassedly at his hands. 'Do all your ideas run to crime?'

'Certainly not! Just things I want to do, like – I want to give a guy a thousand dollars some day. A beggar. When I get my own dough, that's one of the first things I'm gonna do. But didn't you ever feel you wanted to steal something? Or kill somebody? You must have. Everybody feels those things. Don't you think some people get quite a kick out of killing people in wars?'

'No,' Guy said.

Bruno hesitated. 'Oh, they'd never admit it, of course, they're afraid! But you've had people in your life you'd have liked out of the way, haven't you?'

'No.' Steve, he remembered suddenly. Once he had even thought of murdering him.

Bruno cocked his head. 'Sure you have. I see it. Why don't you admit it?'

'I may have had fleeting ideas, but I'd never have done anything about them. I'm not that kind of person.'

'That's exactly where you're wrong! Any kind of person can murder. Purely circumstances and not a thing to do with temperament! People get so far – and it takes just the least little thing to push them over the brink. Anybody. Even your grandmother. I know.'

'I don't happen to agree,' Guy said tersely.

'I tell you I came near murdering my father a thousand times! Who'd you ever feel like murdering? The guys with your wife?'

'One of them,' Guy murmured.

'How near did you come?'

'Not near at all. I merely thought of it.' He remembered the sleepless nights, hundreds of them, and the despair of peace unless he avenged himself. Could something have pushed him over the line then? He heard Bruno's voice mumbling, 'You were a hell of a lot nearer than you think, that's all I can say.' Guy gazed at him puzzledly. His figure had the sickly, nocturnal look of a croupier's, hunched on shirt-sleeved forearms over the table, thin head hanging. 'You read too many detective stories,' Guy said, and having heard himself, did not know where the words had come from.

'They're good. They show all kinds of people can murder.'

'I've always thought that's exactly why they're bad.'

'Wrong again!' Bruno said indignantly. 'Do you know what percentage of murders get put in the papers?'

'I don't know and I don't care.'

'One twelfth. One twelfth! Just imagine! Who do you think the other eleven twelfths are? A lot of little people that don't matter. All the people the cops know they'll never catch.' He started to pour more Scotch, found the bottle empty, and dragged himself up. A gold penknife flashed out of his trousers pocket on a gold chain fine as a string. It pleased Guy aesthetically, as a beautiful piece of jewellery might have. And he found himself thinking, as he watched Bruno slash round the top of a Scotch bottle, that Bruno might murder one day with the little penknife, that he would probably go quite free, simply because he wouldn't much care whether he were caught or not.

Bruno turned, grinning, with the new bottle of Scotch. 'Come to Santa Fe with me, huh? Relax for a couple of days.'

'Thanks, I can't.'

'I got plenty of dough. Be my guest, huh?' He spilled Scotch on the table.

'Thanks,' Guy said. From his clothes, he supposed, Bruno thought he hadn't much money. They were his favourite trousers, these grey flannels. He was going to wear them in Metcalf and in Palm Beach, too, if it wasn't too hot. Leaning back, he put his hands in his pockets and felt a hole at the bottom of the right one.

'Why not?' Bruno handed him his drink. 'I like you a lot, Guy.'

'Why?'

'Because you're a good guy. Decent, I mean. I meet a lot of guys – no pun – but not many like you. I admire you,' he blurted, and sank his lip into his glass.

'I like you, too,' said Guy.

'Come with me, huh? I got nothing to do for two or three days till my mother comes. We could have a swell time.'

'Pick up somebody else.'

'Cheeses, Guy, what d'you think I do, go around picking up travelling companions? I like you, so I ask you to come with me. One day even. I'll cut right over from Metcalf and not even go to El Paso. I'm supposed to see the canyon.'

'Thanks, I've got a job as soon as I finish in Metcalf.'

'Oh.' The wistful, admiring smile again. 'Building something?'

'Yes, a country club.' It still sounded strange and unlike himself, the last thing he would have thought he'd be building, two months ago. 'The new Palmyra in Palm Beach.'

'Yeah?'

Bruno had heard of the Palmyra Club, of course. It was the biggest in Palm Beach. He had even heard they were going to build a new one. He had been to the old one a couple of times.

'You designed it?' He looked down at Guy like a hero-worshipping little boy. 'Can you draw me a picture of it?'

Guy drew a quick sketch of the buildings in the back of Bruno's address book and signed his name, as Bruno wanted. He explained the wall that would drop to make the lower floor one great ballroom extending on to the terrace, the louvre windows he hoped to get permission for that would eliminate air-conditioning. He grew happy as he talked, and tears of excitement came in his eyes, though he kept his voice low. How could he talk so intimately to Bruno, he wondered, reveal the very best of himself? Who was less likely to understand than Bruno?

'Sounds terrific,' Bruno said. 'You mean, you tell them how it's gonna look?'

'No. One has to please quite a lot of people.' Guy put his head back suddenly and laughed.

'You're gonna be famous, huh? Maybe you're famous now.'

There would be photographs in the news magazines, perhaps something in the newsreels. They hadn't passed on his sketches yet, he reminded himself, but he was so sure they would. Myers, the architect he shared an office with in New York, was sure. Anne was positive. And so was Mr Brillhart. The biggest commission of his life. 'I might be famous after this. It's the kind of thing they publicize.'

Bruno began to tell him a long story about his life in college, how he would have become a photographer if something hadn't happened at a certain time with his father. Guy didn't listen. He sipped his drink absently, and thought of the commissions that would come after Palm Beach. Soon, perhaps, an office building in New York. He had an idea for an office building in New York, and he longed to see it come into being. Guy Daniel Haines. *A name.* No longer the irksome, never quite banished awareness that he had less money than Anne.

'Wouldn't it, Guy?' Bruno repeated.

'What?'

Bruno took a deep breath. 'If your wife made a stink now about the divorce. Say she fought about it while you were in Palm Beach and made them fire you, wouldn't that be motive enough for murder?'

'Of Miriam?'

'Sure.'

'No.' Guy said. But the question disturbed him. He was afraid Miriam had heard of the Palmyra job through his mother, that she might try to interfere for the sheer pleasure of hurting him.

'When she was two-timing you, didn't you feel like murdering her?'

'No. Can't you get off the subject?' For an instant, Guy saw both halves of his life, his marriage and his career, side by side as he felt he had never seen them before. His brain swam sickeningly, trying to understand how he could be so stupid and helpless in one and so capable in the other. He glanced at Bruno, who still stared at him, and feeling slightly befuddled, set his glass on the table and pushed it fingers' length away.

'You must have wanted to once,' Bruno said with gentle, drunken persistence.

'No.' Guy wanted to get out and take a walk, but the train kept on and on in a straight line, like something that would never stop. Suppose Miriam did lose him the commission. He was going to live there several months, and he would be expected to keep on a social par with the directors. Bruno understood such things very well. He passed his hand across his moist forehead. The difficulty was, of course, that he wouldn't know what was in Miriam's mind until he saw her. He was tired, and when he was tired, Miriam could invade him like an army. It had happened so often in the two years it had taken him to turn loose of his love for her. It was happening now. He felt sick of Bruno. Bruno was smiling.

'Shall I tell you one of my ideas for murdering my father?'

'No,' Guy said. He put his hand over the glass Bruno was about to refill.

'Which do you want, the busted light socket in the bathroom or the carbon monoxide garage?'

'Do it and stop talking about it!'

'I'll do it, don't think I won't! Know what else I'll do some day? Commit suicide if I happen to feel like committing suicide, and fix it so it looks like my worst enemy murdered me.'

Guy looked at him in disgust. Bruno seemed to be growing indefinite at the edges, as if by some process of deliquescence. He seemed only a voice and a spirit now, the spirit of evil. All he despised, Guy thought, Bruno represented. All the things he would not want to be, Bruno was, or would become.

'Want me to dope out a perfect murder of your wife for you? You might want to use it some time.' Bruno squirmed with self-consciousness under Guy's scrutiny.

Guy stood up. 'I want to take a walk.'

Bruno slammed his palms together. 'Hey! Cheeses, what an idea! We murder for each other, see? I kill your wife and you kill my father! We meet on the train, see, and nobody knows we know each other! Perfect alibis! Catch?'

The wall before his eyes pulsed rhythmically, as if it were about to spring apart. *Murder.* The word sickened him, terrified him. He wanted to break away from Bruno, get out of the room, but a nightmarish heaviness held him. He tried to steady himself by straightening out the wall, by understanding what Bruno was saying, because he could feel there was logic in it somewhere, like a problem or a puzzle to be solved.

Bruno's tobacco-stained hands jumped and trembled on his knees. 'Air-tight alibis!' he shrieked. 'It's the idea of my life! Don't you get it? I could do it some time when you're out of town and you could do it when I was out of town.'

Guy understood. No one could ever, possibly, find out.

'It would give me a great pleasure to stop a career like Miriam's and to further a career like yours.' Bruno giggled. 'Don't you agree she ought to be stopped before she ruins a lot of other people? Sit down, Guy!'

She hasn't ruined me, Guy wanted to remind him, but Bruno gave him no time.

'I mean, just supposing the set-up was that. Could you do it? You could tell me all about where she lived, you know, and I could do the same for you, as good as if you lived there. We could leave fingerprints all over the place and only drive the dicks batty!' He snickered. 'Months apart, of course, and strictly no communication. Christ, it's a cinch!' He stood up and nearly toppled, getting his drink. Then he was saying, right in Guy's face, with suffocating confidence: 'You could do it, huh, Guy? Wouldn't be any hitches, I swear. I'd fix everything, I swear, Guy.'

Guy thrust him away, harder than he had intended. Bruno rose resiliently from the window seat. Guy glanced about for air, but the walls presented an unbroken surface. The room had become a little hell. What was he doing here? How and when had he drunk so much?

'I'm positive you *could*!' Bruno frowned.

Shut up with your damned theories, Guy wanted to shout back, but instead his voice came like a whisper: 'I'm sick of this.'

He saw Bruno's narrow face twist then in a queer way – in a smirk of surprise, a look that was eerily omniscient and hideous. Bruno shrugged affably.

'Okay. I still say it's a good idea and we got the absolutely perfect set-up right here. It's the idea I'll use. With somebody else, of course. Where are you going?'

Guy had at last thought of the door. He went out and opened another door on to the platform where the cooler air smashed him like a reprimand and the train's voice rose to an upbraiding blare. He added his own curses of himself to the wind and the train, and longed to be sick.

'Guy?'

Turning, he saw Bruno slithering past the heavy door.

'Guy, I'm sorry.'

'That's all right,' Guy said at once, because Bruno's face shocked him. It was doglike in its self-abasement.

'Thanks, Guy.' Bruno bent his head, and at that instant the pound-pound-pound of the wheels began to die away, and Guy had to catch his balance.

He felt enormously grateful, because the train was stopping. He slapped Bruno's shoulder. 'Let's get off and get some air!'

They stepped out into a world of silence and total blackness.

'The hell's the idea?' Bruno shouted. 'No lights!'

Guy looked up. There was no moon either. The chill made his body rigid and alert. He heard the homely slap of a wooden door somewhere. A spark grew into a lantern ahead of them, and a man ran with it towards the rear of the train where a box-car door unrolled a square of light. Guy walked slowly towards the light, and Bruno followed him.

Far away on the flat black prairie a locomotive wailed, on and on, and then again, farther away. It was a sound he remembered from childhood, beautiful, pure, lonely. Like a wild horse shaking a white man. In a burst of companionship, Guy linked his arm through Bruno's.

'I don't *wanna* walk!' Bruno yelled, wrenching away and stopping. The fresh air was wilting him like a fish.

The train was starting. Guy pushed Bruno's big loose body aboard.

'Nightcap?' Bruno said dispiritedly at his door, looking tired enough to drop.

'Thanks, I couldn't.'

Green curtains muffled their whispers.

'Don't forget to call me in the morning. I'll leave the door unlocked. If I don't answer, come on in, huh?'

Guy lurched against the walls of green curtains as he made his way to his berth.

Habit made him think of his book as he lay down. He had

left it in Bruno's room. His Plato. He didn't like the idea of its spending the night in Bruno's room, or of Bruno's touching it and opening it.

3

He had called Miriam immediately, and she had arranged to meet him at the high school that lay between their houses.

Now he stood in a corner of the asphalt gamefield, waiting. She would be late, of course. Why had she chosen the high school, he wondered. Because it was her own ground? He had loved her when he had used to wait for her here.

Overhead, the sky was a clear strong blue. The sun poured down moltenly, not yellow but colourless, like something grown white with its own heat. Beyond the trees, he saw the top of a slim reddish building he did not know, that had gone up since he had been in Metcalf two years ago. He turned away. There was no human being in sight, as if the heat had caused everyone to abandon the school building and even the homes of the neighbourhood. He looked at the broad grey steps that spilled from the dark arch of the school doors. He could still remember the inky, faintly sweaty smell on the fuzzy edges of Miriam's algebra book. He could still see the MIRIAM pencilled on the edge of its pages, and the drawing of the girl with the Spencerian marcel wave on the flyleaf, when he opened the book to do her problems for her. Why had he thought Miriam any different from all the others?

He walked through the wide gate between the criss-cross wire fence and looked up College Avenue again. Then he saw her, under the yellow-green trees that bordered the sidewalk. His heart began to beat harder, but he blinked his eyes with deliberate casualness. She walked at her usual rather stolid pace, taking her time. Now her head came into view, haloed by a broad, light-coloured hat. Shadow and sun speckled her figure chaotically. She gave him a relaxed wave, and Guy pulled a hand out of his pocket, returned it, and went back into the gamefield, suddenly tense and shy as a boy. She knows about the Palm Beach job, he thought, that strange girl under the trees. His mother had told him, half an hour ago, that she had mentioned it to Miriam when Miriam last telephoned.

'Hello, Guy.' Miriam smiled and quickly closed her broad orangey-pink lips. Because of the space between her front teeth, Guy remembered.

'How are you, Miriam?' Involuntarily he glanced at her figure, plump, but not pregnant-looking, and it flashed through his mind she might have lied. She wore a brightly-flowered skirt and a white short-sleeved blouse. Her big white pocket-book was of woven patent leather.

She sat down primly on the one stone bench that was in the shade, and asked him dull questions about his trip. Her face had grown fuller where it had always been full, on the lower cheeks, so that her chin looked more pointed. There were little wrinkles under her eyes now, Guy noticed. She had lived a long time, for twenty-two.

'In January,' she answered him in a flat voice. 'In January the child's due.'

It was two months advanced then. 'I suppose you want to marry him.'

She turned her head slightly and looked down. On her short cheek, the sunlight picked out the largest freckles, and Guy saw a certain pattern he remembered and had not thought of since a time when he had been married to her. How sure he had once been that he possessed her, possessed her every frailest thought! Suddenly it seemed that all love was only a tantalizing, a horrible next-best to knowing. He knew not the smallest part of the new world in Miriam's mind now. Was it possible that the same thing could happen with Anne?

'Don't you, Miriam?' he prompted.

'Not *right* now. See, there're complications.'

'Like what?'

'Well, we might not be able to marry as soon as we'd like to.'

'Oh.' *We.* He knew what he would look like, tall and dark, with a long face, like Steve. The type Miriam had always been attracted to. The only type she would have a child by. And she did want this child, he could tell. Something had happened, that had nothing to do with the man, perhaps, that made her want a child. He could see it in the prim, stiff way she sat on the bench, in that self-abandoned trance he had always seen or imagined in pregnant women's faces. 'That needn't delay the divorce though, I suppose.'

'Well, I didn't think so – until a couple of days ago. I thought Owen would be free to marry this month.'

'Oh. He's married now?'

'Yeah, he's married,' she said with a little sigh, almost smiling.

Guy looked down in vague embarrassment and paced a slow step or two on the asphalt. He had known the man would be married. He had expected he would have no intention of marrying her unless he were forced to. 'Where is he? Here?'

'He's in Houston,' she replied. 'Don't you want to sit down?'

'No.'

'You never did like to sit down.'

He was silent.

'Still have your ring?'

'Yeah.' His class ring from Chicago, that Miriam had always admired because it meant he was a college man. She was staring at the ring with a self-conscious smile. He put his hands in his pockets. 'As long as I'm here, I'd like it settled. Can we do it this week?'

'I want to go away, Guy.'

'For the divorce?'

Her stubby hands opened in a limp ambiguous gesture and he thought suddenly of Bruno's hands. He had forgotten Bruno completely, getting off the train this morning. And his book.

'I'm sort of tired of staying here,' she said.

'We can get the divorce in Dallas if you like.' Her friends here knew, he thought, that was all.

'I want to wait, Guy. Would you mind? Just a while?'

'I should think you'd mind. Does he intend to marry you or not?'

'He could marry me in September. He'd be free then, but –'

'But what?' In her silence, in the childlike lick of her tongue on her upper lip, he saw the trap she was in. She wanted this child so much, she would sacrifice herself in Metcalf by waiting until four months before it was born to marry its father. In spite of himself, he felt a certain pity for her.

'I want to go away, Guy. With you.'

There was a real effort at sincerity in her face, so much that he almost forgot what she was asking, and why. 'What is it you want, Miriam? Money to go away somewhere?'

The dreaminess in her grey-green eyes was dispersing like a mist. 'Your mother said you were going to Palm Beach.'

'I might be going there. To work.' He thought of the Palmyra with a twinge of peril. It was slipping away already.

'Take me with you, Guy? It's the last thing I'll ask you. If I could stay with you till December and then get the divorce –'

'Oh,' he said quietly, but something throbbed in his chest, like the breaking of his heart. She disgusted him suddenly, she and all the people around her whom she knew and attracted. Another man's child. Go away with her, be her husband until she gave birth to another man's child.

'If you don't take me, I'll come anyway.'

'Miriam, I could get that divorce now. I don't have to wait to see the child. The law doesn't.' His voice shook.

'You wouldn't do that to me,' Miriam replied with that combination of threat and pleading that had played on both his anger and his love when he loved her, and baffled him.

He felt it baffling him now. And she was right. He wouldn't divorce her now. But it was not because he still loved her, not because she was still his wife and was therefore due his protection, but because he pitied her and because he remembered he had once loved her. He realized now he had pitied her even in New York, even when she wrote him for money. 'I won't take the job if you come out there. There'd be no use in taking it,' he said evenly, but it was gone already, he told himself, so why discuss it?

'I don't think you'd give up a job like that,' she challenged.

He turned away from her twisted smile of triumph. That was where she was wrong, he thought, but he was silent. He took two steps on the gritty asphalt and turned again, with his head high. Be calm, he told himself. What could anger accomplish? Miriam had used to hate him when he reacted like this, because she loved loud arguments. She would love one even this morning, he thought. She had hated him when he reacted like this, until she had learned that in the long run it hurt him more to react like this. He knew he played into her hands now, yet he felt he could react in no other way.

'I haven't even got the job yet, you know. I'll simply send them a telegram saying I don't want it.' Beyond the treetops, he noticed again the new reddish building he had seen before Miriam came.

'And then what?'

'A lot of things. But you won't know about them.'

'Running away?' she taunted. 'Cheapest way out.'

He walked again, and turned. There was Anne. With Anne, he could endure this, endure anything. And in fact, he felt strangely resigned. Because he was with Miriam now, the symbol of the failure of his youth? He bit the tip of his tongue. There was inside him, like a flaw in a jewel, not visible on the surface, a fear and anticipation of failure that he had never been able to mend. At times, failure was a possibility that fascinated him, as at times, in high school and college, when he had allowed himself to fail examinations he might have passed; as when he married Miriam, he thought, against the will of both their families and all their friends. Hadn't he known it couldn't succeed? And now he had given up his biggest commission, without a murmur. He would go to Mexico and have a few days with Anne. It would take all his money, but why not? Could he possibly go back to New York and work without having seen Anne first?

'Is there anything else?' he asked.

'I've said it,' she told him, out of her spaced front teeth.

4

He walked home slowly, approaching Ambrose Street, where he lived, through Travis Street, which was shaded and still. There was a small fruit shop now on the corner of Travis and Delancey Streets, sitting right on somebody's front lawn like a children's play store. Out of the great Washatorium building that marred the west end of Ambrose Street, girls and women in white uniforms were pouring, chattering, on their way to an early lunch.

He was glad he did not meet anyone on the street he had to speak to. He felt slow and quiet and resigned, and even rather happy. Strange how remote – perhaps how foreign – Miriam seemed five minutes after talking with her, how unimportant, really, everything seemed. Now he felt ashamed of his anxiety on the train.

'Not bad, Mama,' he said with a smile when he came home.

His mother had greeted him with an anxious lift of her eyebrows. 'I'm glad to hear that.' She pulled a rocker around and sat down to listen. She was a small woman with light brown hair, with a pretty, rather fine straight-nosed profile still, and a physical energy that seemed to twinkle off in sparks now in the silver of her hair. And she was almost always cheerful. It was this fact that chiefly made Guy feel that he and she were quite different, that had estranged him from her somewhat since the time he had suffered from Miriam. Guy liked to nurse his griefs, discover all he could about them, while his mother counselled him to forget. 'What did she say? You certainly weren't gone very long. I thought you might have had lunch with her.'

'No, Mama.' He sighed and sank down on the brocade sofa.

'Everything's all right, but I'll probably not take the Palmyra job.'

'Oh, Guy. Why not? Is she–? Is it true she's going to have a child?'

His mother was disappointed, Guy thought, but so mildly disappointed, for what the job really meant. He was glad she didn't know what the job really meant. 'It's true,' he said, and let his head go back until he felt the cool of the sofa's wooden frame against the back of his neck. He thought of the gulf that separated his life from his mother's. He had told her very little of his life with Miriam. And his mother, who had known a comfortable, happy upbringing in Mississippi, who kept herself busy now with her big house and her garden and her pleasant, loyal friends in Metcalf – what could she understand of a total malice like Miriam's? Or, for instance, what could she understand of the precarious life he was willing to lead in New York for the sake of a simple idea or two about his work?

'Now what's Palm Beach got to do with Miriam?' she asked finally.

'Miriam wants to come with me there. Protection for a time. And I couldn't bear it.' Guy clenched his hands. He had a sudden vision of Miriam in Palm Beach, Miriam meeting Clarence Brillhart, the manager of the Palmyra Club. Yet it was not the vision of Brillhart's shock beneath his calm, unvarying courtesy, Guy knew, but simply his own revulsion that made it impossible. It was just that he couldn't bear having Miriam anywhere near him when he worked on a project like this one. 'I couldn't bear it,' he repeated.

'Oh,' was all she said, but her silence now was one of understanding. If she made any comment, Guy thought, it was bound to remind him of her old disapproval of their marriage. And she wouldn't remind him at this time. 'You couldn't bear it,' she added, 'for as long as it would take.'

'I couldn't bear it.' He got up and took her soft face in his hands. 'Mama, I don't care a bit,' he said, kissing her forehead. 'I really don't care a row of beans.'

'I don't believe you do care. Why don't you?'

He crossed the room to the upright piano. 'Because I'm going to Mexico to see Anne.'

'Oh, are you?' she smiled, and the gaiety of this first morning with him won out. 'Aren't you the gadabout!'

'Want to come to Mexico?' He smiled over his shoulder. He began to play a saraband that he had learned as a child.

'Mexico!' his mother said in mock horror. 'Wild horses wouldn't get me to Mexico. Maybe you can bring Anne to see me on your way back.'

'Maybe.'

She went over and laid her hands shyly on his shoulders. 'Sometimes, Guy, I feel you're happy again. At the funniest times.'

5

What has happened? Write *immediately*. Or better, telephone collect. We're here at the Ritz for another two weeks. Missed you so on the trip, seems a shame we couldn't have flown down together, but I understand. I wish you well every moment of the day, darling. This must be over soon and we'll get it over. Whatever happens, tell me and let's face it. I often feel you *don't*. Face things, I mean.

You're so close, it's absurd you can't come down for a day or so. I hope you'll be in the mood. I hope there'll be time. Would love to have you here, and you know the family would. Darling, I do love the drawings and I'm so terribly proud of you I can even stand the idea of your being away in the months ahead because you'll be building them. Dad most impressed, too. We talk about you all the time.

> All my love, and all that goes
> with it. Be happy, darling.
> A.

Guy wrote a telegram to Clarence Brillhart, the manager of the Palmyra Club: 'Owing to circumstances, impossible for me to take commission. My deepest regrets and thanks for your championing and constant encouragement. Letter following.'

Suddenly he thought of the sketches they would use in lieu of his – the imitation Frank Lloyd Wright of William Harkness Associates. Worse yet, he thought as he dictated the telegram over the phone, the board would probably ask Harkness to copy some of his ideas. And Harkness would, of course.

He telegraphed Anne that he would fly down Monday and that he was free for several days. And because there was Anne, he did not bother to wonder how many months it would be, how many years, perhaps, before another job as big as the Palmyra would come within his reach.

6

That evening, Charles Anthony Bruno was lying on his back in an El Paso room, trying to balance a gold fountain-pen across his rather delicate, dished-in nose. He was too restless to go to bed, not energetic enough to go down to one of the bars in the neighbourhood and look things over. He had looked things over all afternoon, and he did not think much of them in El Paso. He did not think much of the Grand Canyon either. He thought more of the idea that had come to him night before last on the train. A pity Guy hadn't awakened him that morning. Not that Guy was the kind of fellow to plan a murder with, but he liked him, as a person. Guy was somebody worth knowing. Besides, Guy had left his book, and he could have given it back.

The ceiling fan made a *wuz-wuz-wuz* sound because one of its four blades was missing. If the fourth had been there, he would have been just a little cooler, he thought. One of the taps in the john leaked, the clamp on the reading light over the bed was broken so it hung down, and there were fingerprints all over the closet door. And the best hotel in town, they told him! Why was there always something wrong, maybe only one thing, with every hotel room he had ever been in? Some day he was going to find the perfect hotel room and buy it, even if it was in South Africa.

He sat up on the edge of the bed and reached for the telephone. 'Gimme long-distance.' He looked blankly at a smudge of red dirt his shoe had put on the white counterpane. 'Great Neck 166J . . . Great Neck, yeah.' He waited. 'Long Island . . . In *New York*, lunk, ever hear of it?'

In less than a minute, he had his mother.

'Yeah, I'm here. You still leaving Sunday? You better . . . Well, I took that muleback trip. Just about pooped me, too . . . Yeah, I seen the canyon . . . Okay, but the colours are kind of corny . . . Anyhow, how's things with you?'

He began to laugh. He pushed off his shoes and rolled back on the bed with the telephone, laughing. She was telling him about coming home to find the Captain entertaining two of her friends – two men she had met the night before – who had dropped in, thought the Captain was her father, and proceeded to say all the wrong things.

7

Propped on his elbow in bed, Guy stared at the letter addressed to him in pencil.

'Guess I'll have only one more time to wake you for another good long while,' his mother said.

Guy picked up the letter from Palm Beach. 'Maybe not so long, Mama.'

'What time does your plane leave tomorrow?'

'One-twenty.'

She leaned over and superfluously tucked in the foot of his bed. 'I don't suppose you'll have time to run over and see Ethel?'

'Oh, certainly I will, Mama.' Ethel Peterson was one of his mother's oldest friends. She had given Guy his first piano lessons.

The letter from Palm Beach was from Mr Brillhart. He had been given the commission. Mr Brillhart had also persuaded the board about the louvre windows.

'I've got some good strong coffee this morning,' his mother said from the threshold. 'Like breakfast in bed?'

Guy smiled at her. 'Would I!'

He reread Mr Brillhart's letter carefully, put it back in its envelope, and slowly tore it up. Then he opened the other letter. It was one page, scrawled in pencil. The signature with the heavy flourish below it made him smile again: Charles A. Bruno

Dear Guy:

This is your train friend, remember? You left your book in my room that night & I found a Texas address in it which I trust is still right. Am mailing book to you. Read some in it, myself, didn't know there was so much conversation in Plato.

A great pleasure dining with you that night & hope I may list you among my friends. It would be fine to see you in Santa Fe & if you possibly change your mind, address is: Hotel La Fonda, Santa Fe, New Mex. for next two weeks at least.

I keep thinking about that idea we had for a couple of murders. It could be done, I am sure. I cannot express to you my supremest confidence in the idea! Though I know subject does not interest you.

What's what with your wife as that was very interesting? Please write me soon. Outside of losing wallet in El Paso (stolen right off a bar in front of me) nothing has happened of note. Didn't like El Paso, with apologies to you.

Hoping to hear from you soon,

Your friend,
Charles A. Bruno

P.S. Very sorry for sleeping late and missing you that a.m.

C.A.B.

The letter pleased him somehow. It was pleasant to think of Bruno's freedom.

'Grits!' he said happily to his mother. 'Never get grits with my fried eggs up North!'

He put on a favourite old robe that was too hot for the weather, and sat back in bed with the *Metcalf Star* and the teetery-legged bed-tray that held his breakfast.

Afterwards, he showered and dressed as if there were something he had to do that day, but there wasn't. He had visited the Cartwrights yesterday. He might have seen Peter had a job in New Orleans now. What was Miriam doing, he wondered. Perhaps manicuring her nails on her back porch, or playing checkers with some little girl neighbour who adored her, who wanted to be just like her. Miriam was never one to brood when a plan went askew. Guy lighted a cigarette.

A soft, intermittent *chink* came from downstairs, where his mother or Ursline the cook was cleaning the silver and dropping it piece by piece on to a heap.

Why hadn't he left for Mexico today? The next idle twenty-four hours were going to be miserable, he knew. Tonight, his uncle again, and probably some friends of his mother's dropping over. They all wanted to see him. Since his last visit, the *Metcalf Star* had printed a column about him and his work, mentioning his scholarships, the Prix de Rome that he hadn't been able to use because of the war, the store he had designed in Pittsburg, and the little annexe infirmary of the hospital in Chicago. It read so impressively in a newspaper. It had almost made him feel important, he remembered, the lonely day in New York when the clipping had arrived in his mother's letter.

A sudden impulse to write Bruno made him sit down at his work table, but, with his pen in his hand, he realized he had nothing to say. He could see Bruno in his rust-brown suit, camera strap over his shoulder, plodding up some dry hill in Santa Fe, grinning with his bad teeth at something, lifting his camera unsteadily and clicking. Bruno with a thousand easy dollars in his pocket, sitting in a bar, waiting for his mother. What did he have to say to Bruno? He recapped his fountain pen and tossed it back on the table.

'Mama?' he called. He ran downstairs. 'How about a movie this afternoon?'

His mother said she had already been to movies twice that week. 'You know you don't like movies,' she chided him.

'Mama, I really want to go!' he smiled, and insisted.

8

The telephone rang that night at about eleven. His mother answered it, then came in and called him from the living-room where he sat with his uncle and his uncle's wife and his two cousins, Ritchie and Ty.

'It's long-distance,' his mother said.

Guy nodded. It would be Brillhart, of course, asking for further explanations. Guy had answered his letter that day.

'Hello, Guy,' the voice said. 'Charley.'

'Charley who?'

'Charley Bruno.'

'Oh! – How are you? Thanks for the book.'

'I dint send it yet but I will,' Bruno said with the drunken cheer Guy remembered from the train. 'Coming out to Santa Fe?'

'I'm afraid I can't.'

'What about Palm Beach? Can I visit you there in a couple weeks? I'd like to see how it looks.'

'Sorry, that's all off.'

'Off? Why?'

'Complications. I've changed my mind.'

'Account of your wife?'

'N-no.' Guy felt vaguely irritated.

'She wants you to stay with her?'

'Yes. Sort of.'

'Miriam wants to come out to Palm Beach?'

Guy was surprised he remembered her name.

'You haven't got your divorce, huh?'

'Getting it,' Guy said tersely.

'*Yes, I'm paying for this call!*' Bruno shouted to someone. 'Cheeses!' disgustedly. 'Listen, Guy, you gave up that job account of her?'

'Not exactly. It doesn't matter. It's finished.'

'You have to wait till the child's born for a divorce?'

Guy said nothing.

'The other guy's not going to marry her, huh?'

'Oh, yes, he is –'

'Yeah?' Bruno interrupted cynically.

'I can't talk any longer. We've got guests here tonight. I wish you a pleasant trip, Charley.'

'When can we talk? Tomorrow?'

'I won't be here tomorrow.'

'Oh.' Bruno sounded lost now, and Guy hoped he was. Then the voice again, with sullen intimacy. 'Listen, Guy, if you want anything done, you know, all you have to do is give a sign.'

Guy frowned. A question took form in his mind, and immediately he knew the answer. He remembered Bruno's idea for a murder.

'What do you want, Guy?'

'Nothing. I'm very content. Understand?' But it was drunken bravado on Bruno's part, he thought. Why should he react seriously?

'Guy, I mean it,' the voice slurred, drunker than before.

'Good-bye, Charley,' Guy said. He waited for Bruno to hang up.

'Doesn't sound like everything's fine,' Bruno challenged.

'I don't see that it's any of your business.'

'Guy!' in a tearful whine.

Guy started to speak, but the line clicked and went dead. He had an impulse to ask the operator to trace the call. Then he thought, drunken bravado. And boredom. It annoyed him that

Bruno had his address. Guy ran his hand hard across his hair, and went back into the living-room.

9

All of what he had just told her of Miriam, Guy thought, did not matter so much as the fact he and Anne were together on the gravel path. He took her hand as they walked, and gazed around him at the scene in which every object was foreign – a broad level avenue bordered with giant trees like the Champs-Elysées, military statues on pedestals, and beyond, buildings he did not know. The El Paso de la Reforma. Anne walked beside him with her head still lowered, nearly matching his slow paces. Their shoulders brushed, and he glanced at her to see if she were about to speak, to say he was right in what he had decided, but her lips were still thoughtful. Her pale yellow hair, held by a silver bar at the back of her neck, made lazy movements in the wind behind her. It was the second summer he had seen her when the sun had only begun to tan her face, so her skin about equalled in pigment the colour of her hair. Soon her face would be darker than her hair, but Guy liked her best the way she was now, like something made of white gold.

She turned to him with the faintest smile of self-consciousness on her lips because he had been staring at her. 'You couldn't have borne it, Guy?'

'No. Don't ask me why. I couldn't.' He saw that her smile stayed, tinged with perplexity, perhaps annoyance.

'It's such a big thing to give up.'

It vexed him now. He felt done with it. 'I simply loathe her,' he said quietly.

'But you shouldn't loathe anything.'

He made a nervous gesture. 'I loathe her because I've told you all this while we're walking here!'

'Guy, really!'

'She's everything that should be loathed,' he went on, staring in front of him. 'Sometimes I think I hate everything in the world. No decency, no conscience. She's what people mean when they say America never grows up, America rewards the corrupt. She's the type who goes to the bad movies, acts in them, reads the love-story magazines, lives in a bungalow, and whips her husband into earning more money this year so they can buy on the instalment plan next year, breaks up her neighbour's marriage –'

'Stop it, Guy! You talk so like a child!' She drew away from him.

'And the fact I once loved her,' Guy added, 'loved all of it, makes me ill.'

They stopped, looking at each other. He had had to say it, here and now, the ugliest thing he could say. He wanted to suffer also from Anne's disapproval, perhaps from her turning away and leaving him to finish the walk by himself. She had left him on one or two other occasions, when he had been unreasonable.

Anne said, in that distant, expressionless tone that terrified him, because he felt she might abandon him and never come back, 'Sometimes I can believe you're still in love with her.'

He smiled, and she softened. 'I'm sorry,' he said.

'Oh, Guy!' She put out her hand again, like a gesture of beseeching, and he took it. 'If you'd only grow up!'

'I read somewhere people don't grow emotionally!'

'I don't care what you read. They do. I'll prove it to you if it's the last thing I do.'

He felt secure suddenly. 'What else can I think about now?' he asked perversely, lowering his voice.

'That you were never closer to being free of her than now, Guy. What do you suppose you should think about?'

He lifted his head higher. There was a big pink sign on the top of a building: TOME XX, and all at once he was curious to know what it meant and wanted to ask Anne. He wanted to ask her why everything was so much easier and simpler when he was with her, but pride kept him from asking now, and the question would have been rhetorical anyway, unanswerable by

Anne in words, because the answer was simply Anne. It had been so since the day he met her, in the dingy basement of the Art Institute in New York, the rainy day he had slogged in and addressed the only living thing he saw, the Chinese red raincoat and hood. The red raincoat and hood had turned and said: 'You get to 9A from the first floor. You didn't have to come all the way down here.' And then her quick, amused laugh that mysteriously, immediately, lifted his rage. He had learned to smile by quarter inches, frightened of her, a little contemptuous of her new dark green convertible. 'A car just makes more sense,' Anne said, 'when you live in Long Island.' The days when he was contemptuous of everything and courses taken here and there were no more than tests to make sure he knew all the instructor had to say, or to see how fast he could learn it and leave. 'How do you suppose anybody gets in if not through pull? They can still throw you out if they don't like you.' He had seen it her way finally, the right way, and gone to the exclusive Deems Architectural Academy in Brooklyn for a year, through her father's knowing a man on the board of directors.

'I know you have it in you, Guy,' Anne said suddenly at the end of a silence, 'the capacity to be terribly happy.'

Guy nodded quickly, though Anne was not looking at him. He felt somehow ashamed. Anne had the capacity to be happy. She was happy now, she had been happy before she met him, and it was only he, his problems, that ever seemed to daunt her happiness for an instant. He would be happy, too, when he lived with Anne. He had told her so, but he could not bear to tell her again now.

'What's that?' he asked.

A big round house of glass had come into view under the trees of Chapultepec Park.

'The botanical gardens,' Anne said.

There was no one inside the building, not even a caretaker. The air smelled of warm, fresh earth. They walked around, reading unpronounceable names of plants that might have come from another planet. Anne had a favourite plant. She had watched it grow for three years, she said, visiting it on successive summers with her father.

'Only I can't even remember these names,' she said.

'Why should you remember?'

They had lunch at Sanborn's with Anne's mother, then walked around in the store until it was time for Mrs Faulkner's afternoon nap. Mrs Faulkner was a thin, nervously energetic woman, tall as Anne, and for her age as attractive. Guy had come to be devoted to her, because she was devoted to him. At first, in his mind, he had built up the greatest handicaps for himself from Anne's wealthy parents, but not one of them had come true, and gradually he had shed them. That evening, the four of them went to a concert at the Bellas Artes, then had a late supper at the Lady Baltimore Restaurant across the street from the Ritz.

The Faulkners were sorry he wouldn't be able to stay the summer with them in Acapulco. Anne's father, an importer, intended to build a warehouse on the docks there.

'We can't expect to interest him in a warehouse if he's building a whole country club,' Mrs Faulkner said.

Guy said nothing. He couldn't look at Anne. He had asked her not to tell her parents about Palm Beach until after he left. Where would he go next week? He might go to Chicago and study for a couple of months. He had stored away his possessions in New York, and his landlady awaited his word as to whether to rent his apartment or not. If he went to Chicago, he might see the great Saarinen in Evanston and Tim O'Flaherty, a young architect who had had no recognition yet, but whom Guy believed in. There might be a job or two in Chicago. But New York was too dismal a prospect without Anne.

Mrs Faulkner laid her hand on his forearm and laughed. 'He wouldn't smile if he got all New York to build over, would you, Guy?'

He hadn't been listening. He wanted Anne to take a walk with him later, but she insisted on his coming up to their suite at the Ritz to see the silk dressing-gown she had bought for her cousin

Teddy, before she sent it off. And then, of course, it was too late for a walk.

He was staying at the Hotel Montecarlo, about ten blocks from the Hotel Ritz, a great shabby building that looked like the former residence of a military general. One entered it through a wide carriage drive, paved in black and white tile like a bathroom floor. This gave into a huge dark lobby, also tile floored. There was a grotto-like bar-room and a restaurant that was always empty. Stained marble stairs wound around the patio, and going up behind the bellhop yesterday, Guy had seen, through open doorways and windows, a Japanese couple playing cards, a woman kneeling at prayer, people writing letters at tables or merely standing with a strange air of captivity. A masculine gloom and an untraceable promise of the supernatural oppressed the whole place, and Guy had liked it instantly, though the Faulkners, including Anne, chaffed him about his choice.

His cheap little room in a back corner was crammed with pink and brown painted furniture, had a bed like a fallen cake, and a bath down the hall. Somewhere down in the patio, water dripped continuously, and the sporadic flush of toilets sounded torrential.

When he got back from the Ritz, Guy deposited his wristwatch, a present from Anne, on the pink bed table, and his billfold and keys on the scratched brown bureau, as he might have done at home. He felt very content as he got into bed with his Mexican newspaper and a book on English architecture that he had found at the Alameda book-store that afternoon. After a second plunge at the Spanish, he leaned his head back against the pillow and gazed at the offensive room, listened to the little ratlike sounds of human activity from all parts of the building. What was it that he liked, he wondered. To immerse himself in ugly, uncomfortable, undignified living so that he gained new power to fight it in his work? Or was it a sense of hiding from Miriam? He would be harder to find here than at the Ritz.

Anne telephoned him the next morning to say that a telegram

had come for him. 'I just happened to hear them paging you,' she said. 'They were about to give you up.'

'Would you read it to me, Anne?'

Anne read: ' "Miriam suffered miscarriage yesterday. Upset and asking to see you. Can you come home? Mama." – Oh, Guy!'

He felt sick of it, all of it. 'She did it herself,' he murmured.

'You don't know, Guy.'

'I know.'

'Don't you think you'd better see her?'

His fingers tightened on the telephone. 'I'll get the Palmyra back anyway,' he said. 'When was the telegram sent?'

'The ninth. Tuesday, at 4 p.m.'

He sent a telegram off to Mr Brillhart, asking if he might be reconsidered for the job. Of course he would be, he thought, but how asinine it made him. Because of Miriam. He wrote to Miriam:

This changes both our plans, of course. Regardless of yours, I mean to get the divorce now. I shall be in Texas in a few days. I hope you will be well by then, but if not, I can manage whatever is necessary alone.

Again my wishes for your quick recovery.

Guy

Shall be at this address until Sunday.

He sent it airmail special delivery.

Then he called up Anne. He wanted to take her to the best restaurant in the city that night. He wanted the most exotic cocktails in the Ritz Bar to start with, all of them.

'You really feel happy?' Anne asked, laughing, as if she couldn't quite believe him.

'Happy and – strange. *Muy extranjero.*'

'Why?'

'Because I didn't think it was fated. I didn't think it was part of my destiny. The Palmyra, I mean.'

'I did.'

'Oh, you did!'

'Why do you think I was so mad at you yesterday?'

He really did not expect an answer from Miriam, but Friday morning when he and Anne were in Xochimilco, he felt prompted to call his hotel to see if a message had come. There was a telegram waiting. And after saying he would pick it up in a few minutes, he couldn't wait, once he was back in Mexico City, he telephoned the hotel again from a drugstore in the Socalo. The Montecarlo clerk read it to him: ' "Have to talk with you first. Please come soon. Love Miriam." '

'She'll make a bit of a fuss,' Guy said after he repeated it to Anne. 'I'm sure the other man doesn't want to marry her. He's got a wife now.'

'Oh.'

He glanced at her as they walked, wanting to say something to her about her patience with him, with Miriam, with all of it. 'Let's forget it,' he smiled, and began to walk faster.

'Do you want to go back now?'

'Certainly not! Maybe Monday or Tuesday. I want these few days with you. I'm not due in Florida for another week. That's if they keep to the first schedule.'

'Miriam won't follow you now, will she?'

'This time next week,' Guy said, 'she won't have a single claim on me.'

10

At her dressing-table in Hotel La Fonda, Santa Fe, Elsie Bruno sat removing the night's dry-skin cream from her face with a cleansing tissue. Now and then, with wide, absent blue eyes, she leaned closer to the mirror to examine the little mesh of wrinkles below her lids and the laugh lines that curved from the base of her nose. Though her chin was somewhat recessive, the lower part of her face projected, thrusting her full lips forward in a manner quite different from Bruno's face. Santa Fe, she thought, was the only place she could see the laugh lines in the mirror when she sat all the way back at her dressing-table.

'This light around here – might as well be an X-ray,' she remarked to her son.

Bruno, slumped in his pyjamas in a rawhide chair, cast a puffy eye over at the window. He was too tired to go and pull the shade down. 'You look good, Mom,' he croaked. He lowered his pursed lips to the glass of water that rested on his hairless chest, and frowned thoughtfully.

Like an enormous walnut in feeble, jittery squirrel hands, an idea, bigger and closer than any idea he had ever known, had been revolving in his mind for several days. When his mother left town, he intended to crack open the idea and start thinking in earnest. His idea was to go and get Miriam. The time was ripe, and the time was now. Guy needed it now. In a few days, a week even, it might be too late for the Palm Beach thing, and he wouldn't.

Her face had grown fatter in these few days in Santa Fe, Elsie thought. She could tell by the plumpness of her cheeks compared to the small taut triangle of her nose. She hid the laugh lines with a smile at herself, tilted her curly blonde head, and blinked her eyes.

'Charley, should I pick up that silver belt this morning?' she asked casually, as if she spoke to herself. The belt was two hundred and fifty something, but Sam would send another thousand on to California. It was such a good-looking belt, like nothing in New York. What else was Santa Fe good for but silver?

'What else is he good for?' Bruno murmured.

Elsie picked up her shower cap and turned to him with her quick broad smile that had no variations. 'Darling,' coaxingly.

'Umm-m?'

'You won't do anything you shouldn't while I'm gone?'

'No, Ma.'

She left the shower cap perched on the crown of her head, looked at a long narrow red nail, then reached for a sandpaper stick. Of course, Fred Wiley would be only too happy to buy the silver belt for her – he'd probably turn up at the station with something atrocious and twice as expensive anyway – but she didn't want Fred on her neck in California. With the least encouragement, he would come to California with her. Better that he only swore eternal love at the station, wept a little, and went straight home to his wife.

'I must say last night was funny though,' Elsie went on. 'Fred saw it first.' She laughed, and the sandpaper stick flew in a blur.

Bruno said coolly, 'I had nothing to do with it.'

'All right, darling, you had nothing to do with it!'

Bruno's mouth twisted. His mother had awakened him at four in the morning, in hysterics, to tell him there was a dead bull in the Plaza. A bull sitting on a bench with a hat and coat on, reading a newspaper. Typical of Wilson's collegiate pranks. Wilson would be talking about it today, Bruno knew, elaborating on it till he thought of something dumber to do. Last night in La Placita, the hotel bar, he had planned a murder – while Wilson dressed a dead bull. Even in Wilson's tall stories about his war service, he had never claimed to have killed anybody, not even a Jap. Bruno closed his eyes, thinking contentedly of last night. Around ten o'clock, Fred Wiley and a lot of other baldheads had trooped into La Placita half crocked, like a musical comedy stagline, to take his mother to a party. He'd been invited too, but he had told his mother he had a date with Wilson, because he needed time to think. And last night he had decided yes. He had been thinking really since Saturday when he talked to Guy, and here it was Saturday again, and it was tomorrow or never, when his mother left for California. He was sick of the question, could he do it. How long had the question been with him? Longer than he could remember. He *felt* like he could do it. Something kept telling him that the time, the circumstances, the cause would never be better. A pure murder, without personal motives! He didn't consider the possibility of Guy's murdering his father a motive, because he didn't count on it. Maybe Guy could be persuaded, maybe not. The point was, now was the time to act, because the set-up was so perfect. He'd called Guy's house again last night to make sure he still wasn't back from Mexico. Guy had been in Mexico since Sunday, his mother said.

A sensation like a thumb pressing at the base of his throat made him tear at his collar, but his pyjama jacket was open all the way down the front. Bruno began to button it dreamily.

'You won't change your mind and come with me?' his mother asked, getting up. 'If you did, I'd go up to Reno. Helen's there now and so's George Kennedy.'

'Only one reason I'd like to see you in Reno, Mom.'

'Charley –' She tipped her head to one side and back again. 'Have patience? If it weren't for Sam, we wouldn't be here, would we?'

'Sure, we would.'

She sighed. 'You won't change your mind?'

'I'm having fun here,' he said through a groan.

She looked at her nails again. 'All I've heard is how bored you are.'

'That's with Wilson. I'm not gonna see him again.'

'You're not going to run back to New York?'

'What'd I do in New York?'

'Grannie'd be so disappointed if you fell down again this year.'

'When did I ever fall down?' Bruno jested weakly, and suddenly felt sick enough to die, too sick even to throw up. He knew the feeling, it lasted only a minute, but God, he thought, let there not be time for breakfast before the train, don't let her say the word breakfast. He stiffened, not moving a muscle, barely breathing between his parted lips. With one eye shut, he watched her move towards him in her pale blue silk wrapper, a hand on her hip, looking as shrewd as she could which wasn't shrewd at all, because her eyes were so round. And she was smiling besides.

'What've you and Wilson got up your sleeves?'

'That punk?'

She sat down on the arm of his chair. 'Just because he steals your thunder,' she said, shaking him slightly by the shoulder.

'Don't do anything too awful, darling, because I haven't got the money just now to throw around cleaning up after you.'

'Stick him for some more. Get me a thousand, too.'

'Darling.' She laid the cool backs of her fingers against his forehead. 'I'll miss you.'

'I'll be there day after tomorrow probably.'

'Let's have fun in California.'

'Sure.'

'Why're you so serious this morning!'

'I'm not, Ma.'

She tweaked the thin dangling hair over his forehead, and went on into the bathroom.

Bruno jumped up and shouted against the roar of her running bath, 'Ma, I got money to pay my bill here!'

'What, angel?'

He went closer and repeated it, then sank back in the chair, exhausted with the effort. He did not want his mother to know about the long-distance calls to Metcalf. If she didn't, everything was working out fine. His mother hadn't minded very much his not staying on, hadn't really minded enough. Was she meeting this jerk Fred on the train or something? Bruno dragged himself up, feeling a slow animosity rising in him against Fred Wiley. He wanted to tell his mother he was staying on in Santa Fe for the biggest experience of his life. She wouldn't be running the water in there now, paying no attention to him, if she knew a fraction of what it meant. He wanted to say, Ma, life's going to be a lot better for both of us soon, because this is the beginning of getting rid of the Captain. Whether Guy came through with his part of the deal or not, if he was successful with Miriam, he would have proved a point. A perfect murder. Some day, another person he didn't know yet would turn up and some kind of a deal could be made. Bruno bent his chin down to his chest in sudden anguish. How could he tell his mother? Murder and his mother didn't go together. 'How gruesome!' she would say. He looked at the bathroom door with a hurt, distant expression. It had dawned on him that he couldn't tell anyone, ever. Except Guy. He sat down again.

'Sleepyhead!'

He blinked when she clapped her hands. Then he smiled. Dully, with a wistful realization that much would happen before he saw them again, he watched his mother's legs flex as she tightened her stockings. The slim lines of her legs always gave him a lift, made him proud. His mother had the best-looking legs he had ever seen on anyone, no matter what age. Ziegfeld had picked her, and hadn't Ziegfeld known his stuff? But she had married right back into the kind of life she had run away from. He was going to liberate her soon, and she didn't know it.

'Don't forget to mail *that*,' his mother said.

Bruno winced as the two rattlesnakes' heads tipped over towards him. It was a tie rack they had bought for the Captain, made of interlocking cowhorns and topped by two stuffed baby rattlers sticking their tongues out at each other over a mirror. The Captain hated tie racks, hated snakes, dogs, cats, birds—what didn't he hate? He would hate the corny tie rack, and that was why he had talked his mother into getting it for him. Bruno smiled affectionately at the tie rack. It hadn't been hard to talk his mother into getting it.

11

He stumbled on a goddamned cobblestone, then drew himself up pridefully and tried to straighten his shirt in his trousers. Good thing he had passed out in an alley and not on a street, or the cops might have picked him up and he'd have missed the train. He stopped and fumbled for his wallet, fumbled more wildly than he had earlier to see if the wallet was there. His hands shook so, he could hardly read the 10.20 a.m. on the railroad ticket. It was now 8.10 according to several clocks. If this was Sunday. Of course it was Sunday, all the Indians were in clean shirts. He kept an eye out for Wilson, though he hadn't seen him all day yesterday and it wasn't likely he would be out now. He didn't want Wilson to know he was leaving town.

The Plaza spread suddenly before him, full of chickens and kids and the usual old men eating piñones for breakfast. He stood still and counted the pillars of the Governor's palace to see if he could count seventeen, and he could. It was getting so the pillars weren't a good gauge any more. On top of a bad hangover, he ached now from sleeping on the goddamned cobblestones. Why'd he drunk so much, he wondered, almost tearfully. But he had been all alone, and he always drank more alone. Or was that true? And who cared anyway? He remembered one brilliant and powerful thought that had come to him last night watching a televised shuffleboard game: *the way to see the world was to see it drunk.* Everything was created to be seen drunk. Certainly this wasn't the way to see the world, with his head splitting every time he turned his eyes. Last night he'd wanted to celebrate his last night in Santa Fe. Today he'd be in Metcalf, and he'd have to be sharp. But had he ever known a hangover a few drinks couldn't fix? A hangover might even help, he thought: he had a habit of doing things slowly and cautiously with a hangover. Still, he hadn't planned anything, even yet. He could plan on the train.

'Any mail?' he asked mechanically at the desk, but there wasn't any.

He bathed solemnly and ordered hot tea and a raw egg sent up to make a prairie oyster, then went to the closet and stood a long while, wondering vaguely what to wear. He decided on the red-brown suit in honour of Guy. It was rather inconspicuous, too, he noticed when he had it on, and it pleased him that he might have chosen it unconsciously for this reason also. He gulped the prairie oyster and it stayed down, flexed his arms but suddenly the room's Indian decor, the loony tin lamps, and the strips hanging down the walls were unbearable, and he began to shake all over again in his haste to get his things and leave. What things? He didn't need anything really. Just the paper on which he had written everything he knew about Miriam. He got it from the back pocket of his suitcase and stuck it into the inside pocket of his jacket. The gesture made him feel like a business man. He put a white handkerchief into his breast pocket, then left the room and locked the door. He figured he could be back tomorrow night, sooner if he could possibly do it tonight and catch a sleeper back.

Tonight!

He could hardly believe it as he walked towards the bus station, where one caught the bus for Lamy, the railroad terminal. He had thought he would be so happy and excited – or maybe quiet and grim – and he wasn't at all. He frowned suddenly, and his pallid, shadowy-eyed face looked much younger. Was something going to take the fun out of it after all? What would take it out? But something always had taken the fun out of everything he had ever counted on. This time he wouldn't let it. He made himself smile. Maybe it was the hangover that had made him doubt. He went into a bar and bought a fifth from a barman he knew, filled his flask, and asked for an empty pint bottle to put the rest in. The barman looked, but he didn't have one.

At Lamy Bruno went on to the station, carrying nothing but the half-empty bottle in a paper bag, not even a weapon. He hadn't planned yet, he kept reminding himself, but a lot of planning didn't always mean a murder was a success. Witness the –

'Hey, Charley! Where you going?'

It was Wilson, with a gang of people. Bruno forced himself to walk towards them, wagging his head boredly. They must have just got off a train, he thought. They looked tired and seedy.

'Where you been for two days?' Bruno asked Wilson.

'Las Vegas. Didn't know I was there until I was there, or I'd have asked you. Meet Joe Hanover. I told you about Joe.'

'H'lo, Joe.'

'What're you so mopey about?' Wilson asked with a friendly shove.

'Oh, Charley's hung over!' shrieked one of the girls, her voice like a bicycle bell right in his ear.

'Charley Hangover, meet Joe Hanover!' Joe Hanover said, convulsed.

'Haw haw.' Bruno tugged his arm away gently from a girl with a lei around her neck. 'Hell, I gotta catch this train.' His train was waiting.

'Where *you* going?' Wilson asked, frowning so his black eyebrows met.

'I hadda see someone in Tulsa,' Bruno mumbled, aware he mixed his tenses, thinking he must get away *now*. Frustration made him want to weep, lash out at Wilson's dirty red shirt with his fists.

Wilson made a movement as if he would wipe Bruno away like a chalk streak on a blackboard. 'Tulsa!'

Slowly, with a try at a grin, Bruno made a similar gesture and turned away. He walked on, expecting them to come after him, but they didn't. At the train, he looked back and saw the group moving like a rolling thing out of the sunlight into the darkness below the station roof. He frowned at them, feeling something conspiratorial in their closeness. Did they suspect something? Were they whispering about him? He boarded the train casually, and it began to move before he found his seat.

When he awakened from his nap, the world seemed quite changed. The train was speeding silkily through cool bluish mountainland. Dark green valleys were full of shadows. The sky was grey. The air-conditioned car and the cool look of things outside was as refreshing as an icepack. And he was hungry. In the diner he had a delicious lunch of lamb chops, French fries and salad, and fresh peach pie washed down with two Scotch and sodas, and strolled back to his seat feeling like a million dollars.

A sense of purpose, strange and sweet to him, carried him along in an irresistible current. Merely in gazing out the window, he felt a new co-ordination of mind and eye. He began to realize what he intended to do. He was on his way to do a murder which not only would fulfil a desire of years, but would benefit a friend. It made Bruno very happy to do things for his friends.

And his victim deserved her fate. Think of all the other good guys he would save from ever knowing her! The realization of his importance dazzled his mind, and for a long moment he felt completely and happily drunk. His energies that had been dissipated, spread like a flooded river over land as flat and boring as the Llano Estacado he was crossing now, seemed gathered in a vortex whose point strove towards Metcalf like the aggressive thrust of the train. He sat on the edge of his seat and wished Guy were opposite him again. But Guy would try to stop him, he knew; Guy wouldn't understand how much he wanted to do it or how easy it was. But for Christ's sake, he ought to understand how useful! Bruno ground his smooth, hard rubberlike fist into his palm, wishing the train would go faster. All over his body, little muscles twitched and quivered.

He took out the paper about Miriam, laid it on the empty seat opposite him, and studied it earnestly. *Miriam Joyce Haines, about twenty-two,* said his handwriting in precise, inked characters, for this was his third copy. *Rather pretty. Red hair. A little plump, not very tall. Pregnant so you could tell probably since a month. Noisy, social type. Probably flashy dressed. Maybe short curly hair, maybe a long permanent.* It wasn't very much, but it was the best he could do. A good thing she had red hair at least. Could he really do it tonight, he wondered. That depended on whether he could find her right away. He might have to go through the whole list of Joyces and Haineses. He thought she'd be living with her family probably. Once he saw her, he was sure he would recognize her. The little bitch! He hated her already. He thought of the instant he would see her and recognize her, and his feet gave an expectant jump on the floor. People came and went in the aisle, but Bruno did not look up from the paper.

She's going to have a child, Guy's voice said. The little floozy! Women who slept around made him furious, made him ill, like the mistresses his father used to have, that had turned all his school holidays into nightmares because he had not known if his mother knew and was only pretending to be happy, or if she did not know at all. He recreated every word he could of his and Guy's conversation on the train. It brought Guy close to him. Guy, he considered, was the most worthy fellow he had ever met. He had earned the Palm Beach job, and he deserved to keep it. Bruno wished he could be the one to tell Guy he still had it.

When Bruno finally replaced the paper in his pocket and sat back with one leg comfortably crossed, his hands folded on his knee, anyone seeing him would have judged him a young man of responsibility and character, probably with a promising future. He did not look in the pink of health, to be sure, but he did reflect poise and an inner happiness seen in few faces, and in Bruno's never before. His life up to now had been pathless, and seeking had known no direction, finding had revealed no meaning. There had been crises – he loved crises and created them sometimes among his acquaintances and between his father and mother – but he had always stepped out of them in time to avoid participation. This, and because he occasionally found it impossible to show sympathy even when it was his mother who was hurt by his father, had led his mother to think that a part of him was cruel, while his father and many other people believed him heartless. Yet an imagined coolness in a stranger, a friend he telephoned in a lonely dusk who was unable or unwilling to spend the evening with him, could plunge him into sulking, brooding melancholy. But only his mother knew this. He stepped out of crises because he found pleasure in depriving himself of excitement, too. So long had he been frustrated in his hunger for a meaning of his life, and in his amorphous desire to perform an act that would give it meaning, that he had come to prefer frustration, like some habitually unrequited lovers. The sweetness of fulfilment of anything he had felt he would never know. A quest with direction and hope he had always felt, from the start, too discouraged to attempt. Yet there had always been the energy to live one more day. Death held no terror at all, however. Death was only one more adventure untried. If it came on some perilous business, so much the better. Nearest, he thought, was the time he had driven a racing car blindfolded on a straight road with gas pedal on the floor. He never heard his friend's gunshot that meant stop, because he was lying unconscious in a ditch with a broken hip. At times he was so bored he contemplated the dramatic finality of suicide. It had never occurred to him that facing death unafraid might be brave, that his attitude was as resigned as that of the swamis of India, that to commit suicide required a particular kind of despondent nerve. Bruno had that kind of nerve always. He was actually a little ashamed of ever considering suicide, because it was so obvious and dull.

Now, on the train to Metcalf, he had direction. He had not felt so alive, so real and like other people since he had gone to Canada as a child with his mother and father – also on a train, he remembered. He had believed Quebec full of castles that he would be allowed to explore, but there had not been one castle, not even time to look for any, because his paternal grandmother had been dying, which was the only reason they had come anyway, and since then he had never placed full confidence in the purpose of any journey. But he did in this one.

In Metcalf, he went immediately to a telephone book and checked on the Haineses. He was barely conscious of Guy's address as he frowned down the list. No Miriam Haines, and he hadn't expected any. There were seven Joyces. Bruno scribbled a list of them on a piece of paper. Three were at the same address, 1235 Magnolia Street, and one of them there was Mrs M. J. Joyce. Bruno's pointed tongue curled speculatively over his upper lip. Certainly a good bet. Maybe her mother's name was Miriam, too. He should be able to tell a lot from the neighbourhood. He didn't think Miriam would live in a fancy neighbourhood. He hurried towards a yellow taxi parked at the kerb.

12

It was almost nine o'clock. The long dusk was sliding steeply into night, and the residential blocks of small flimsy-looking wooden houses were mostly dark, except for a glow here and there on a front porch where people sat in swings and on front steps.

'Lemme out here, this is okay,' Bruno said to the driver. Magnolia Street and College Avenue, and this was the one-thousand block. He began walking.

A little girl stood on the sidewalk, staring at him.

'Hyah,' Bruno said, like a nervous command for her to get out of the way.

'H'lo,' said the little girl.

Bruno glanced at the people on the lighted porch, a plump man fanning himself, a couple of women in the swing. Either he was tighter than he thought or luck was going to be with him, because he certainly had a hunch about 1235. He couldn't have dreamt up a neighbourhood more likely for Miriam to live in. If he was wrong, he'd just try the rest. He had the list in his pocket. The fan on the porch reminded him it was hot, apart from his own feverlike temperature that had been annoying him since late afternoon. He stopped and lighted a cigarette, pleased that his hands did not shake at all. The half bottle since lunch had fixed his hangover and put him in a slow mellow mood. Crickets chirruped everywhere around him. It was so quiet, he could hear a car shift gears two blocks away. Some young fellows came around a corner, and Bruno's heart jumped, thinking one might be Guy, but none of them was.

'You ol' jassack!' one said.

'Hell, I tol' her I ain't foolin' with no man don't give his brother an even break . . .'

Bruno looked after them haughtily. It sounded like another language. They didn't talk like Guy at all.

On some houses, Bruno couldn't find a number. Suppose he couldn't find 1235? But when he came to it, 1235 was very legible in tin numerals over the front porch. The sight of the house brought a slow pleasant thrill. Guy must have hopped up those steps very often, he thought, and it was this fact alone that really set it apart from the other houses. It was a small house like all the others on the block, only its yellow-tan clapboards were more in need of paint. It had a driveway at the side, a scraggly lawn, and an old Chevvy sedan sitting at the kerb. A light showed at a downstairs window and one in a back corner window upstairs that Bruno thought might be Miriam's room. But why didn't he *know*? Maybe Guy really hadn't told him enough!

Nervously, Bruno crossed the street and went back a little the way he had come. He stopped and turned and stared at the house, biting his lip. There was no one in sight, and no porch lighted except one down at the corner. He could not decide if the faint sound of a radio came from Miriam's house or the one next to it. The house next to it had two lighted windows downstairs. He might be able to walk up the driveway and take a look at the back of 1235.

Bruno's eyes slid alertly to the next-door front porch as the light came on. A man and woman came out, the woman sat down in the swing, and the man went down the walk. Bruno backed into the niche of a projecting garage front.

'Pistachio if they haven't got peach, Don,' Bruno heard the woman call.

'I'll take vanilla,' Bruno murmured, and drank some out of his flask.

He stared quizzically at the yellow-tan house, put a foot up behind him to lean on, and felt something hard against his thigh: the knife he had bought in the station at Big Springs, a hunting knife with a six-inch blade in a sheath. He did not want to use a knife if he could avoid it. Knives sickened him in a funny way. And a gun made noise. How would he do it? Seeing her would suggest a way. Or would it? He had thought seeing the house would suggest something, and he still felt like this was the house, but it didn't suggest anything. Could that mean this wasn't the house? Suppose he got chased off for snooping before he even found out. Guy hadn't told him enough, he really hadn't! Quickly he took another drink. He mustn't start to worry, that would spoil everything! His knee buckled. He wiped his sweaty hands on his thighs and wet his lips with a shaky tongue. He pulled the paper with the Joyce addresses out of his breast pocket and slanted it towards the street light. He still couldn't see to read. Should he leave and try another address, maybe come back here?

He would wait fifteen minutes, maybe half an hour.

A preference for attacking her out of doors had taken root in his mind on the train, so all his ideas began from a simple physical approach to her. This street was almost dark enough, for instance, very dark there under the trees. He preferred to use his bare bands, or to hit her over the head with something. He did not realize how excited he was until he felt his body start now with his thoughts of jumping to right or left, as it might be, when he attacked her. Now and then it crossed his mind how happy Guy would be when it was done. Miriam had become an object, small and hard.

He heard a man's voice, and a laugh, he was sure from the lighted upstairs room in 1235, then a girl's smiling voice: 'Stop that? – Please? Plee-ee-ease?' Maybe Miriam's voice. Babyish and stringy, but somehow strong like a strong string, too.

The light blinked out and Bruno's eyes stayed at the dark window. Then the porch light flashed on and two men and a girl – *Miriam* – came out. Bruno held his breath and set his feet on the ground. He could see the red in her hair. The bigger fellow was redheaded, too – maybe her brother. Bruno's eyes caught a hundred details at once, the chunky compactness of her figure, the flat shoes, the easy way she swung around to look up at one of the men.

'Think we ought to call her, Dick?' she asked in that thin voice. 'It's kinda late.'

A corner of the shade in the front window lifted. 'Honey? Don't be out too long!'

'No, Mom.'

They were going to take the car at the kerb.

Bruno faded towards the corner, looking for a taxi. Fat chance in this dead burg! He ran. He hadn't run in months, and he felt fit as an athlete.

'Taxi!' He didn't even see a taxi, then he did and dove for it.

He made the driver circle and come into Magnolia Street in

the direction the Chevvy had been pointed. The Chevvy was gone. Darkness had closed in tight. Far away he saw a red tail-light blinking under trees.

'Keep going!'

When the tail-light stopped for a red and the taxi closed some of the distance, Bruno saw it was the Chevvy and sank back with relief.

'Where do you want to go?' asked the driver.

'Keep going!' Then as the Chevvy swung into a big avenue, 'Turn right.' He sat up on the edge of his seat. Glancing at a kerb, he saw 'Crockett Boulevard' and smiled. He had heard of Crockett Boulevard in Metcalf, the widest longest street.

'Who're the people's names you want to go to?' the driver asked. 'Maybe I know 'em.'

'Just a minute, just a minute,' Bruno said, unconsciously assuming another personality, pretending to search through the papers he had dragged from his inside pocket, among them the paper about Miriam. He snickered suddenly, feeling very amused, very safe. Now he was pretending to be the dopey guy from out of town, who had even misplaced the address of where he wanted to go. He bent his head so the driver could not see him laughing, and reached automatically for his flask.

'Need a light?'

'Nope, nope, thank you.' He took a hot swallow. Then the Chevvy backed into the avenue, and Bruno told the driver to keep going.

'Where?'

'Get going and shut up!' Bruno shouted, his voice falset to with anxiety.

The driver shook his head and made a click with his tongue. Bruno fumed, but they had the Chevvy in sight. Bruno thought they would never stop driving and that Crockett Boulevard must cross the whole state of Texas. Twice Bruno lost and found the Chevvy. They passed roadstands and drive-in movies, then darkness put up a wall on either side. Bruno began to worry. He couldn't tail them out of town or down a country road.

Then a big arch of lights appeared over the toad. WELCOME TO
LAKE METCALF'S KINGDOM OF FUN, it said, and the Chevvy drove
under it and into a parking lot. There were all kinds of lights
ahead in the woods and the jingle of merry-go-round music. An
amusement park! Bruno was delighted.

'Four bucks,' said the driver sourly, and Bruno poked a five
through the front window.

He hung back until Miriam and the two fellows and a new
girl they had picked up had gone through the turnstile, then he
followed them. He stretched his eyes wide for a good look at
Miriam under the lights. She was cute in a plump college-girl
sort of way, but definitely second-rate, Bruno judged. The red
socks with the red sandals infuriated him. How could Guy have
married such a thing? Then his feet scraped and he stood still:
she wasn't pregnant! His eyes narrowed in intense perplexity.
Why hadn't he noticed from the first? But maybe it wouldn't
show yet. He bit his underlip hard. Considering how plump
she was, her waist looked even flatter than it ought to. Maybe a
sister of Miriam's. Or she had had an abortion or something. Or
a miscarriage. Miss Carriage! How *do* you do? Swing it, sister!
She had fat little hips under a tight grey skirt. He moved on as
they did, following evenly, as if magnetized. Had Guy lied about
her being pregnant? But Guy wouldn't lie. Bruno's mind swam
in contradictions. He stared at Miriam with his head cocked.
Then something made a connection in his mind before he was
aware of looking for it: if something had happened to the child,
then all the more reason why he should erase her, because Guy
wouldn't be able to get his divorce. She could be walking around
now if she had had an abortion, for instance.

She stood in front of a sideshow where a gypsy woman was
dropping things into a big fish bowl. The other girl started
laughing, leaning all over the redheaded fellow.

'Miriam!'

Bruno leapt off his feet.

'Oooh, yes!' Miriam went across to the frozen-custard stand.
They all bought frozen custards. Bruno waited boredly smiling,

looking up at the ferris wheel's arc of lights and the tiny people swinging in benches up there in the black sky. Far off through the trees, he saw lights twinkling on water. It was quite a park. He wanted to ride the ferris wheel. He felt wonderful. He was taking it easy, not getting excited. The merry-go-round played 'Casey would waltz with the strawberry blonde . . .' Grinning, he turned to Miriam's red hair, and their eyes met, but hers moved on and he was sure she hadn't noticed him, but he mustn't do that again. A rush of anxiety made him snicker. Miriam didn't look at all smart, he decided, which amused him, too. He could see why Guy would loathe her. He loathed her, too, with all his guts! Maybe she was lying to Guy about having a baby. And Guy was so honest himself, he believed her. Bitch!

When they moved on with their frozen custards, he released the swallow-tailed bird he had been fingering in the balloon seller's box, then wheeled around and bought one, a bright yellow one. It made him feel like a kid again, whipping the stick around, listening to the tail's *squee-wee-wee*!

A little boy walking by with his parents stretched his hand towards it, and Bruno had an impulse to give it to him, but he didn't.

Miriam and her friends entered a big lighted section where the bottom of the ferris wheel was and a lot of concessions and sideshows. The roller coaster made a *tat-tat-tat-tat-tat* like a machine-gun over their heads. There was a clang and a roar as someone sent the red arrow all the way to the top with a sledge-hammer. He wouldn't mind killing Miriam with a sledge hammer, he thought. He examined Miriam and each of the three to see if any seemed aware of him, but he was sure they weren't. If he didn't do it tonight, he mustn't let any of them notice him. Yet somehow he was sure he would do it tonight. Something would happen that he could. This was his night. The cooler night air bathed him, like some liquid that he frolicked in. He waved the bird in wide circles. He liked Texas, Guy's state! Everybody looked happy and full of energy. He let Miriam's group blend into a crowd while he took a gulp from his flask. Then he loped after them.

They were looking at the ferris wheel, and he hoped they would decide to ride it. They really did things big in Texas, Bruno thought, looking up admiringly at the wheel. He had never seen a ferris wheel big as this. It had a five-pointed star in blue lights inside it.

'Ralph, how 'bout it?' Miriam squealed, poking the last of the frozen-custard cone into her mouth with her hand against her face.

'Aw, 's ain't no fun. H'bout the merry-go-round?'

And they all went. The merry-go-round was like a lighted city in the dark woods, a forest of nickel-plated poles crammed with zebras, horses, giraffes, bulls, and camels all plunging down or upward, some with necks arched out over the platform, frozen in leaps and gallops as if they waited desperately for riders. Bruno stood still, unable to take his dazzled eyes from it even to watch Miriam, tingling to the music that promised movement at any instant. He felt he was about to experience again some ancient, delicious childhood moment that the steam calliope's sour hollowness, the stitching hurdy-gurdy accompaniment, and the drum-and-cymbal crash brought almost to the margin of his grasp.

People were choosing mounts. And Miriam and her friends were eating again, Miriam diving into a popcorn bag Dick held for her. The pigs! Bruno was hungry, too. He bought a frankfurter, and when he looked again, they were boarding the merry-go-round. He scrambled for coins and ran. He got the horse he had wanted, a royal blue one with an upreared head and an open mouth, and as luck would have it, Miriam and her friends kept weaving back through the poles towards him, and Miriam and Dick took the giraffe and the horse right in front of him. Luck was with him tonight! Tonight he should be gambling!

Just like the strain – te-te-dum –
Of a haunting refrain – te-te-dum –
She'll start upon – BOOM! a marathon – BOOM!

Bruno loved the song and so did his mother. The music made him suck in his belly and sit his horse like a ramrod. He swung his feet gaily in the stirrups. Something swatted him in the back of the head, he turned belligerently, but it was only some fellows rough-housing with one another.

They started off slowly and militantly to 'The Washington Post March'. Up, up, up he went and down, down, down went Miriam on her giraffe. The world beyond the merry-go-round vanished in a light-streaked blur. Bruno held the reins in one hand as he had been taught to do in his polo lessons, and ate the frankfurter with the other.

'Yeeee-hooo!' yelled the redheaded fellow.

'Yeeee-hooo!' Bruno yelled back. 'I'm a Texan!'

'Katie?' Miriam leaned forward on the giraffe's neck, and her grey skirt got round and tight. 'See the fellow over there in the check shirt?'

Bruno looked. He saw the fellow in the checked shirt. He looked a little like Guy, Bruno thought, and thinking of this, he missed what Miriam said about him. Under the bright lights, he saw that Miriam was covered with freckles. She looked increasingly loathsome, so he began not to want to put his hands on her soft sticky-warm flesh. Well, he still had the knife. A clean instrument.

'A clean instrument!' Bruno shouted jubilantly, for no one could possibly hear him. His was the outside horse, and next to him was a boxed double-seat thing made out of swans, which was empty. He spat into it. He flung away the rest of the frankfurter and wiped the mustard off his fingers on the horse's mane.

'Casey would waltz with the strawberry blonde, while the band – played – aaaawn!' Miriam's date sang out with vehemence.

They all joined in and Bruno with them. The whole merry-go-round was singing. If they only had drinks! Everybody should be having a drink!

'His brain was so loaded, it nearly exploded,' sang Bruno at the cracking top of his lungs, 'the poor girl would shake with alaa-arm!'

'Hi, Casey!' Miriam cooed to Dick, opening her mouth to catch the popcorn he was trying to throw into it.

'Yak-yak!' Bruno shouted.

Miriam looked ugly and stupid with her mouth open, as if she were being strangled and had turned pink and bloated. He could not bear to look at her, and still grinning, turned his eyes away. The merry-go-round was slowing. He hoped they would stay for another ride, but they got off, linked arms, and began to walk towards the twinkling lights on the water.

Bruno paused under the trees for another little nip from the nearly empty flask.

They were taking a rowboat. The prospect of a cool row was delightful to Bruno. He engaged a boat, too. The lake looked big and black, except for the lightless twinkles, full of drifting boats with couples necking in them. Bruno got close enough to Miriam's boat to see that the redheaded fellow was doing the rowing, and that Miriam and Dick were squeezing each other and giggling in the back seat. Bruno bent for three deep strokes that carried him past their boat, then let his oars trail.

'Want to go to the island or loaf around?' the redheaded fellow asked.

Petulantly, Bruno slumped sideways on the seat, waiting for them to make up their minds. In the nooks along the shore, as if from little dark rooms, he heard murmurs, soft radios, laughter. He tipped his flask and drained it. What would happen if he shouted 'Guy!'? What would Guy think if he could see him now? Maybe Guy and Miriam had been out on dates on this lake, maybe in the same rowboat he sat in now. His hands and the lower part of his legs tingled cosily with the liquor. If he had Miriam here in the boat with him, he would hold her head under the water with pleasure. Here in the dark. Pitch dark and no moon. The water made quick licking sounds against his boat. Bruno writhed in sudden impatience. There was the sucking sound of a kiss from Miriam's boat, and Bruno gave it back to them with a pleasurable groan thrown in. *Smack, smack!* They must have heard him, because there was a burst of laughter.

He waited until they had paddled past, then followed leisurely. A black mass drew closer, pricked here and there with the spark of a match. The island. It looked like a neckers' paradise. Maybe Miriam would be at it again tonight, Bruno thought, giggling.

When Miriam's boat landed, he rowed a few yards to one side and climbed ashore, and set his boat's nose up on a little log so it would be easy to recognize from the others. The sense of purpose filled him once more, stronger and more imminent than on the train. In Metcalf hardly two hours, and here he was on an island with her! He pressed the knife against him through his trousers. If he could just get her alone and clap his hand over her mouth – or would she be able to bite? He squirmed with disgust at the thought of her wet mouth on his hand.

Slowly he followed their slow steps, up rough ground where the trees were close.

'We cain't sit here, the ground's wet,' whined the girl called Katie.

'Sit on mah coat if y'wanta,' a fellow said.

Christ, Bruno thought, those dumb Southern accents!

'When I'm walkin' with m'honey down honeymoon lane . . .' somebody sang, off in the bushes.

Night murmurs. Bugs. Crickets. And a mosquito at his ear. Bruno boxed his ear and the ear rang maddeningly, drowning out the voices.

'. . . shove off.'

'Why cain't we find a place?' Miriam yapped.

'Ain't no place an' watch whatcha step in!'

'Watcha step-ins, gals!' laughed the redheaded fellow.

What the hell *were* they going to do? He was bored! The music of the merry-go-round sounded tired and very distant, only the *tings* coming through. Then they turned around right in his face, so he had to move off to one side as if he were going somewhere. He got tangled in some thorny underbrush and occupied himself getting free of it while they passed him. Then he followed, downward. He thought he could smell Miriam's perfume, if it wasn't the other girl's, a sweetness like a steamy bathroom that repelled him.

'. . . and now,' said a radio, 'coming in very cautiously . . . Leon . . . *Leon* . . . lands a hard right to the Babe's face *andlistentothecrowd!*' A roar.

Bruno saw a fellow and a girl wallowing down there in the bushes as if they were fighting, too.

Miriam stood on slightly higher ground, not three yards away from him now, and the others slid down the bank towards the water. Bruno inched closer. The lights on the water silhouetted her head and shoulders. Never had he been so close!

'Hey!' Bruno whispered, and saw her turn. 'Say, isn't your name Miriam?'

She faced him, but he knew she could barely see him. 'Yeah. Who're you?'

He came a step nearer. 'Haven't I met you somewhere before?' he asked cynically, smelling the perfume again. She was a warm ugly black spot. He sprang with such concentrated aim, the wrists of his spread hands touched.

'Say what d'you –?'—

His hands captured her throat on the last word, stifling its abortive uplift of surprise. He shook her. His body seemed to harden like rock, and he heard his teeth crack. She made a grating sound in her throat, but he had her too tight for a scream. With a leg behind her, he wrenched her backward, and they fell to the ground together with no sound but of a brush of leaves. He sunk his fingers deeper, enduring the distasteful pressure of her body under his so her writhing would not get them both up. Her throat felt hotter and fatter. Stop, stop, stop! He willed it! And the head stopped turning. He was sure he had held her long enough, but he did not lessen his grip. Glancing behind him, he saw nothing coming. When he relaxed his fingers, it felt as if he had made deep dents in her throat as in a piece of dough. Then she made a sound like an ordinary cough that terrified him like the rising dead, and he fell on her again, hitched himself on to his knees to do it, pressing her with a force he thought would break his thumbs. All the power in him he poured out through his hands. And if it was not enough? He heard himself whimper. She was still and limp now.

'Miriam?' called the girl's voice.

Bruno sprang up and stumbled straight away towards the centre of the island, then turned left to bring him out near his boat. He found himself scrubbing something off his hands with his pocket handkerchief. Miriam's spit. He threw the handkerchief down and swept it up again, because it was monogrammed. He was thinking! He felt great! It was done!

'Mi-ri-am!' with lazy impatience.

But what if he hadn't finished her, if she were sitting up and talking now? The thought shot him forward and he almost toppled down the bank. A firm breeze met him at the water's edge. He didn't see his boat. He started to take any boat, changed his mind, then a couple of yards farther to the left found it, perched on the little log.

'Hey, she's fainted!'

Bruno shoved off, quickly, but not hurrying.

'Help, somebody!' said the girl's half gasp, half scream.

'Gawd! – Huh-*help*!'

The panic in the voice panicked Bruno. He rowed for several choppy strokes, then abruptly stopped and let the boat glide over the dark water. What was he getting scared about, for Christ's sake? Not a sign of anyone chasing him.

'Hey!'

'F'God's sake, she's *dead*! Call somebody!'

A girl's scream was a long arc in silence and somehow the scream made it final. A beautiful scream, Bruno thought with a queer, serene admiration. He approached the dock easily, behind another boat. Slowly, as slowly as he had ever done anything, he paid the boatkeeper.

'On the island!' said another shocking, excited voice from a boat. 'Girl's dead, they said!'

'Dead?'

'Somebody call the cops!'

Feet ran on the wooden dock behind him.

Bruno idled towards the gates of the park. Thank God he was so tight or hung over or something he could move so slowly! But a fluttering, unfightable terror rose in him as he passed through the turnstile. Then it ebbed quickly. No one was even looking at him. To steady himself, he concentrated on wanting a drink. There was a place up the road with red lights that looked like a bar, and he went straight towards it.

'Cutty,' he said to the barman.

'Where you from, son?'

Bruno looked at him. The two men on the right were looking at him, too. 'I want a Scotch.'

'Can't get no hard liquor round here, man.'

'What is this, part of the park?' His voice cracked like the scream.

'Can't get no hard liquor in the state of Texas.'

'Gimme some of that!' Bruno pointed to the bottle of rye the men had on the counter.

'Here. Anybody wants a drink that bad.' One of the men poured some rye in a glass and pushed it over.

It was rough as Texas going down, but sweet when it got there. Bruno offered to pay him, but the man refused.

Police sirens sounded, coming closer.

A man came in the door.

'What happened? Accident?' somebody asked him.

'I didn't see anything,' the man said unconcernedly.

My brother! Bruno thought, looking the man over, but it didn't seem the thing to do to go over and talk to him.

He felt fine. The man kept insisting he have another drink, and Bruno had three fast. He noticed a streak on his hand as he lifted the glass, got out his handkerchief, and calmly wiped between his thumb and forefinger. It was a smear of Miriam's orangey lipstick. He could hardly see it in the bar's light. He thanked the man with the rye, and strolled out into the darkness, walking along the right side of the road, looking for a taxi. He had no desire to look back at the lighted park. He wasn't even thinking about it, he told himself. A streetcar passed, and he ran for it. He enjoyed its bright interior, and read all the placards. A wriggly little boy sat across the aisle, and Bruno began chatting with him. The thought of calling Guy and seeing him kept crossing his mind, but of course Guy wasn't here. He wanted some kind of celebration. He might call Guy's mother again, for the hell of it, but on second thought, it didn't seem wise. It was the one lousy note in the evening, the fact he couldn't see Guy, or even talk or write to him for a long while. Guy would be in for some questioning, of course. But he was free! It was done, done, done! In a burst of well-being, he ruffled the little boy's hair.

The little boy was taken aback for a moment, then in response to Bruno's friendly grin, he smiled, too.

At the Atchison, Topeka and Santa Fe Railroad terminal, he got an upper berth on a sleeper leaving at 1.30 a.m., which gave him an hour and a half to kill. Everything was perfect and he felt terribly happy. In a drugstore near the station, he bought a pint of Scotch to refill his flask. He thought of going by Guy's house to see what it looked like, debated it carefully, and decided he could. He was just heading for a man standing by the door, to ask directions – he knew he shouldn't go there in a taxi – when he realized he wanted a woman. He wanted a woman more than ever before in his life, and that he did pleased him prodigiously. He hadn't wanted one since he got to Santa Fe, though twice Wilson had got him into it. He veered away right in the man's face, thinking one of the taxi drivers outside would be better to ask. He had the shakes, he wanted a woman so badly! A different kind of shakes from liquor shakes.

'Ah don' know,' said the blank, freckle-faced driver leaning against the fender.

'What d'you mean, you don't know?'

'Don' know, that's all.'

Bruno left him in disgust.

Another driver down the sidewalk was more obliging. He wrote Bruno an address and a couple of names on the back of a company card, though it was so close by, he didn't even have to drive him there.

13

Guy leaned against the wall by his bed in the Montecarlo, watching Anne turn the pages of the family album he had brought from Metcalf. These had been wonderful days, his last two with Anne. Tomorrow he left for Metcalf. And then Florida. Mr Brillhart's telegram had come three days ago, saying the commission was still his. There was a stretch of six months' work ahead, and in December the commencement of their own house. He had the money to build it now. And the money for the divorce.

'You know,' he said quietly, 'if I didn't have Palm Beach, if I had to go back to New York tomorrow and work, I could, and take anything.' But almost as he said it, he realized that Palm Beach had given him his courage, his momentum, his will, or whatever he chose to call it, that without Palm Beach these days with Anne would give him only a sense of guilt.

'But you don't have to,' Anne said finally. She bent lower over the album.

He smiled. He knew she had hardly been listening to him. And, in fact, what he had said didn't matter, as Anne knew. He leaned over the album with her, identifying the people that she asked about, watching amusedly as she examined the double page of his pictures that his mother had collected, from babyhood to about twenty. He was smiling in every one of them, a shock of black hair setting off a sturdier, more careless-looking face than he had now.

'Do I look happy enough there?' he asked.

She winked at him. 'And very handsome. Any of Miriam?' She let the remaining pages slip past her thumbnail.

'No,' Guy said.

'I'm awfully glad you brought this.'

'My mother would have my neck if she knew it was in Mexico.' He put the album back in his suitcase so he wouldn't possibly leave it behind. 'It's the most humane way of meeting families.'

'Guy, did I put you through much?'

He smiled at her plaintive tone. 'No! I never minded a bit!' He sat down on the bed and pulled her back with him. He had met all of Anne's relatives, by twos and threes, by dozens at the Faulkners' Sunday suppers and parties. It was a family joke how many Faulkners and Weddells and Morrisons there were, all living in New York State or in Long Island. Somehow he liked the fact she had so many relatives. The Christmas he had spent at the Faulkners' house last year had been the happiest of his life. He kissed both her cheeks, then her mouth. When he put his head down, he saw Anne's drawings on the Montecarlo stationery on the counterpane, and idly began to push them into a neat stack. They were ideas for designs that had come to her after their visit to the Museo Nacionale this afternoon. Their lines were black and definite, like his own rough sketches. 'I'm thinking about the house, Anne.'

'You want it big.'

He smiled. 'Yes.'

'Let's have it big.' She relaxed in his arms. They both sighed, like one person, and she laughed a little as he wrapped her closer.

It was the first time she had agreed to the size of the house. The house was to be Y-shaped, and the question had been whether to dispense with the front arm of it. But the idea sang in Guy's head only with both arms. It would cost much, much more than twenty thousand, but Palm Beach would bring a flock of private commissions, Guy expected, that would be fast, well-paid jobs. Anne had said her father would like nothing better than to make them a wedding present of the front wing, but to Guy that seemed as unthinkable as removing it. He could see the house shining white and sharp against the brown bureau across the room. It projected from a certain white rock he had seen near a town called Alton in lower Connecticut. The house was long, low, and flat-roofed, as if alchemy had created it from the rock itself, like a crystal.

'I might call it "The Crystal", Guy said.

Anne stared up reflectively at the ceiling. 'I'm not so fond of naming houses – houses' names. Maybe I don't like "Crystal".'

Guy felt subtly hurt. 'It's a lot better than "Alton". Of all the insipid names! That's New England for you. Take Texas now –'

'All right, you take Texas and I'll take New England.' Anne smiled, stopping Guy in his tracks, because in reality she liked Texas and Guy liked New England.

Guy looked at the telephone, with a funny premonition it was going to ring. He felt rather giddy in his head, as if he had taken some mildly euphoric drug. It was the altitude, Anne said, that made people feel that way in Mexico City. 'I feel as if I could call up Miriam tonight and talk to her and everything would be all right,' Guy said slowly, 'as if I could say just the right thing.'

'There's the telephone,' Anne said, perfectly serious.

Seconds passed, and he heard Anne sigh.

'What time is it?' she asked, sitting up. 'I told Mother I'd be back by twelve.'

'Eleven-seven.'

'Aren't you sort of hungry?'

They ordered something from the restaurant downstairs. Their ham and eggs were an unrecognizable dish of vermilion colour, but quite good, they decided.

'I'm glad you got to Mexico,' Anne said. 'It's been like something I knew so well and you didn't, something I wanted you to know. Only Mexico City isn't like the rest.' She went on, eating slowly, 'It has a nostalgia like Paris or Vienna and you want to come back no matter what's happened to you here.'

Guy frowned. He had been to Paris and Vienna with Robert Treacher, a Canadian engineer, one summer when neither of them had any money. It hadn't been the Paris and Vienna Anne had known. He looked down at the buttered sweet roll she had given him. At times he wanted passionately to know the flavour of every experience Anne had ever known, what had happened to her in every hour of her childhood. 'What do you mean, no matter what's happened to me here?'

'I mean whether you've been sick. Or robbed.' She looked up at him and smiled. But the lamp's light that made a glow through her smoke-blue eyes, a crescent glow on their darker rims, lent a mysterious sadness to her face. 'I suppose it's contrasts that make it attractive. Like people with incredible contrasts.'

Guy stared at her, his finger crooked in the handle of his coffee cup. Somehow her mood, or perhaps what she said, made him feel inferior. 'I'm sorry I don't have any incredible contrasts.'

'Oh-ho-ho!' Then she burst out in a laugh, her familiar gay laugh that delighted him even when she laughed at him, even when she had no intention of explaining herself.

He sprang up. 'How about some cake. I'm going to produce a cake like a jinni. A wonderful cake!' He got the cookie tin out of the corner of his suitcase. He had not thought of the cake until that moment, the cake his mother had baked him with the blackberry jam he had praised at his breakfasts.

Anne telephoned the bar downstairs and ordered a very special liqueur that she knew of. The liqueur was a rich purple like the purple cake, in stemmed glasses hardly bigger around than a finger. The waiter had just gone, they were lifting the glasses, when the telephone rang, in nervous, iterant rings.

'Probably Mother,' Anne said.

Guy answered it. He heard a voice talking distantly to an operator. Then the voice came louder, anxious and shrill, his mother's voice:

'Hello?'

'Hello, Mama.'

'Guy, something's happened.'

'What's the matter?'

'It's Miriam!'

'What about her?' Guy pressed the receiver hard against his ear. He turned to Anne, and saw her face change as she looked at him.

'She's been killed, Guy. Last night –' She broke off.

'What, Mama?'

'It happened last night.' She spoke in the shrill, measured tones that Guy had heard only once or twice before in his life. 'Guy, she was murdered.'

'Murdered!'

'Guy, *what*?' Anne asked, getting up.

'Last night at the lake. They don't know anything.'

'You're –'

'Can you come home, Guy?'

'Yes, Mama. – How?' he asked stupidly, wringing the telephone as if he could wring information from its two old-fashioned parts. 'How?'

'Strangled.' The one word, then silence.

'Did you –?' he began. 'Is –?'

'Guy, what is it?' Anne held to his arm.

'I'll be home as fast as I can, Mama. Tonight. Don't worry. I'll see you very soon.' He hung up slowly and turned to Anne. 'It's Miriam. Miriam's been killed.'

Anne whispered, 'Murdered – did you say?'

Guy nodded, but it suddenly struck him there might be a mistake. If it were just a report –

'When?'

But it was last night. 'Last night, she said.'

'Do they know who?'

'No. I've got to go tonight.'

'My God.'

He looked at Anne, standing motionless in front of him. 'I've got to go tonight,' he said again, dazedly. Then he turned and went to the telephone to call for a plane reservation, but it was Anne who got the reservation for him, talking rapidly in Spanish.

He began to pack. It seemed to take hours getting his few possessions into his suitcase. He stared at the brown bureau, wondering if he had already looked through it to see if everything were out of its drawers. Now, where he had seen the vision of the white house, a laughing face appeared, first the crescent mouth, then the face – Bruno's face. The tongue curved lewdly over the upper lip, and then the silent convulsed laughter came again, shaking the stringy hair over the forehead. Guy frowned at Anne.

'What's the matter, Guy?'

'Nothing,' he said. How *did* he look now?

14

Supposing Bruno had done it? He couldn't have, of course, but just supposing he had? Had they caught him? Had Bruno told them the murder was a plan of theirs? Guy could easily imagine Bruno hysterical, saying anything. There was no predicting what a neurotic child like Bruno would say. Guy searched his hazy memory of their conversation on the train and tried to recall if in jest or anger or drunkenness he had said anything that might have been taken as a consent to Bruno's insane idea. He hadn't. Against this negative answer, he weighed Bruno's letter that he remembered word for word: *that idea we had for a couple of murders. It could be done, I am sure. I cannot express to you my supremest confidence –*

From the plane window, Guy looked down into total blackness. Why wasn't he more anxious than he was? Up the dim cylinder of the plane's body, a match glowed at someone's cigarette. The scent of Mexican tobacco was faint, bitter, and sickening. He looked at his watch: 4.25.

Towards dawn he fell asleep, yielding to the shaking roar of the motors that seemed bent on tearing the plane apart, tearing his mind apart, and scattering the pieces in the sky. He awakened to a grey overcast morning, and a new thought: Miriam's lover had killed her. It was so obvious, so likely. He had killed her in a quarrel. One read such cases so often in the newspapers, the victims so often women like Miriam. There was a front-page story about a girl's murder in the tabloid *El Grafico* he had bought at the airport – he hadn't been able to find an American paper, though he had almost missed the plane looking for one and a picture of her grinning Mexican lover holding the knife with which he had killed her, and Guy started to read it, becoming bored in the second paragraph.

A plain-clothes man met him at the Metcalf airport and asked if he would mind answering a few questions. They got into a taxi together.

'Have they found the murderer?' Guy asked him.

'No.'

The plain-clothes man looked tired, as if he had been up all night, like the rest of the reporters and clerks and police in the old North Side courthouse. Guy glanced around the big wooden room, looking for Bruno before he was aware of doing so. When he lighted a cigarette, the man next to him asked him what kind it was, and accepted the one Guy offered him. They were Anne's Belmonts that he had pocketed when he was packing.

'Guy Daniel Haines, 717 Ambrose Street, Metcalf . . . When did you leave Metcalf? . . . And when did you get to Mexico City?'

Chairs scraped. A noiseless typewriter started bumping after them.

Another plain-clothes man with a badge, with his jacket open and a swagbelly protruding, strolled closer. 'Why did you go to Mexico?'

'To visit some friends.'

'Who?'

'The Faulkners. Alex Faulkner of New York.'

'Why didn't you tell your mother where you were going?'

'I did tell her.'

'She didn't know where you were staying in Mexico City,' the plain-clothes man informed him blandly, and referred to his notes. 'You sent your wife a letter Sunday asking for a divorce. What did she reply?'

'That she wanted to talk with me.'

'But you didn't care to talk with her any more, did you?' asked a clear tenor voice.

Guy looked at the young police officer, and said nothing.

'Was her child to be yours?'

He started to answer, but was interrupted.

'Why did you come to Texas last week to see your wife?'

'Didn't you want a divorce pretty badly, Mr Haines?'

'Are you in love with Anne Faulkner?'

Laughter.

'You know your wife had a lover, Mr Haines. Were you jealous?'

'You were depending on that child for your divorce, weren't you?'

'That's all!' someone said.

A photograph was thrust in front of him, and the image spun with his anger before it straightened to a long dark head, handsome and stupid brown eyes, a cleft, manly chin – a face that might have been a movie actor's, and no one had to tell him this was Miriam's lover, because this was the kind of face she had liked three years ago.

'No,' Guy said.

'Haven't you and he had some talks together?'

'That's all!'

A bitter smile pulled at the corner of his mouth, yet he felt he might have cried, too, like a child. He hailed a taxi in front of the courthouse. On the ride home, he read the double column on the front of the *Metcalf Star*:

QUEST CONTINUES FOR GIRL'S SLAYER

June 12 – The quest continues for the slayer of Mrs Miriam Joyce Haines of this city, victim of strangulation by an unknown assailant on Metcalf Island Sunday night.

Two fingerprint experts arrive today who will endeavour to establish classifications of fingerprints taken from several oars and rowboats of the Lake Metcalf rowboat docks. But police and detectives fear that obtainable fingerprints are hazy. Authorities yesterday afternoon expressed the opinion that the crime might have been the act of a maniac. Apart from dubious fingerprints and several heelprints around the scene of the attack, police officials have not yet uncovered any vital clue.

Most important testimony at the inquest, it is believed, will come from Owen Markman, 30, longshoreman of Houston, and a close friend of the murdered woman.

Interment of Mrs Haines's body will take place today at Remington Cemetery. The cortège departs from Howell Funeral Home on College Avenue at 2.00 p.m. this afternoon.

Guy lighted a cigarette from the end of another. His hands were still shaking, but he felt vaguely better. He hadn't thought of the possibility of a maniac. A maniac reduced it to a kind of horrible accident.

His mother sat in her rocker in the living-room with a handkerchief pressed to her temple, waiting for him, though she did not get up when he came in. Guy embraced her and kissed her cheek, relieved to see she hadn't been crying.

'I spent yesterday with Mrs Joyce,' she said, 'but I just can't go to the funeral.'

'There isn't any need to, Mama.' He glanced at his watch and saw it was already past two. For an instant, he felt that Miriam might have been buried alive, that she might awaken and scream in protest. He turned, and passed his hand across his forehead.

'Mrs Joyce,' his mother said softly, 'asked me if you might know something.'

Guy faced her again. Mrs Joyce resented him, he knew. He hated her now for what she might have said to his mother. 'Don't see them again, Mama. You don't have to, do you?'

'No.'

'And thank you for going over.'

Upstairs on his bureau, he found three letters and a small square package with a Santa Fe store label. The package contained a narrow belt of braided lizard skin with a silver buckle formed like an H. A note enclosed said:

Lost your Plato book on way to post office. I hope this will help make up.

Charley

Guy picked up the pencilled envelope from the Santa Fe hotel. There was only a small card inside. On the card's back was printed:

NICE TOWN METCALF

Turning the card, he read mechanically:

24 HOUR
DONOVAN TAXI SERVICE
RAIN OR SHINE
Call 2-3333
SAFE FAST COURTEOUS

Something had been erased beneath the message on the back. Guy held the card to the light and made out one word: Ginnie. It was a Metcalf taxi company's card, but it had been mailed from Santa Fe. It doesn't mean anything, doesn't prove anything, he thought. But he crushed the card and the envelope and the package wrappings into his waste-basket. He loathed Bruno, he realized. He opened the box in the waste-basket and put the belt in, too. It was a handsome belt, but he happened also to loathe lizard and snake skin.

Anne telephoned him that night from Mexico City. She wanted to know everything that had happened, and he told her what he knew.

'They don't have any suspicion who did it?' she asked.

'They don't seem to.'

'You don't sound well, Guy. Did you get any rest?'

'Not yet.' He couldn't tell her now about Bruno. His mother had said that a man had called twice, wanting to talk to him, and Guy had no doubt who it was. But he knew he could not tell Anne about Bruno until he was sure. He could not begin.

'We've just sent those affidavits, darling. You know, about your being here with us?'

He had wired her for them after talking to one of the police detectives. 'Everything'll be all right after the inquest,' he said.

But it troubled him the rest of the night that he had not told Anne about Bruno. It was not the horror that he wished to spare her. He felt it was some sense of personal guilt that he himself could not bear.

There was a report going about that Owen Markman had not wanted to marry Miriam after the loss of the child, and that she had started a breach-of-promise action against him. Miriam really had lost the child accidentally, Guy's mother said. Mrs Joyce had told her that Miriam had tripped on a black silk nightgown that she particularly liked, that Owen had given her, and had fallen downstairs in her house. Guy believed the story implicitly. A compassion and remorse he had never before felt for Miriam had entered his heart. Now she seemed pitiably ill-fated and entirely innocent.

15

'Not more than seven yards and not less than five,' the grave, self-assured young man in the chair replied. 'No, I did not see anyone.'

'I think about fifteen feet,' said the wide-eyed girl, Katherine Smith, who looked as frightened as if it had just happened. 'Maybe a little more,' she added softly.

'About thirty feet. I was the first one down at the boat,' said Ralph Joyce, Miriam's brother. His red hair was like Miriam's, and he had the same grey-green eyes, but his heavy square jaw took away the resemblance. 'I wouldn't say she had any enemy. Not enough to do something like this.'

'I didn't hear one thing,' Katherine Smith said earnestly, shaking her head.

Ralph Joyce said he hadn't heard anything, and Richard Schuyler's positive statement ended it:

'There weren't any sounds.'

The facts repeated and repeated lost their horror and even their drama for Guy. They were like dull blows of a hammer, nailing the story in his mind forever. The nearness of the three others was the unbelievable. Only a maniac would have dared come so near, Guy thought, that was certain.

'Were you the father of the child Mrs Haines lost?'

'Yes.' Owen Markman slouched forward over his locked fingers. A glum, hangdog manner spoilt the dashing good looks Guy had seen in the photograph. He wore grey buckskin shoes, as if he had just come from his job in Houston. Miriam would not have been proud of him today, Guy thought.

'Do you know anyone who might have wanted Mrs Haines to die?'

'Yes.' Markman pointed at Guy. 'Him.'

People turned to look at him. Guy sat tensely, frowning straight at Markman, for the first time really suspecting Markman.

'Why?'

Owen Markman hesitated a long while, mumbled something, then brought out one word: 'Jealousy.'

Markman could not give a single credible reason for jealousy, but after that accusation of jealousy came from all sides. Even Katherine Smith said, 'I guess so.'

Guy's lawyer chuckled. He had the affidavits from the Faulkners in his hand. Guy hated the chuckle. He had always hated legal procedure. It was like a vicious game in which the objective seemed not to disclose the truth but to enable one lawyer to tilt at another, and unseat him on a technicality.

'You gave up an important commission –' the coroner began.

'I did not give it up,' Guy said. 'I wrote them before I had the commission, saying I didn't want it.'

'You telegraphed. Because you didn't want your wife to follow you there. But when you learned in Mexico that your wife had lost her child, you sent another telegram to Palm Beach that you wished to be considered for the commission. Why?'

'Because I didn't believe she'd follow me there then. I suspected she'd want to delay the divorce indefinitely. But I intended to see her – this week to discuss the divorce.' Guy wiped the perspiration from his forehead, and saw his lawyer purse his lips ruefully. His lawyer hadn't wanted him to mention the divorce in connection with his change of mind about the commission. Guy didn't care. It was the truth, and they could make of it what they wished.

'In your opinion was her husband capable of arranging for such a murder, Mrs Joyce?'

'Yes,' said Mrs Joyce with the faintest quiver, her head high. The shrewd dark red lashes were almost closed, as Guy had so often seen them, so that one never knew where her eyes rested. 'He wanted his divorce.'

There was an objection that Mrs Joyce had said a few moments before that her daughter wanted the divorce and Guy Haines did not because he still loved her. 'If both wanted a divorce, and it has been proven Mr Haines did, why wasn't there a divorce?'

The court was amused. The fingerprint experts could not come to agreement on their classifications. A hardware dealer, into whose store Miriam had come the day before her death, got tangled up as to whether her companion had been male or female, and more laughter camouflaged the fact he had been instructed to say a man. Guy's lawyer harangued on geographical fact, the inconsistences of the Joyce family, the affidavits in his hand, but Guy was sure that his own straightforwardness alone had absolved him from any suspicion.

The coroner suggested in his summation that the murder would seem to have been committed by a maniac unknown to the victim and the other parties. A verdict was brought in of 'person or persons unknown', and the case was turned over to the police.

A telegram arrived the next day, just as Guy was leaving his mother's house:

ALL GOOD WISHES FROM THE GOLDEN WEST.

UNSIGNED

'From the Faulkners,' he said quickly to his mother.

She smiled. 'Tell Anne to take good care of my boy.' She pulled him down gently by his ear and kissed his cheek.

Bruno's telegram was still wadded in his hand when he got to the airport. He tore it into tiny bits and dropped them into a wire trash-basket at the edge of the field. Every one of the pieces blew through the wire and went dancing out across the asphalt, gay as confetti in the windy sunlight.

16

Guy struggled to find a definite answer about Bruno – had he or hadn't he? – and then gave it up. There was too much incredible in the possibility that Bruno had done it. What weight did the Metcalf taxi company's card have? It would be like Bruno to find such a card in Santa Fe and mail it on to him. If it were not the act of a maniac, as the coroner and everyone else believed, wasn't it far more likely that Owen Markman had arranged it?

He closed his mind to Metcalf, to Miriam, and to Bruno, and concentrated on the work for Palm Beach which, he saw from the first day, would demand all that he had in diplomacy, technical knowledge, and sheer physical strength. Except for Anne, he closed his mind to all his past that, for all his idealistic aims and the fighting for them, and the small success he had known, seemed miserable and grubbing compared to the magnificent main building of the country club. And the more he immersed himself in the new effort, the more he felt recreated also in a different and more perfect form.

Photographs from newspapers and news magazines took pictures of the main building, the swimming pool, the bath-houses, and the terracing in the early stages of construction. Members of the club were also photographed inspecting the grounds, and Guy knew that below their pictures would be printed the amount of money each had donated to the cause of princely recreation. Sometimes he wondered if part of his enthusiasm might be due to a consciousness of the money behind the project, to the lavishness of space and materials he had to work with, to the flattery of the wealthy people who continually invited him to their homes. Guy never accepted their invitations. He knew he might be losing himself the small commissions he would need next winter, but he also knew he could never force himself to the social responsibilities that most architects assumed as a matter of course. Evenings when he did not want to be alone, he caught a bus to Clarence Brillhart's house a few miles away, and they had dinner together, listened to phonograph records, and talked. Clarence Brillhart, the Palmyra Club manager, was a retired broker, a tall, white-haired old gentleman whom Guy often thought he would have liked as a father. Guy admired most of all his air of leisure, as imperturbable on the bustling, hectic construction grounds as in his own home. Guy hoped he might be like him in his own old age. But he felt he moved too fast, had always moved too fast. There was inevitably, he felt, a lack of dignity in moving fast.

Most evenings Guy read, wrote long letters to Anne, or merely went to bed, for he was always up by five and often worked all day with a blowtorch or mortar and trowel. He knew almost all the workmen by name. He liked to judge the temperament of each man, to know how it contributed or did not contribute to the spirit of his buildings. 'It is like directing a symphony,' he wrote to Anne. In the dusks, when he sat smoking his pipe in a thicket of the golf course, gazing down on the four white buildings, he felt that the Palmyra project was going to be perfect. He knew it when he saw the first horizontals laid across the spaced marble uprights of the main building. The Pittsburgh store had been marred at the last moment by the client's change of mind about the window area. The hospital annexe in Chicago had been ruined, Guy thought, by the cornice that was of darker stone than he had intended. But Brillhart permitted no interference, the Palmyra was going to be as perfect as his original conception, and Guy had never created anything before that he felt would be perfect.

In August, he went North to see Anne. She was working in the design department of a textile company in Manhattan. In the autumn, she planned to go into partnership in a shop with another woman designer she had met. Neither of them mentioned Miriam until the fourth and last day of Guy's visit. They were standing by the brook behind Anne's house, in their last few minutes together before Anne drove him to the airport.

'Do you think it was Markman, Guy?' Anne asked him suddenly. And when Guy nodded: 'It's terrible – but I'm almost sure.'

Then one evening when he returned from Brillhart's house to the furnished room where he lived, a letter from Bruno awaited him with one from Anne. The letter was from Los Angeles, forwarded by his mother from Metcalf. It congratulated him on his work in Palm Beach, wished him success, and begged for just a word from him. The P.S. said:

Hope you are not annoyed at this letter. Have written many letters and not mailed them. Phoned your mother for your address, but she wouldn't give it to me. Guy, honestly there is nothing to worry about or I wouldn't have written. Don't you know I'd be the first one to be careful? Write soon. I may go to Haiti soon. Again your friend and admirer. C.A.B.

A slow ache fell through him to his feet. He could not bear to be alone in his room. He went out to a bar, and almost before he knew what he was doing, had two ryes and then a third. In the mirror behind the bar, he saw himself glance at his sunburnt face, and it struck him that his eyes looked dishonest and furtive. *Bruno had done it*. It came thundering down with a weight that left no possibility of doubt any longer, like a cataclysm that only a madman's unreason could have kept suspended all this while. He glanced about in the little bar as if he expected the walls to topple down on him. *Bruno had done it.* There was no mistaking Bruno's personal pride in his, Guy's, freedom now. Or the P.S. Or possibly even the trip to Haiti. But what did Bruno *mean?* Guy scowled at the face in the mirror and dropped his eyes, looked down at his hands, the front of his tweed jacket, his flannel trousers, and it flashed through his mind he had put these clothes on this morning as a certain person and that he would take them off tonight as another person, the person he would be from now on. He *knew* now. This was an instant – He could not say just what was happening, but he felt his entire life would be different, must be different, from now on.

If he knew Bruno had done it, why didn't he turn him in? What did he feel about Bruno besides hatred and disgust? Was he afraid? Guy didn't clearly know.

He resisted an impulse to telephone Anne until it was too late, and finally, at three in the morning, could resist no longer. Lying on his bed in the darkness, he talked to her very calmly, about commonplace matters, and once he even laughed. Even Anne did not notice anything wrong, he thought when he had hung up. He felt somehow slighted, and vaguely alarmed.

His mother wrote that the man who had called while he was in Mexico, and said his name was Phil, had called again to ask how he might reach him. She was worried that it might have something to do with Miriam, and wondered if she should tell the police.

Guy wrote back to her: 'I found out who the annoying telephoner was. Phil Johnson, a fellow I knew in Chicago.'

17

'Charley, what're all these clippings?'

'Friend of mine, Ma!' Bruno shouted through the bathroom door. He turned the water on harder, leaned on the basin, and concentrated on the bright nickel-plated drain-stop. After a moment, he reached for the Scotch bottle he kept under towels in the clothes hamper. He felt less shaky with the glass of Scotch and water in his hand, and spent a few seconds inspecting the silver braid on the sleeve of his new smoking jacket. He liked the jacket so much, he wore it as a bathrobe also. In the mirror, the oval lapels framed the portrait of a young man of leisure, of reckless and mysterious adventure, a young man of humour and depth, power and gentleness (witness the glass held delicately between thumb and forefinger with the air of an imperial toast) – a young man with two lives. He drank to himself.

'Charley?'

'Minute, Mom!'

He cast a wild eye about the bathroom. There was no window. Lately it happened about twice a week. Half an hour or so after he got up, he felt as if someone were kneeling on his chest and stifling him. He closed his eyes and dragged air in and out of his lungs as fast as he could. Then the liquor took. It bedded his leaping nerves like a hand passing down his body. He straightened and opened the door.

'Shaving,' he said.

His mother was in tennis shorts and a halter, bending over his unmade bed where the clippings were strewn. 'Who was she?'

'Wife of a fellow I met on the train coming down from New York. Guy Haines.' Bruno smiled. He liked to say Guy's name. 'Interesting, isn't it? They haven't caught the murderer yet.'

'Probably a maniac,' she sighed.

Bruno's face sobered. 'Oh, I doubt it. Circumstances are too complicated.'

Elsie stood up and slid her thumb inside her belt. The bulge just below her belt disappeared, and for a moment she looked as Bruno had seen her all her life until this last year, trim as a twenty-year-old down to her thin ankles. 'Your friend Guy's got a nice face.'

'Nicest fellow you ever saw. It's a shame he's dragged in on it. He told me on the train he hadn't seen his wife in a couple of years. Guy's no more a murderer than I am!' Bruno smiled at his inadvertent joke, and to cover it added, 'His wife was a roundheels anyway –'

'Darling.' She took him by the braid-edged lapels. 'Won't you watch your language a little for the duration? I know Grannie's horrified sometimes.'

'Grannie wouldn't know what a roundheels means,' Bruno said hoarsely.

Elsie threw her head back and shrieked.

'Ma, you're getting too much sun. I don't like your face that dark.'

'I don't like yours that pale.'

Bruno frowned. The leathery look of his mother's forehead offended him painfully. He kissed her suddenly on the cheek.

'Promise me you'll sit in the sun a half-hour today anyway. People come thousands of miles to get to California, and here you sit in the house!'

Bruno frowned down his nose. 'Ma, you're not interested in my friend!'

'I am interested in your friend. You haven't told me much about him.'

Bruno smiled shyly. No, he had been very good. He had let the clippings lie out in his room only today for the first time, because he was sure now both he and Guy were safe. If he talked a quarter of an hour about Guy now, his mother would probably forget, too. If it were even necessary that she forget. 'Did you read all that?' He nodded towards the bed.

'No, not all that. How many drinks this morning?'

'One.'

'I smell two.'

'All right, Mom, I had two.'

'Darling, won't you watch the morning drinks? Morning drinks are the end. I've seen alcoholic after alcoholic –'

'Alcoholic is a nasty word.' Bruno resumed his slow circuit of the room. 'I feel better since I drink a little more, Ma. You said yourself I'm more cheerful and my appetite's better. Scotch is a very pure drink. Some people it agrees with.'

'You drank too much last night, and Grannie knows it. Don't think she doesn't notice, you know.'

'About last night don't ask me.' Bruno grinned and waved his hand.

'Sammie's coming over this morning. Why don't you get dressed and come down and keep score for us?'

'Sammie gives me ulcers.'

She walked to the door as gaily as if she had not heard. 'Promise me you'll get some sun today anyway.'

He nodded and moistened his dry lips. He did not return her smile as she closed the door, because he felt as if a black lid had fallen on him suddenly, as if he had to escape something before it was too late. He had to see *Guy* before it was too late! He had to get rid of his father before it was too late! He had things to do! He did not want to be here, in his grandmother's house furnished just like his own house in Louis Quinze, eternal Louis Quinze! But he did not know where else he wanted to be. He was not happy if he were long away from his mother, was he? He bit his underlip and frowned, though his small grey eyes were quite blank. Why did she say he didn't need a drink in the mornings? He needed it more than any other drink of the day. He flexed his shoulders in a slow rotary movement. Why should he feel low? The clippings on the bed were about him. Week after week went by and the dumb police got nothing on him, nothing except the heelprints, and he had thrown his shoes away long ago! The party last week with Wilson in the San Francisco hotel was nothing to what he would do now if he had Guy to celebrate with. A perfect murder! How many people could do a perfect murder on an island with a couple of hundred other people around?

He was not like the dopes in the newspapers who killed 'to see what it felt like', and never had a bloody thing to report except sometimes a sick-making, 'It wasn't as good as I expected.' If he were interviewed, he would say, 'It was terrific! There's nothing

in the world like it!' ('Would you ever do it again, Mr Bruno?')
'Well, I might,' reflectively, with caution, as an arctic explorer
when asked if he will winter up north again next year might
reply uncommittingly to a reporter. ('Can you tell us a little bit
about your sensations?') He would tip the microphone towards
him, look up, and muse, while the world awaited his first word.
How had it felt? Well, there's only *it*, see, and nothing to compare
it with. She was a rotten woman anyway, you understand. It
was like killing a hot little rat, only she was a girl so it made it
a murder. The very warmth of her had been disgusting, and he
remembered thinking that before he took his fingers away, the
heat would really have stopped coming, that after he left her,
she would grow chill and hideous, like she really was. ('Hideous,
Mr Bruno?') Yes, hideous. ('Do you think a corpse is hideous?')
Bruno frowned. No, he did not really think he thought a corpse
was hideous. If the victim was evil, like Miriam, people ought
to be pretty glad to see the corpse, oughtn't they? ('Power, Mr
Bruno?') Oh, yes, he had felt terrific power! That was it. He had
taken away a life. Now, nobody knew what life was, everybody
defended it, the most priceless possession, but he had taken one
away. That night there had been the danger, the ache of his hands,
the fear in case she made a sound, but the instant when he felt
that life had left her, everything else had fallen away, and only
the mysterious *fact* of the thing he did remained, the mystery
and the miracle of stopping life. People talked about the mystery
of birth, of beginning life, but how explainable that was! Out of
two live germ cells! What about the mystery of stopping life? Why
should life stop because he held a girl's throat too tightly? What
was life anyway— What did Miriam feel after he took his hands
away? Where was she? No, he didn't believe in a life after death.
She was stopped, and that was just the miracle. Oh, he could say
a great deal at his interview with the press! ('What significance
did it have for you that your victim was female?') Where had
that question come from? Bruno hesitated, then recovered his
poise. Well, the fact she was a female had given him greater
enjoyment. No, he did not therefore conclude that his pleasure

had partaken of the sexual. No, he did not hate women either. Rather not! Hate is akin to love, you know. Who said that? He didn't believe it for a minute. No, all he would say was that he wouldn't have enjoyed it quite so much, he thought, if he had killed a man. Unless it was his father.

The telephone . . .

Bruno had been staring at it. Every telephone suggested Guy. He could reach Guy now with two well-placed calls, but a call might annoy Guy. Guy might still be nervous. He would wait for Guy to write. A letter should come any day now; because Guy must have got his letter the end of last week. The one thing Bruno needed to make his happiness complete was to hear Guy's voice, to have a word from him saying he was happy. The bond between Guy and him now was closer than brotherhood. How many brothers liked their brothers as much as he liked Guy?

Bruno threw a leg out the window and stood up on the wrought-iron balcony. The morning sunshine did feel rather good. The lawn was broad and smooth as a golf course all the way to the ocean. Then he saw Sammie Franklin, dressed in white tennis clothes with his rackets under his arm, grinning his way towards his mother. Sammie was big and flabby, like a softened-up boxer. He reminded Bruno of another Hollywood stooge who had hung around his mother when they were here three years ago. Alexander Phipps. Why did he even remember their phony names? He heard Sammie's chuckle as he extended his hand to his mother, and an old antagonism fluttered up in Bruno and lay still again. *Merde.* Disdainfully he took his eyes from Sammie's broad flannel backsides, and examined the view from left to right. A couple of pelicans flew loggily over a hedge and plopped down on the grass. Far out on the pale water he saw a sailboat. Three years ago he had begged his grandmother to get a sailboat, and now that she had one, he never felt like using it.

The tennis balls *wokked* around the tan stucco corner of the house. Chimes sounded from downstairs, and Bruno went back into his room, so he would not know what time it was. He liked to see a clock by accident as late as possible in the day, and find it was later than he had thought. If there was no letter from Guy in the noon mail, he thought, he might catch a train to San Francisco. On the other hand, his last memory of San Francisco was not pleasant. Wilson had brought a couple of Italian fellows up to the hotel, and Bruno had bought all the dinners and several bottles of rye. They had called Chicago on his telephone. The hotel had chalked up two calls to Metcalf, and he couldn't remember the second at all. And the last day, he had been twenty dollars short on the bill. He didn't have a cheque account, so the hotel, the best hotel in town, had held his suitcase until his mother wired the money. No, he wouldn't go back to San Francisco.

'Charley?' called the high, sweet voice of his grandmother.

He saw the curved handle of the door start to move, made an involuntary lunge for the clippings on his bed, then circled back to the bathroom instead. He shook tooth powder into his mouth. His grandmother could smell liquor like a dry sourdough in the Klondike.

'Aren't you ready to have some breakfast with me?' his grandmother asked.

He came out combing his hair. 'Gee, you're all dressed up!' She turned her small unsteady figure around for him like a fashion model, and Bruno smiled. He liked the black lace dress with the pink satin showing through it. 'Looks like one of those balconies out there.'

'Thank you, Charley. I'm going into town the latter part of the morning. I thought you might like to come with me.'

'Could be. Yeah, I'd like that, Grannie,' he said good-naturedly.

'So it's *you've* been clipping my *Times*! I thought it was one of the servants. You must be getting up awfully early these mornings.'

'Yep,' Bruno said agreeably.

'When I was young, we used to get poems out of newspapers for our scrapbooks. We made scrapbooks out of everything under the sun. What're you going to do with these?'

'Oh, just keep 'em.'

'Don't you make scrapbooks?'

'Nope.' She was looking at him, and Bruno wanted her to look at the clippings.

'Oh, you're just a *ba-aby*!' She pinched his cheek. 'Hardly a bit of fuzz on your chin yet! I don't know why your mother's worried about you –'

'She's not worried.'

'– when you just need time to grow up. Come on down to breakfast with me. Yes, pyjamas and all.'

Bruno gave her his arm on the stairs.

'I've got the least bit of shopping to do,' said his grandmother as she poured his coffee, 'and then I thought we'd do something nice. Maybe a good movie – with a murder in it – or maybe the amusement park. I haven't been to an amusement park in *a-ages*!'

Bruno's eyes opened as wide as they could.

'Which would you like? Well, we can look over the movies when we get there.'

'I'd like the amusement park, Grannie.'

Bruno enjoyed the day, helping her in and out of the car, piloting her around the amusement park, though there was not much after all his grandmother could do or eat. But they rode the ferris wheel together. Bruno told his grandmother about the big ferris wheel in Metcalf, but she did not ask him when he had been there.

Sammie Franklin was still at the house when they came home, staying for dinner. Bruno's eyebrows drew together at the first sight of him. He knew his grandmother cared as little for Sammie as he did, and Bruno felt suddenly a great tenderness for her, because she accepted Sammie so uncomplainingly, accepted any mongrel his mother brought on the place. What had he and his mother been doing all day? They had been to a movie, they said, one of Sammie's movies. And there was a letter for him upstairs in his room.

Bruno ran upstairs. The letter was from Florida. He tore it open with his hands shaking like ten hangovers. He had never wanted a letter so badly, not even at camp, when he had waited for letters from his mother.

Dear Charles,

I do not understand your message to me, or for that matter your great interest in me. I know you very slightly, but enough to assure me that we have nothing in common on which to base a friendship. May I ask you please not to telephone my mother again or communicate with me?

Thank you for trying to return the book to me. Its loss is of no importance.

Guy Haines

Bruno brought it up closer and read it again, his eyes lingering incredulously on a word here and there. His pointed tongue stretched over his upper lip, then disappeared suddenly. He felt shorn. It was a feeling like grief, or like a death. Worse! He glanced about his room, hating the furniture, hating his possessions. Then the pain centred in his chest, and reflexively he began to cry.

After dinner, Sammie Franklin and he got into an argument about vermouths. Sammie said the drier the vermouth, the more one had to put into a martini, though he admitted he was not a martini drinker. Bruno said he was not a martini drinker either, but he knew better than that. The argument went on even after his grandmother said good night and left them. They were on the upstairs terrace in the dark, his mother in the glider and he and Sammie standing by the parapet. Bruno ran down to the bar for the ingredients to prove his point. They both made martinis and tasted them, and though it was clear Bruno was right, Sammie kept holding out, and chuckling as if he didn't quite mean what he said either, which Bruno found insufferable.

'Go to New York and learn something!' Bruno shouted. His mother had just left the terrace.

'How do you know what you're saying anyway?' Sammie

retorted. The moonlight made his fat grinning face blue-green and yellow, like gorgonzola cheese. 'You're pickled all day. You –'

Bruno caught Sammie by the shirtfront and bent him backwards over the parapet. Sammie's feet rattled on the tiles. His shirt split. When he wriggled sideways to safety, the blue had left his face and it was a shadowless yellow-white.

'Th-the hell's the matter with you?' he bellowed. 'You'd a shoved me over, wouldn't you?'

'No, I wouldn't!' Bruno shrieked, louder than Sammie. Suddenly he couldn't breathe, like in the mornings. He took his stiff, sweaty hands down from his face. He had done a murder, hadn't he? Why should he do another? But he had seen Sammie squirming on the points of the iron fence right below, and he had wanted him there. He heard Sammie stirring a highball fast. Bruno stumbled over the threshold of the french window into the house.

'And *stay* out!' Sammie shouted after him.

The shaking passion in Sammie's voice sent a throb of fear through him. Bruno said nothing as he passed his mother in the hall. Going downstairs, he clung to the banister with both hands, cursing the ringing, aching, unmanageable mess in his head, cursing the martinis he had drunk with Sammie. He staggered into the living-room.

'Charley, what did you do to Sammie?' His mother had followed him in.

'Ah, whad I do to Sammie!' Bruno shoved his hand towards her blurred figure and sat down on the sofa with a bounce.

'Charley – come back and apologize.' The white blur of her evening dress came closer, one brown arm extended towards him.

'Are you sleeping with that guy? *Are you sleeping with that guy?*' He knew he had only to lie back on the sofa and he would pass out like a light, so he lay back, and never felt her arm at all.

In the month after Guy returned to New York, his restlessness, his dissatisfaction with himself, with his work, with Anne, had focused gradually on Bruno. It was Bruno who made him hate to look at pictures of the Palmyra now, Bruno who was the real cause of his anxiety that he had blamed on the dearth of commissions since he had come back from Palm Beach. Bruno who had made him argue so senselessly with Anne the other evening about not getting a better office, not buying new furniture and a rug for this one. Bruno who had made him tell Anne he did not consider himself a success, that the Palmyra meant nothing. Bruno who had made Anne turn quietly away from him that evening and walk out the door, who had made him wait until he heard the elevator door close, before he ran down the eight flights of stairs and begged her to forgive him.

And who knew? Perhaps it was Bruno who kept him from getting jobs now. The creation of a building was a spiritual act. So long as he harboured his knowledge of Bruno's guilt, he corrupted himself in a sense. Such a thing could be perceived in him, he felt. Consciously, he had made up his mind to let the police trap Bruno. But as the weeks went by and they didn't, he was plagued by a feeling that he should act himself. What stopped him' was both an aversion to accusing a man of murder and a senseless but lingering doubt that Bruno might not be guilty. That Bruno had committed the crime struck him at times as so fantastic, all his previous conviction was momentarily wiped out. At times, he felt he would have doubted even if Bruno had sent him a written confession. And yet, he had to admit to himself that he was *sure* Bruno had done it. The weeks that went by without the police picking up any strong trail seemed to confirm it. As Bruno had said, how could they with no motivation? His letter to Bruno in September had silenced him all the autumn, but just before he left Florida, a sober note from Bruno had said he would be back in New York in December and he hoped to be able to have a talk with him. Guy was determined to have nothing to do with him.

Still he fretted, about everything and about nothing, but chiefly about his work. Anne told him to be patient. Anne reminded him that he had already proven himself in Florida. In greater measure than ever before, she offered him the tenderness and reassurance he needed so, yet he found that in his lowest, most stubborn moments he could not always accept it.

One morning in mid-December, the telephone rang as Guy sat idly studying his drawings of the Connecticut house.

'Hello, Guy. This is Charley.'

Guy recognized the voice, felt his muscles tensing for a fight. But Myers was within earshot across the room.

'How are you?' Bruno asked with smiling warmth. 'Merry Christmas.'

Slowly Guy put the telephone back in its cradle.

He glanced over at Myers, the architect with whom he shared the big one-room office. Myers was still bent over his drawing-board. Under the edge of the green window-shade, the bobbing pigeons still pecked at the grain he and Myers had sprinkled on the sill a few moments ago.

The telephone rang again.

'I'd like to see you, Guy,' Bruno said.

Guy stood up. 'Sorry. I don't care to see you.'

'What's the matter?' Bruno forced a little laugh. 'Are you nervous, Guy?'

'I just don't care to see you.'

'Oh. Okay,' said Bruno, hoarse with hurt.

Guy waited, determined not to retreat first, and finally Bruno hung up.

Guy's throat was dry, and he went to the drinking fountain in the corner of the room. Behind the fountain, sunlight lay in a precise diagonal across the big aerial photograph of the four nearly finished Palmyra buildings. He turned his back to it. He'd been asked to make a speech at his old school in Chicago, Anne would remind him. He was to write an article for a leading architectural magazine. But so far as commissions went, the Palmyra Club might have been a public declaration that he was to be boycotted. And why not? Didn't he owe the Palmyra to Bruno? Or at any rate to a murderer?

On a snowy evening a few days later, as he and Anne came down the brownstone steps of his West Fifty-third Street apartment house, Guy saw a tall bareheaded figure standing on the sidewalk gazing up at them. A tingle of alarm travelled to his shoulders, and involuntarily his hand tightened on Anne's arm.

'Hello,' Bruno said, his voice soft with melancholy. His face was barely visible in the dusk.

'Hello,' Guy replied, as if to a stranger, and walked on.

'Guy!'

Guy and Anne turned at the same time. Bruno came towards them, hands in the pockets of his overcoat.

'What is it?' Guy asked.

'Just wanted to say hello. Ask how you are.' Bruno stared at Anne with a kind of perplexed, smiling resentment.

'I'm fine,' Guy said quietly. He turned away, drawing Anne with him.

'Who is he?' Anne whispered.

Guy itched to look back. He knew Bruno would be standing where they had left him, knew he would be looking after them, weeping perhaps. 'He's a fellow who came around looking for work last week.'

'You can't do anything for him?'

'No. He's an alcoholic.'

Deliberately Guy began to talk about their house, because he knew there was nothing else he could talk about now and possibly sound normal. He had bought the land, and the foundations were being laid. After New Year's, he was going up to Alton and stay several days. During the movie, he speculated as to how he could shake Bruno off, terrify him so that he would be afraid to contact him.

What did Bruno want with him? Guy sat with his fists clenched at the movie. The *next* time, he would threaten Bruno with police investigation. And he would carry it through, too. What vast harm was there in suggesting he be investigated?

But what did Bruno want with him?

19

Bruno had not wanted to go to Haiti, but it offered escape. New York or Florida or anywhere in the American continent was torture so long as Guy was there, too, and would not see him. To blot out his pain and depression, he had drunk a great deal at home in Great Neck, and to occupy himself had measured the house and the grounds in paces, measured his father's room with tailor's tape, moving doggedly, stooping, measuring and remeasuring, like a tireless automaton that wavered only slightly off its track now and then, betraying the fact it was drunk and not deranged. Thus he spent ten days after seeing Guy, waiting for his mother and her friend Alice Leffingwell to get ready to go to Haiti.

There were moments when he felt his whole being in some as yet inscrutable stage of metamorphosis. There was the deed he had done, which in his hours alone in the house, in his room, he felt sat upon his head like a crown, but a crown that no one else could see. Very easily and quickly, he could break down in tears. There was the time he had wanted a caviar sandwich for lunch, because he deserved the finest, big black caviar, and when there had been only red in the house, had told Herbert to go out and get some black. He had eaten a quarter of the toasted sandwich, sipping a Scotch and water with it, then had almost fallen asleep staring at the triangle of toasted bread that finally had begun to lift at one corner. He had stared at it until it was no longer a sandwich, the glass with his drink no longer a glass, and only the golden liquid in it part of himself, and he had gulped it all. The empty glass and the curling toast had been live things that mocked him and challenged his right to use them. A butcher's truck had departed down the driveway just then and Bruno had frowned after it, because everything had suddenly come alive and was fleeing to escape him – the truck, the sandwich, and the glass, the trees that couldn't run away but were disdainful, like the house that imprisoned him. He had hit both his fists against the wall simultaneously, then seized the sandwich and broken its insolent triangular mouth and burnt it, piece by piece, in the empty fireplace, the caviar popping like little people, dying, each one a life.

Alice Leffingwell, his mother and he, and a crew of four including two Puerto Ricans left for Haiti in mid-January on the steam yacht, *Fairy Prince*, which Alice had spent all autumn and winter wresting from her former husband. The trip was a celebration of her third divorce, and she had invited Bruno and his mother months before. Bruno's delight in the voyage inspired him to a pretence of indifference and boredom during the first days. No one noticed. Alice and his mother spent whole afternoons and evenings chattering together in the cabin, and in the mornings they slept. To justify his happiness to himself at such a dull prospect as being cooped up on a ship for a month with an old bag like Alice, Bruno convinced himself he had been under quite a strain watching out the police didn't get on his trail, and that he needed leisure to dope out the details of how his father could be got rid of. He also reasoned that the more time elapsed, the more likely Guy would be to change his attitude.

On shipboard, he detailed two or three key plans for the murder of his father, of which any other plans laid on the estate would be mere variations. He was very proud of his plans – one with gun in his father's bedroom, one with knife and two choices of escape, and one with either gun or knife or strangulation in the garage where his father put his car every evening at 6.30. The disadvantage of the last plan was lack of darkness, but it had compensations in comparative simplicity. He could all but hear in his ears the efficient *click-click* of his plans' operations. Yet whenever he finished a careful drawing, he felt obliged to tear it up for safety. He was eternally making drawings and tearing them up. The sea from Bar Harbour to the southernmost of the Virgin Islands was strewn with the subdivided seeds of his ideas when the *Fairy Prince* rounded Cape Maisi bound for Port-au-Prince.

'A princely harbour for my *Prince!*' cried Alice, relaxing her mind in a lull of conversation with his mother.

Around the corner from them, in the shade, Bruno fumbled up the paper he had been drawing on and lifted his head. In the left quarter of the horizon, land was visible in a grey fuzzy line. Haiti. Seeing it made it seem more distant and foreign than when he had not seen it. He was going farther and farther away from Guy. He pulled himself from the deck-chair and went over to the port rail. They would spend days in Haiti before they moved on, and then they would move farther south. Bruno stood perfectly still, feeling frustration corrode him internally as the tropical sun did externally now, on the pale backs of his legs. Abruptly, he ripped the plan to pieces and released them by opening his hands over the side. The wind perversely carried the pieces forward.

As important as the plans, of course, was to find someone for the job. He would do it himself, he thought, if not for the fact Gerard, his father's private detective, would nail him no matter how carefully he planned it. Besides, he wanted to put his no-motivation scheme to the test again. Matt Levine or Carlos – the trouble was he knew them. And it was dangerous to try to negotiate without knowing if the person would agree. Bruno had seen Matt several times, and hadn't been able to mention it.

Something happened in Port-au-Prince that Bruno would never forget. He fell off the gangplank coming back aboard ship the second afternoon.

The steamy heat had stupefied him and rum had made it worse, made him hotter. He was on his way from Hotel La Citadelle to the ship to get his mother's evening shoes, when he stopped in a bar near the waterfront for a Scotch with ice. One of the Puerto Ricans of the crew, whom Bruno had disliked since the first moment he saw him, was in the bar and blind drunk, roaring around as if he owned the town, the *Fairy Prince*, and the rest of Latin America. He called Bruno a 'wite bum-m' and a lot of other things Bruno could not understand but which made everybody laugh. Bruno left the bar with dignity, too tired and disgusted to fight, with a quiet determination to report it to Alice and get the Puerto Rican fired and blacklisted. A block away from the ship, the Puerto Rican caught up with him and kept on talking. Then, crossing the gangplank, Bruno lurched against the handrope and fell off into the filthy water. He couldn't say the Puerto Rican had pushed him, because he hadn't. The Puerto Rican and another sailor, also laughing, fished him out and dragged him in to his bed. Bruno crawled off the bed and got his bottle of rum. He drank some straight, then flopped on the bed and fell asleep in his wet underwear.

Later, his mother and Alice came in and shook him awake.

'What happened?' they kept asking, giggling so they could hardly talk. 'What happened, Charley?'

Their figures were fuzzy but their laughs were sharp. He recoiled from Alice's fingers on his shoulder. He couldn't talk, but he knew what he wanted to say. What were they doing in his room if they didn't have a message from Guy?

'What? What guy?' asked his mother.

'G'way!' he shouted, and he meant both of them.

'Oh, he's out,' said his mother deploringly, as if he were a hospital case nearly dead. 'Poor boy. Poor, poor boy.'

Bruno jerked his head this way and that to avoid the cool washcloth. He hated them both and he hated Guy! He had killed for him, dodged police for him, kept quiet when he asked him to, fallen in the stinking water for him, and Guy didn't even want to see him! Guy spent his time with a girl! Guy wasn't scared or unhappy, just didn't have time for him! Three times he had seen her around Guy's house in New York! If he had her here, he would kill her just like he had killed Miriam!

'Charley, Charley, hush!'

Guy would get married again and never have time for him. See what sympathy he'd get now when this girl played him for a

106

sucker! He'd been seeing her in Mexico, not just visiting friends. No wonder he'd wanted Miriam out of the way! And he hadn't even mentioned Anne Faulkner on the train! Guy had used him. Maybe Guy would kill his father whether he liked it or not. Anybody can do a murder. Guy hadn't believed it, Bruno remembered.

20

'Have a drink with me,' Bruno said. He had appeared out of nowhere, in the middle of the sidewalk.

'I don't care to see you. I'm not asking questions. I don't care to see you.'

'I don't care if you ask questions,' Bruno said with a weak smile. His eyes were wary. 'Come across the street. Ten minutes.'

Guy glanced around him. Here he is, Guy thought. Call the police. Jump him, throw him down to the sidewalk. But Guy only stood rigidly. He saw that Bruno's hands were rammed in his pockets, as if he might have a gun.

'Ten minutes,' Bruno said, luring him with the tentative smile.

Guy hadn't heard a word from Bruno in weeks. He tried to summon back the anger of that last evening in the snow, of his decision to turn Bruno over to the police. This was the critical moment. Guy came with him. They walked into a bar on Sixth Avenue and took a back booth.

Bruno's smile grew wider. 'What're you scared about, Guy?'

'Not a thing.'

'Are you happy?'

Guy sat stiffly on the edge of his seat. He was sitting opposite a murderer, he thought. Those hands had crushed Miriam's throat.

'Listen, Guy, why didn't you tell me about Anne?'

'What about Anne?'

'I'd have liked to know about her, that's all. On the train, I mean.'

'This is our last meeting, Bruno.'

'Why? I just want to be friends, Guy.'

'I'm going to turn you over to the police.'

'Why didn't you do that in Metcalf?' Bruno asked with the lowest pink gleam in his eyes, as only he could have asked it, impersonally, sadly, yet with triumph. Oddly, Guy felt his inner voice had asked him the question in the same way.

'Because I wasn't sure enough.'

'What do I have to do, make a written statement?'

'I can still turn you over for investigation.'

'No, you can't. They've got more on you than on me.' Bruno shrugged.

'What're you talking about?'

'What do you think they'd get on me? Nothing.'

'I could tell them!' He was suddenly furious.

'If I wanted to say you paid me for it,' Bruno frowned self-righteously, 'the pieces would fit like hell!'

'I don't care about pieces.'

'Maybe you don't, but the law does.'

'What pieces?'

'That letter you wrote Miriam,' Bruno said slowly, 'the cover-up of that job cancelling. The whole convenient trip to Mexico.'

'You're insane!'

'Face it, Guy! You're not making any sense!' Bruno's voice rose hysterically over the jukebox that had started up near them. He pushed his hand flat across the table towards Guy, then closed it in a fist. 'I like you, Guy, I swear. We shouldn't be talking like this!'

Guy did not move. The edge of the bench cut against the back of his legs. 'I don't want to be liked by you.'

'Guy, if you say anything to the police, you'll only land us both in prison. Don't you see?'

Guy had thought of it, even before now. If Bruno clung to his lies, there could be a long trial, a case that might never be decided unless Bruno broke down, and Bruno wouldn't break down. Guy could see it in the monomaniacal intensity with which Bruno stared at him now. Ignore him, Guy thought. Keep away. Let the police catch him. He's insane enough to kill you if you make a move.

'You didn't turn me in in Metcalf because you like me, Guy. You like me in a way.'

'I don't like you in the least.'

'But you're not going to turn me in, are you?'

'No,' Guy said between his teeth. Bruno's calm amazed him. Bruno was not afraid of him at all. 'Don't order me another drink. I'm leaving.'

'Wait a minute.' Bruno got money from his wallet and gave it to the waiter.

Guy sat on, held by a sense of inconclusiveness.

'Good-looking suit.' Bruno smiled, nodding towards Guy's chest.

His new grey flannel chalk-stripe suit. Bought with the Palmyra money, Guy thought, like his new shoes and the new alligator briefcase beside him on the seat.

'Where do you have to go?'

'Downtown.' He was to meet a prospective client's representative at the Fifth Avenue Hotel at seven. Guy stared at Bruno's hard, wistful eyes, feeling sure Bruno thought he was on his way to meet Anne now. 'What's your game, Bruno?'

'You know,' Bruno said quietly. 'What we talked about on the train. The exchange of victims. You're going to kill my father.'

Guy made a sound of contempt. He had known it before Bruno said it, had suspected it since Miriam's death. He stared into Bruno's fixed, still wistful eyes, fascinated by their cool insanity. Once as a child he had stared at a mongoloid idiot on a streetcar, he remembered, like this, with a shameless curiosity that nothing could shake. Curiosity and fear.

'I told you I could arrange every detail.' Bruno smiled at the corner of his mouth, amusedly, apologetically. 'It'd be very simple.'

He hates me, Guy thought suddenly. He'd love to kill me, too.

'You know what I'll do if you don't.' Bruno made a gesture of snapping his fingers, but his hand on the table was carelessly limp. 'I'll just put the police on to you.'

Ignore him, Guy thought, ignore him! 'You don't frighten me in the least. It'd be the easiest thing in the world to prove you insane.'

'I'm no more insane than you are!'

It was Bruno who ended the interview a moment later. He had a seven o'clock appointment with his mother, he said.

The next encounter, so much shorter, Guy felt he lost, too, though at the time he thought he had won. Bruno tried to intercept him one Friday afternoon as he was leaving his office on the way to Long Island to see Anne. Guy simply brushed past him and climbed into a taxi. Yet a feeling of having physically run away shamed him, began to undermine a certain dignity that had up to then been intact. He wished he had said something to Bruno. He wished he had faced him for an instant.

21

In the next days, there was hardly an evening when Bruno was not standing on the sidewalk across the street from his office building. Or if not there, standing across the street from where he lived, as if Bruno knew the evenings he would come straight home. There was never a word now, never a sign, only the tall figure with the hands in the pockets of the long, rather military overcoat that fit him closely, like a stovepipe. There was only the eyes following him, Guy knew, though he did not look back until he was out of sight. For two weeks. Then the first letter came.

It was two sheets of paper: the first a map of Bruno's house and the grounds and roads around it and the course Guy would take, neatly drawn with dotted and ruled ink lines, and the second a typed, closely written letter lucidly setting forth the plan for the murder of Bruno's father. Guy tore it up, then immediately regretted it. He should have kept it as evidence against Bruno. He kept the pieces.

But there was no need to have kept them. He received such a letter every two or three days. They were all mailed from Great Neck, as if Bruno stayed out there now – he had not seen Bruno since the letters began – writing perhaps on his father's typewriter the letters that must have taken him two or three hours to prepare. The letters were sometimes drunken. It showed in the typing mistakes and in the emotional bursts of the last paragraphs. If he were sober, the last paragraph was affectionate and reassuring as to the ease of the murder. If he were drunk, the paragraph was either a gush of brotherly love or a threat to haunt Guy all his life, ruin his career and his 'love affair', and a reminder that Bruno had the upper hand. All the necessary information might have been got from any one of the letters, as if Bruno anticipated he might tear most of them up unopened. But despite his determination to tear up the next, Guy would open it when it came, curious as to the variations in the last paragraph. Of Bruno's three plans, the one with a gun, using the back entrance of the house, came most often, though each letter invited him to take his choice.

The letters affected him in a perverse way. After the shock of the first, the next few bothered him hardly at all. Then as the tenth, twelfth, fifteenth appeared in his mailbox, he felt they hammered at his consciousness or his nerves in a manner that he could not analyse. Alone in his room he would spend quarter hours trying to isolate his injury and repair it. His anxiety was unreasonable, he told himself, unless he thought Bruno would turn on him and try to murder him. And he didn't really. Bruno had never threatened that. But reasoning could not alleviate the anxiety, or make it less exhausting.

The twenty-first letter mentioned Anne. 'You wouldn't like Anne to know your part in Miriam's murder, would you? What girl would marry a murderer? Certainly not Anne. The time is getting short. The first two weeks in March is my deadline. Until then it would be easy.'

Then the gun came. It was handed him by his landlady, a big package in brown paper. Guy gave a short laugh when the black gun toppled out. It was a big Luger, shiny and new looking except for a chip off the cross-hatched handle.

Some impulse made Guy take his own little revolver from the back of his top drawer, made him heft his own beautiful pearl-handled gun over his bed where the Luger lay. He smiled at his action, then brought the Texas gun up closer to his eyes and studied it. He had seen it in a glutted pawnshop window on lower Main Street in Metcalf when he was about fifteen, and had bought it with money from his paper route, not because it was a gun but because it was beautiful. Its compactness, the economy of its short barrel had delighted him. The more he had learned of mechanical design, the more pleased he had been with his gun. He had kept it in various top drawers for fifteen years. He opened the chamber and removed the bullets, three of them, and turned the cylinder around with six pulls of the trigger, admiring the deep-pitched clicks of its perfect machinery. Then he slipped the bullets back, put the gun into its lavender-coloured flannel bag, and replaced it in his drawer.

How should he get rid of the Luger? Drop it over an embankment into the river? Into some ashcan? Throw it out with his trash? Everything he thought of seemed either suspect or melodramatic. He decided to slip it under his socks and underwear in a bottom drawer until something better occurred to him. He thought suddenly of Samuel Bruno, for the first time as a person. The presence of the Luger brought the man and his potential death into juxtaposition in his mind. Here in his room was the complete picture of the man and his life, according to Bruno, the plan for his murder – a letter had been waiting in his box that morning, too, and lay on his bed now unopened – and the gun with which he was supposed to kill him. Guy got one of Bruno's recent letters from among a few in the bottom drawer.

Samuel Bruno [Bruno seldom referred to him as 'my father'] is the finest example of the worst that America produces. He comes of low-class peasants in Hungary, little better than animals. He picked a wife of good family, with his usual greed, once he could afford her. All this time my mother quietly bore his unfaithfulness, having some concept of the sacredness of marriage contract. Now in his old age he tries to act pius before it is too late, but it is too late. I wish I could kill him myself but I have explained to you due to Gerard, his private detective, it is impossible. If you ever had anything to do with him, he would be your personal enemy, too. He is the kind of man who thinks all your ideas about architecture as beauty and about adiquate houses for everyone are idiotic & doesn't care what kind of factory he has as long as the roof doesn't leak and ruin his machinery. It may interest you to know his employees are on strike now. See *N.Y. Times* last Thurs. p. 31 bottom left. They are striking for a living wage. Samuel Bruno does not hesitate to rob his own son . . .

Who would believe such a story if he told it? Who would accept such fantasy? The letter, the map, the gun – They seemed like props of a play, objects arranged to give a verisimilitude to a story that wasn't real and never could be real. Guy burnt the letter. He burnt all the letters he had, then hurried to get ready for Long Island.

He and Anne were going to spend the day driving, walking in the woods, and tomorrow drive up to Alton. The house would be finished by the end of March, which would give them a leisurely two months before the wedding to furnish it. Guy smiled as he gazed out the train window. Anne had never said she wanted a June wedding; it was simply drifting that way. She had never said she wanted a formal wedding, only, 'Let's not have anything too slapdash.' Then when he had told her he wouldn't mind a formal wedding if she wouldn't, she had let out a long 'Oh-h!' and grabbed him and kissed him. No, he didn't want another three-minute wedding with a stranger for a witness. He began sketching on the back of an envelope the twenty-storey office building he had learned last week he had a good chance of being commissioned for, that he had been saving as a surprise for Anne. He felt the future had suddenly become the present. He had everything he wanted. Running down the platform steps, he saw Anne's leopard coat in the little crowd by the station door. Always he would remember the times she waited for him here, he thought, the shy dance of impatience she did when she caught sight of him, the way she smiled and half turned round, as if she wouldn't have waited half a minute longer.

'Anne!' He put his arm around her and kissed her cheek.

'You didn't wear a hat.'

He smiled because it was exactly what he had expected her to say. 'Well, neither did you.'

'I'm in the car. And it's snowing.' She took his hand and they ran across the crisp lane towards the cars. 'I've got a surprise!'

'So have I. What's yours?'

'Sold five designs yesterday on my own.'

Guy shook his head. 'I can't beat that. I've just got one office building. Maybe.'

She smiled and her eyebrows went up. 'Maybe? Yes!'

'Yes, yes, yes!' he said, and kissed her again.

That evening, standing on the little wooden bridge over the stream back of Anne's house, Guy started to say, 'Do you know what Bruno sent me today? A gun.' Then, not that he had come close to saying it, but the remoteness of Bruno and his connection with him from his and Anne's life shocked him with a terrible realization. He wanted no secrets from Anne, and here was one bigger than all he had told her. Bruno, the name that haunted him, would mean nothing to Anne.

'What is it, Guy?'

She knew there was something, he thought. She always knew. 'Nothing.'

He followed her as she turned and walked towards the house. The night had blackened the earth, made the snowy ground hardly distinguishable from woods and sky. And Guy felt it again – the sense of hostility in the clump of woods east of the house.

Before him, the kitchen door spilled a warm yellow light some way on to the lawn. Guy turned again, letting his eyes rest on the blackness where the woods began. The feeling he had when he gazed there was discomforting and relieving at once, like biting on an ailing tooth.

'I'll walk around again,' he said.

Anne went in, and he turned back. He wanted to see if the sensation were stronger or weaker when Anne was not with him. He tried to feel rather than see. It was still there, faint and evasive, where the darkness deepened at the baseline of the woods. Nothing of course. What chance combination of shadow and sound and his own thoughts had created it?

He slipped his hands into his overcoat pockets and moved stubbornly closer.

The dull snap of a twig plummeted his consciousness to earth, focused it at a certain point. He sprinted towards it. A crackling of bushes now, and a moving black figure in the blackness. Guy released all his muscles in a long drive, caught it, and recognized the hoarse intake of breath as Bruno's. Bruno plunged in his arms like a great powerful fish underwater, twisted and hit him an agonizing blow on the cheekbone. Clasping each other, they both fell, fighting to free arms, fighting as if they both fought death. Bruno's fingers scratched frenziedly at his throat, though Guy kept his arm straight. Bruno's breath hissed in and out between his drawn-back lips. Guy hit the mouth again with his right fist that felt broken, that would no longer close.

'Guy!' Bruno burst out indignantly.

Guy caught him by the front of his collar. Suddenly they both stopped fighting.

'You knew it was me!' Bruno said in a fury. 'Dirty bastard!'

'What're you doing here?' Guy pulled him to his feet.

The bleeding mouth spread wider, as if he were going to cry. 'Lemme go!'

Guy shoved him. He fell like a sack to the ground and tottered up again.

'Okay, kill me if you want to! You can say it's self-defence!' Bruno whined.

Guy glanced towards the house. They had struggled a long way into the woods. 'I don't want to kill you. I'll kill you next time I find you here.'

Bruno laughed, the single victorious clap.

Guy advanced menacingly. He did not want to touch Bruno again. Yet a moment before, he had fought with 'Kill, kill!' in his mind. Guy knew there was nothing he could do to stop Bruno's smile, not even kill him. 'Clear out.'

'You ready to do that job in two weeks?'

'Ready to turn you over to the police.'

'Ready to turn yourself over?' Bruno jeered shrilly. 'Ready to tell Anne all about it, huh? Ready to spend the next twenty years in jail? Sure, I'm ready!' He brought his palms together gently. His eyes seemed to glow with a red light. His swaying figure was like that of an evil spirit's that might have stepped from the twisted black tree behind him.

'Get someone else for your dirty work,' Guy muttered.

'Look who's talking! I want you, and I've got you! Okay!' A laugh. 'I'll start. I'll tell your girl friend all about it. I'll write her tonight.' He lurched away, tripped heavily, and staggered on, a loose and shapeless thing. He turned and shouted, 'Unless I hear from *you* in a day or so.'

Guy told Anne he had fought with a prowler in the woods. He suffered only a reddened eye from the battle, but he saw no way to stay on at the house, not go to Alton tomorrow, except by feigning injury. He had been hit in the stomach, he said. He didn't feel well. Mr and Mrs Faulkner were alarmed, and insisted to the policeman who came to look over the grounds that they have a police guard for the next few nights. But a guard was not enough. If Bruno came back, Guy wanted to be there himself. Anne suggested that he stay on Monday, so he would have someone to look after him in case he were sick. Guy did stay on.

Nothing had ever shamed him so much, he thought, as the two days in the Faulkner house. He was ashamed that he felt the need to stay, ashamed that on Monday morning he went into Anne's room and looked on the writing-table where the maid put her mail to see if Bruno had written. He hadn't. Anne left each morning for her shop in New York before the mail was delivered. On Monday morning, Guy looked through the four or five letters on her writing-table, then hurried out like a thief, afraid the maid might see him. But he often came into her room when she was not there, he reminded himself. Sometimes when the house was filled with people, he would escape to Anne's room for a few moments. And she loved to find him there. At the threshold, he leaned his head back against the door jamb, picking out the disorder in the room – the unmade bed, the big art books that didn't fit in the bookshelves, her last designs thumb-tacked to a strip of green cork down one wall, on the corner of the table a glass of bluish water that she had neglected to empty, the brown and yellow silk scarf over the chair back, that she had evidently changed her mind about. The gardenia scent of the cologne she had touched to her neck at the last moment still lingered in the air. He longed to merge his life with hers.

Guy stayed until Tuesday morning when there was no letter from Bruno either, and then went in to Manhattan. Work had piled up. A thousand things nettled him. The contract with the Shaw Realty Company for the new office building still had not been settled. He felt his life disorganized, without direction, more chaotic than when he had heard of Miriam's murder. There was no letter from Bruno that week except one that awaited him, that had arrived Monday. It was a short note saying thank God his mother was better today and he could leave the house. His mother had been dangerously ill for three weeks with pneumonia, he said, and he had stayed with her.

Thursday evening when Guy got back from a meeting of an architectural club, his landlady Mrs McCausland said he had had three calls. The telephone rang as they stood in the hall. It was Bruno, sullen and drunk. He asked if Guy was ready to talk sense.

'I didn't think so,' Bruno said. 'I've written Anne.' And he hung up.

Guy went upstairs and took a drink himself. He didn't believe Bruno had written or intended to write. He tried for an hour to read, called Anne to ask how she was, then restlessly went out and found a late movie.

On Saturday afternoon, he was supposed to meet Anne in Hempstead, Long Island, to see a dog show there. If Bruno had written the letter, Anne would have got it by Saturday morning, Guy thought. But obviously she hadn't. He could tell from her wave to him from the car where she sat waiting for him. He asked her if she had enjoyed the party last night at Teddy's. Her cousin Teddy had had a birthday.

'Wonderful party. Only no one wanted to go home. It got so late I stayed over. I haven't even changed my clothes yet.' And she shot the car through the narrow gate and into the road.

Guy closed his teeth. The letter might be waiting for her at home then. All at once, he felt sure the letter *would* be waiting for her, and the impossibility of stopping it now made him weak and speechless.

He tried desperately to think of something to say as they walked along the rows of dogs.

'Have you heard anything from the Shaw people?' Anne asked him.

'No.' He stared at a nervous dachshund and tried to listen as Anne said something about a dachshund that someone in her family had.

She didn't know yet, Guy thought, but if she didn't know by today, it would be only a matter of time, a matter of a few days more, perhaps, until she did know. Know what, he kept asking himself, and going over the same answer, whether for reassurance or self-torture, he did not know: that on the train last summer he had met the man who murdered his wife, that he had consented to the murder of his wife. That was what Bruno would tell her, with certain details to make it convincing. And in a courtroom, for that matter, if Bruno distorted only slightly their conversation on the train, couldn't it amount to an agreement between murderers? The hours in Bruno's compartment, that tiny hell, came back suddenly very clearly. It was hatred that had inspired him to say as much as he had, the same petty hatred that had made him rage against Miriam in Chapultepec Park last June. Anne had been angry then, not so much at what he had said as at his hatred. Hatred, too, was a sin. Christ had preached against hatred as against adultery and murder. Hatred was the very seed of evil. In a Christian court of justice, wouldn't he be at least partially guilty of Miriam's death? Wouldn't Anne say so?

'Anne,' he interrupted her. He had to prepare her, he thought. And he had to *know*. 'If someone were to accuse me of having had a part in Miriam's death, what would you –? Would you –?'

She stopped and looked at him. The whole world seemed to stop moving, and he and Anne stood at its still centre.

'Had a part? What do you mean, Guy?'

Someone jostled him. They were in the middle of the walk. 'Just that. Accused me, nothing more.'

She seemed to search for words.

'Just accused me,' Guy kept on. 'I just want to know. Accused me for no reason. It wouldn't matter, would it?' Would she still marry him, he wanted to ask, but it was such a pitiful, begging question, he could not ask it.

'Guy, why do you say that?'

'I just want to know, that's all!'

She pressed him back so they would be out of the traffic of the path. 'Guy, *has* someone accused you?'

'No!' he protested. He felt awkward and vexed. 'But if someone did, if someone tried to make out a strong case against me –'

She looked at him with that flash of disappointment, of surprise and mistrust that he had seen before when he said or did something out of anger, or out of a resentment, that Anne did not approve, did not understand. 'Do you expect someone to?' she asked.

'I just want to know!' He was in a hurry and it seemed so simple!

'At times like this,' she said quietly, 'you make me feel we're complete strangers.'

'I'm sorry,' he murmured. He felt she had cut an invisible bond between them.

'I don't think you're sorry, or you wouldn't keep on doing this!' She looked straight at him, keeping her voice low though her eyes had filled with tears. 'It's like that day in Mexico when you indulged yourself in that tirade against Miriam. I don't care – I don't like it, I'm not that kind of person! You make me feel I don't know you at all!'

Don't love you, Guy thought. It seemed she gave him up then, gave up trying to know him or to love him. Desperate, slipping, Guy stood there unable to make a move or say a word.

'Yes, since you ask me,' Anne said, 'I think it would make a difference if someone accused you. I'd want to ask why you expected it. Why do you?'

'I don't!'

She turned away from him, walked to the blind end of the lane, and stood with her head bent.

Guy came after her. 'Anne, you do know me. You know me better than anyone in the world knows me. I don't want any secrets from you. It came to my mind and I asked you!' He felt he made a confession, and with the relief that followed it, he felt suddenly sure – as sure as he had been before that Bruno had written the letter – that Bruno hadn't and wouldn't.

She brushed a tear from the corner of her eye quickly, indifferently. 'Just one thing, Guy. Will you stop expecting the worst – about everything?'

'Yes,' he said. 'God, yes.'

'Let's go back to the car.'

He spent the day with Anne, and they had dinner that evening at her house. There was no letter from Bruno. Guy put the possibility from his mind, as if he had passed a crisis.

On Monday evening at about eight, Mrs McCausland called him to the telephone. It was Anne.

'Darling – I guess I'm a little upset.'

'What's the matter?' He knew what was the matter.

'I got a letter. In this morning's mail. About what you were talking about Saturday.'

'What is it, Anne?'

'About Miriam – typewritten. And it's not signed.'

'What does it say? Read it to me.'

Anne read shakily, but in her distinct speech, ' "Dear Miss Faulkner. It may interest you to know that Guy Haines had more to do with his wife's murder than the law thinks at present. But the truth will out. I think you should know in case you have any plans for marrying such a dual personality. Apart from that, this writer knows that Guy Haines will not remain a free man much longer." Signed, "A friend." '

Guy closed his eyes. 'God!'

'Guy, do you know who it could be? – Guy? Hello?'

'Yes,' he said.

'Who?'

He knew from her voice she was merely frightened, that she believed in him, was afraid only for him. 'I don't know, Anne.'

'Is that true, Guy?' she asked anxiously. 'You should know. Something should be done.'

'I don't know,' Guy repeated, frowning. His mind seemed tied in an inextricable knot.

'You must know. *Think*, Guy. Someone you might call an enemy?'

'What's the postmark?'

'Grand Central. It's perfectly plain paper. You can't tell a thing from that.'

'Save it for me.'

'Of course, Guy. And I won't tell anyone. The family, I mean.' A pause. 'There must be someone, Guy. You suspected someone Saturday – didn't you?'

'I didn't.' His throat closed up. 'Sometimes these things happen, you know, after a trial.' And he was aware of a desire to cover Bruno as carefully as if Bruno had been himself, and he guilty. 'When can I see you, Anne? Can I come out tonight?'

'Well, I'm – sort of expected to go with Mother and Dad to a benefit thing. I can mail you the letter. Special delivery, you'll get it tomorrow morning.'

So it came the next morning, along with another of Bruno's plans, and an affectionate but exhorting last paragraph in which he mentioned the letter to Anne and promised more.

22

Guy sat up on the edge of his bed, covered his face in his hands, then deliberately brought his hands down. It was the night that took up the body of his thoughts and distorted it, he felt, the night and the darkness and the sleeplessness. Yet the night had its truth also. In the night, one approached truth merely at a certain slant, but all truth was the same. If he told Anne the story, wouldn't she consider he had been partially guilty? Marry him? How could she? What sort of beast was he that he could sit in a room where a bottom drawer held plans for a murder and the gun to do it with?

In the frail pre-dawn light, he studied his face in the mirror. The mouth slanted downward to the left, unlike his. The full underlip was thinner with tension. He tried to hold his eyes to an absolute steadiness. They stared back above pallid semi-circles, like a part of him that had hardened with accusation, as if they gazed at their torturer.

Should he dress and go out for a walk or try to sleep? His step on the carpet was light, unconsciously avoiding the spot by the armchair where the floor squeaked. *You would skip these squeaking steps just for safety*, Bruno's letters said. *My father's door is just to the right as you know. I have gone over everything and there is no room for a hitch anywhere. See on map where the butler's*

(Herbert's) room is. This is the closest you'll come to anyone. The hall floor squeaks there where I marked X . . . He flung himself on the bed. *You should not try to get rid of the Luger no matter what happens between the house and the RR station.* He knew it all by heart, knew the sound of the kitchen door and the colour of the hall carpet.

If Bruno should get someone else to kill his father, he would have ample evidence in these letters to convict Bruno. He could avenge himself for what Bruno had done to him. Yet Bruno would merely counter with his lies that would convict him of planning Miriam's murder. No, it would be only a matter of time until Bruno got someone. If he could weather Bruno's threats only a while longer, it would all be over and he could sleep. If he did it, he thought, he wouldn't use the big Luger, he would use the liule revolver –

Guy pulled himself up from the bed, aching, angry, and frightened by the words that had just passed through his mind. 'The Shaw Building,' he said to himself, as if announcing a new scene, as if he could derail himself from the night's tracks and set himself on the day's. *The Shaw Building. The ground is all grass covered to the steps in back, except for gravel you won't have to touch . . . Skip four, skip three, step wide at the top. You can remember it, it's got a syncopated rhythm.*

'Mr Haines!'

Guy started, and cut himself. He laid his razor down and went to the door.

'Hello, Guy. Are you ready yet?' asked the voice on the telephone, lewd in the early morning, ugly with the complexities of night. 'Want some more?'

'You don't bother me.'

Bruno laughed.

Guy hung up, trembling.

The shock lingered through the day, tremulous and traumatic. He wanted desperately to see Anne that evening, wanted desperately that instant of glimpsing her from some spot where he had promised to wait. But he wanted also to deprive himself of her. He took a long walk up Riverside Drive to tire himself, but slept badly nevertheless, and had a series of unpleasant dreams. It would be different, Guy thought, once the Shaw contract was signed, once he could go ahead on his work.

Douglas Frear of the Shaw Realty Company called the next morning as he had promised. 'Mr Haines,' said his slow, hoarse voice, 'we've received a most peculiar letter concerning you.'

'What? What kind of a letter?'

'Concerning your wife. I didn't know – Shall I read it to you?'

'Please.'

' "To Whom It May Concern: No doubt it will interest you to learn that Guy Daniel Haines, whose wife was murdered last June, had more of a role in the deed than the courts know. This is from one who knows, and who knows also that there will be a retrial soon which will show his real part in the crime." – I trust it's a crank letter, Mr Haines. I just thought you should know about it.'

'Of course.' In the corner, Myers worked over his drawing-board as calmly as on any other morning of the week.

'I think I heard about – uh – the tragedy last year. There's no question of a retrial, is there?'

'Certainly not. That is, I've heard nothing about it.' Guy cursed his confusion. Mr Frear wanted only to know if he would be free to work.

'Sorry we haven't quite made up our minds on that contract, Mr Haines.'

The Shaw Realty Company waited until the following morning to tell him they weren't entirely satisfied with his drawings. In fact, they were interested in the work of another architect.

How had Bruno found out about the building, Guy wondered. But there were any number of ways. It might have been mentioned in the papers – Bruno kept himself well informed on architectural news – or Bruno might have called when he knew he was out of the office, casually got the information from Myers. Guy looked at Myers again, and wondered if he had ever spoken on the telephone with Bruno. The possibility had a flavour of the unearthly.

Now that the building was gone, he began to see it in terms of what it would not mean. He would not have the extra money he had counted on by summer. Nor the prestige, the prestige with the Faulkner family. It did not once occur to him – as much at the root of his anguish as any of the other reasons – that he had suffered frustration in seeing a creation come to nothing.

It would be only a matter of time until Bruno informed the next client, and the next. This was his threat to ruin his career. And his life with Anne? Guy thought of her with a flash of pain. It seemed to him that he was forgetting for long intervals that he loved her. Something was happening between them, he could not say what. He felt Bruno was destroying his courage to love. Every slightest thing deepened his anxiety, from the fact he had lost his best pair of shoes by forgetting what repair shop he had taken them to, to the house at Alton, which already seemed more than they should have taken on, which he doubted they could fill.

In the office, Myers worked on his routine, drafting agency jobs, and Guy's telephone never rang. Once Guy thought, even Bruno doesn't call because he wants it to build up and build up, so his voice will be welcome when it comes. And disgusted with himself, Guy went down in the middle of the day and drank martinis in a Madison Avenue bar. He was to have had lunch with Anne, but she had called and broken the appointment, he could not remember why. She had not sounded precisely cool, but he thought she had not given any real reason for not lunching with him. She certainly hadn't said she was going shopping for something for the house, or he would have remembered it. Or would he have? Or was she retaliating for his breaking his promise to come out to dinner with her family last Sunday? He had been too tired and too depressed to see anyone last Sunday. A quiet, unacknowledged quarrel seemed to be going on between himself and Anne. Lately, he felt too miserable to inflict himself on her, and she pretended to be too busy to see him when he asked to see her. She was busy planning for the house, and busy quarrelling with him. It did not make sense. Nothing in the world made sense except to escape from Bruno. There was no way of doing that that made sense. What would happen in a court would not make sense.

He lighted a cigarette, then noticed he already had one. Hunched over the shiny black table, he smoked them both. His arms and hands with the cigarettes seemed mirrored. What was he doing here at 1.15 in the afternoon, growing swimmy on his third martini, making himself incapable of work, assuming he had any? Guy Haines who loved Anne, who had built the Palmyra? He hadn't even the courage to throw his martini glass into the corner. Quicksand. Suppose he sank completely. Suppose he did kill for Bruno. It would be so simple, as Bruno said, when the house was empty except for his father and the butler, and Guy knew the house more exactly than his home in Metcalf. He could leave clues against Bruno, too, leave the Luger in the room. This thought became a single point of concreteness. His fists closed reflexively against Bruno, then the impotence of his clenched hands before him on the table shamed him. He must not let his mind go there again. That was exactly what Bruno wanted his mind to do.

He wet his handkerchief in the glass of water and daubed his face. A shaving cut began to sting. He looked at it in the mirror beside him. It had started to bleed, a tiny red mark just to one side of the faint cleft in his chin. He wanted to throw his fist at the chin in the mirror. He jerked himself up and went to pay his bill.

But having been there once, it was easy for his mind to go there again. In the nights when he could not sleep, he enacted the murder, and it soothed him like a drug. It was not murder but an act he performed to rid himself of Bruno, the slice of a knife that cut away a malignant growth. In the night, Bruno's father was not a person but an object, as he himself was not a person but a force. To enact it, leaving the Luger in the room, to follow Bruno's progress to conviction and death, was a catharsis.

Bruno sent him an alligator billfold with gold corners and his initials G.D.H. inside. 'I thought this looked like you, Guy,' said the note inside. 'Please don't make things tough. I am very fond of you. As ever, Bruno.' Guy's arm moved to fling it into a trash-basket on the street, then he slipped it into his pocket. He hated to throw away a beautiful thing. He would think of something else to do with it.

That same morning, Guy declined an invitation to speak on a radio panel. He was in no condition to work and he knew it. Why did he even keep coming to the office? He would have been delighted to stay drunk all day, and especially all night. He watched his hand turning and turning the folded compass on his desk top. Someone had once told him that he had hands like a Capuchin monk. Tim O'Flaherty in Chicago. Once when they had sat eating spaghetti in Tim's basement apartment, talking of Le Corbusier and the verbal eloquence that seemed innate in architects, a natural concomitant of the profession, and how fortunate it was, because generally you had to talk your way. But it had all been possible then, even with Miriam draining him, merely a clean invigorating fight ahead, and somehow right with all its difficulties. He turned the compass over and over, sliding his fingers down it and turning it, until he thought the noise might be bothering Myers and stopped.

'Pull out of it, Guy,' Myers said amiably.

'It isn't anything one snaps out of. One either cracks up or doesn't,' Guy retorted with a dead calm in his voice, and then, unable to stop himself, 'I don't want advice, Myers. Thanks.'

'Listen, Guy –' Myers stood up, smiling, lanky, tranquil. But he did not come beyond the corner of his desk.

Guy got his coat from the tree by the door. 'I'm sorry. Let's forget it.'

'I know what's the matter. Pre-wedding nerves. I had them, too. What do you say we go down and have a drink?'

Myers' familiarity piqued a certain sense of dignity that Guy was never aware of until it was affronted. He could not bear to look at Myers' untroubled, empty face, his smug banality.

'Thanks,' he said, 'I really don't feel like it.' He closed the door softly behind him.

23

Guy glanced again at the row of brownstones across the street, sure he had seen Bruno. His eyes smarted and swam, fighting the dusk. He *had* seen him, there by the black iron gate, where he was not. Guy turned and ran up his steps. He had tickets to a Verdi opera tonight. Anne was going to meet him at the theatre at 8.30. He didn't feel like seeing Anne tonight, didn't want Anne's kind of cheering, didn't want to exhaust himself pretending he felt better than he did. She was worried about his not sleeping. Not that she said much, but that little annoyed him. Above all, he didn't want to hear Verdi. Whatever had possessed him to buy tickets to Verdi? He had wanted to do something to please Anne, but at best she wouldn't like it very much, and wasn't there something insane about buying tickets for something neither of them liked?

Mrs McCausland gave him a number he was supposed to call. He thought it looked like the number of one of Anne's aunts. He hoped Anne might be busy tonight.

'Guy, I don't see how I can make it,' Anne said. 'These two people Aunt Julie wanted me to meet aren't coming until after dinner.'

'All right.'

'And I can't duck out on it.'

'It's perfectly all right.'

'I am sorry though. Do you know I haven't seen you since Saturday?'

Guy bit the end of his tongue. An actual repulsion against her clinging, her concern, even her clear, gentle voice that had before been like an embrace itself – all this seemed a revelation he no longer loved her.

'Why don't you take Mrs McCausland tonight? I think it'd be nice if you did.'

'Anne, I don't care at all.'

'There haven't been any more letters, Guy?'

'No.' The third time she had asked him!

'I do love you. You won't forget, will you?'

'No, Anne.'

He fled upstairs to his room, hung up his coat and washed, combed his hair, and immediately there was nothing to do, and he wanted Anne. He wanted her terribly. Why had he been so mad as to think he didn't want to see her? He searched his pockets for Mrs McCausland's note with the telephone number, then ran downstairs and looked for it on the hall floor. It had vanished – as if someone had deliberately snatched it away to thwart him. He peered through the etched glass of the front door. Bruno, he thought, Bruno had taken it.

The Faulkners would know her aunt's number. He would see her, spend the evening with her, even if it meant spending the evening with her Aunt Julie. The telephone in Long Island rang and rang and nobody answered. He tried again to think of her aunt's last name, and couldn't.

His room seemed filled with palpable, suspenseful silence. He glanced at the low bookshelves he had built around the walls, at the ivy Mrs McCausland had given him in the wall brackets, at the empty red plush chair by the reading lamp, at his sketch in black and white over his bed entitled 'Imaginary Zoo', at the monk's cloth curtains that concealed his kitchenette. Almost boredly he went and moved the curtains aside and looked behind them. He had a definite feeling someone was waiting for him in the room, though he was not in the least frightened. He picked up the newspaper and started to read.

A few moments later, he was in a bar drinking a second martini. He had to sleep, he reasoned, even if it meant drinking alone, which he despised. He walked down to Times Square, got a haircut, and on the way home bought a quart of milk and a couple of tabloids. After he wrote a letter to his mother, he thought, he would drink some milk, read the papers, and go to bed. Or there might even be Anne's telephone number on the floor when he came in. But there wasn't.

At about two in the morning, he got up from bed and wandered about the room, hungry and unwilling to eat. Yet one night last week, he remembered, he had opened a can of sardines and devoured them on the blade of a knife. The night was a time for bestial affinities, for drawing closer to oneself. He plucked a notebook from the bookshelf and turned through it hastily. It was his first New York notebook, when he was about twenty-two. He had sketched indiscriminately – the Chrysler Building, the Payne Whitney Psychiatric Clinic, barges on the East River, workmen leaning on electric drills that bit horizontally into rock. There was a series on the Radio City building, with notes on space, on the opposite page the same building with the amendations he would make, or perhaps an entirely new building of his own conception. He closed the book quickly because it was good, and he doubted if he could do as well now. The Palmyra seemed the last spurt of that generous, happy energy of his youth. The sob he had been suppressing contracted his chest with a sickening, familiar pain – familiar from the years after Miriam. He lay down on his bed in order to stop the next.

Guy awakened to Bruno's presence in the dark, though he heard nothing. After the first small start at the suddenness, he felt no surprise at all. As he had imagined, in nights before this, he was quite happy that Bruno had come. *Really* Bruno? Yes. Guy saw the end of his cigarette now, over by the bureau.

'Bruno?'

'Hi,' Bruno said softly. 'I got in on a pass key. You're ready now, aren't you?' Bruno sounded calm and tired.

Guy raised himself to one elbow. Of course Bruno was there. The orangey end of his cigarette was there. 'Yes,' Guy said, and felt the yes absorbed by the darkness, not like the other nights when the yes had been silent, not even going out from him. It undid the knot in his head so suddenly that it hurt him. It was what he had been waiting to say, what the silence in the room had been waiting to hear. And the beasts beyond the walls.

Bruno sat down on the side of the bed and gripped both his arms above the elbows. 'Guy, I'll never see you again.'

'No.' Bruno smelled abominably of cigarettes and sweet brilliantine, of the sourness of drink, but Guy did not draw back from him. His head was still at its delicious business of untying.

'I tried to be nice to him these last couple days,' Bruno said. 'Not nice, just decent. He said something tonight to my mother, just before we went out –'

'I don't want to hear it!' Guy said. Time and again he had stopped Bruno because he didn't want to know what his father had said, what he looked like, anything about him.

They were both silent for several seconds, Guy because he would not explain, and Bruno because he had been silenced.

Bruno snuffled with a disgusting rattle. 'We're going to Maine tomorrow, starting by noon positively. My mother and me and the chauffeur. Tomorrow night is a good night but any night except Thursday night is just the same. Any time after eleven . . .'

He kept talking, repeating what Guy knew already, and Guy did not stop him, because he knew he was going to enter the house and it would all come true.

'I broke the lock on the back door two days ago, slamming it when I was tight. They won't get it fixed, they're too busy. But if they do –' He pressed a key into Guy's hand. 'And I brought you these.'

'What is it?'

'Gloves. Ladies' gloves, but they'll stretch.' Bruno laughed.

Guy felt the thin cotton gloves.

'You got the gun, huh? Where is it?'

'In the bottom drawer.'

Guy heard him stumble against the bureau and heard the drawer pull out. The lampshade crackled, the light came on, and Bruno stood there huge and tall in a new polo coat so pale it was nearly white, in black trousers with a thin white stripe in them. A white silk muffler hung long around his neck. Guy examined him from his small brown shoes to his stringy oiled hair, as if from his physical appearance he could discover what had caused his change of feeling, or even what the feeling was. It was familiarity and something more, something brotherly. Bruno clicked the gun shut and turned to him. His face was heavier than the last time Guy had seen it, flushed and more alive than he remembered ever having seen it. His grey eyes looked bigger with his tears and rather golden. He looked at Guy as if he tried to find words, or as if he pled with Guy to find them. Then he moistened the thin parted lips, shook his head, and reached an arm out towards the lamp. The light went out.

When he was gone, it hardly seemed he was gone. There were just the two of them in the room still, and sleep.

A grey glaring light filled the room when Guy awakened. The clock said 3.25. He imagined more than remembered that he had got up to go to the telephone that morning, that Myers had called to ask why he had not come in, and that he had said he didn't feel well. The devil with Myers. He lay there blinking his dullness away, letting it seep into the thinking part of his brain that tonight he was going to do it, and after tonight it would all be over. Then he got up and slowly went about his routine of shaving, showering, and dressing, aware that nothing he did mattered at all until the hour between eleven and midnight, the hour there was neither hurry nor delay about, that was coming just as it should. He felt he moved on certain definite tracks now, and that he could not have stopped himself or got off them if he had wanted to.

In the middle of his late breakfast in a coffee shop down the street, an eerie sensation came over him that the last time he had seen Anne he had told her everything that he was going to do, and that she had listened placidly, knowing she must for his sake, because he absolutely had to do what he was going to do. It seemed so natural and inevitable, he felt everyone in the world must know it, the man sitting beside him unconcernedly eating, Mrs McCausland, sweeping her hall as he went out, who had given him an especially maternal smile and asked if he was feeling well. March 12 FRIDAY, said the day-by-day calendar on the coffee-shop wall. Guy stared at it a moment, then finished his meal.

He wanted to keep moving. He decided by the time he walked up Madison Avenue, then Fifth to the end of Central Park, down Central Park West to Pennsylvania Station, it would be time to catch the train to Great Neck. He began to think of his course of action for tonight, but it bored him like something in school he had already studied too much, and he stopped. The brass barometers in a Madison Avenue window had a special appeal now, as if he were soon to have a holiday and possess them and play with them. Anne's sailboat, he thought, didn't have a barometer as handsome as any of these or he would have noticed it. He must get one before they sailed south on their honeymoon. He thought of his love, like a rich possession. He had reached the north end of Central Park, when it occurred to him he didn't have the gun with him. Or the gloves. And it was a quarter to eight. A fine, stupid beginning! He hailed a cab and hurried the driver back to his house.

There was plenty of time after all, so much that he wandered about his room absently for a while. Should he bother to wear crêpe-soled shoes? Should he wear a hat? He got the Luger out of the bottom drawer and laid it on the bureau. There was a single plan of Bruno's under the gun and he opened it, but immediately every word was so familiar, he threw it into the waste-basket. Momentum smoothed his movements again. He got the purple cotton gloves from the table by his bed. A small yellow card fluttered from them. It was a ticket to Great Neck.

He stared at the black Luger which more than before struck him as outrageously large. Idiotic of *someone* to have made a gun so big! He got his own little revolver from the top drawer. Its pearl handle gleamed with a discreet beauty. Its short slender barrel looked inquisitive, willing, strong with a reserved and gallant strength. Still, he mustn't forget he'd been going to leave the Luger in the bedroom, because it was Bruno's gun. But it didn't seem worth it now, to carry the heavy gun just for that. He really felt no enmity towards Bruno now, and that was the odd thing.

For a moment, he was utterly confused. Of course take the Luger, the Luger was in the plan! He put the Luger in his overcoat pocket. His hand moved for the gloves on the bureau top. The gloves were purple and the flannel bag of his revolver was lavender. Suddenly it seemed fitting he should take the small revolver, because of the similar colours, so he put the Luger back in the bottom drawer and dropped the little revolver into his pocket. He did not check to see if anything else should be done, because he could simply feel, having gone over Bruno's plans so often, that he had done everything. At last he got a glass of water and poured it into the ivy in the wall brackets. A cup of coffee might make him more alert, he thought. He would get one at the Great Neck station.

There was a moment on the train, when a man bumped his shoulder, when his nerves seemed to go quivering up and up to a pitch at which he thought something *must* happen, and a flurry of words rushed to his mind, almost to his tongue: *It's not really a gun in my pocket. I've never thought of it as a gun. I didn't buy it because it was a gun.* And immediately he felt easier, because he knew he was going to kill with it. He was like Bruno. Hadn't he sensed it time and time again, and like a coward never admitted it? Hadn't he known Bruno was like himself? Or why had he liked Bruno? He loved Bruno. Bruno had prepared every inch of the way for him, and everything would go well because everything always went well for Bruno. The world was geared for people like Bruno.

It was drizzling in a fine, directionless mist as he stepped off the train. Guy walked straight to the row of buses Bruno had described. The air through the open window was colder than New York's, and fresh with open country. The bus moved out of the lighted community centre and into a darker road with houses along both sides. He remembered he hadn't stopped for coffee in the station. The omission threw him into a state of irritation just short of making him get off the bus and go back for it. A cup of coffee might make all the difference in the world. Yes, his life! But at the Grant Street stop, he stood up automatically, and the feeling of moving on established tracks returned to comfort him.

His step had a moist elastic sound on the dirt road. Ahead of him, a young girl ran up some steps, along a front walk, and the closing of the door behind her sounded peaceful and neighbourly. There was the vacant lot with the solitary tree, and off to the left, darkness and the woods. The street lamp Bruno had put in all his maps wore an oily blue and gold halo. A car approached slowly, its headlights rolling like wild eyes with the road's bumps, and passed him.

He came upon it suddenly, and it was as if a curtain had lifted on a stage scene he knew already: the long seven-foot-high wall of white plaster in the foreground, darkened here and there by a cherry tree that overhung it, and beyond, the triangle of white housetop. The Doghouse. He crossed the street. From up the road came the grit of slow steps. He waited against the darker north side of the wall until the figure came into view. It was a policeman, strolling with hands and stick behind him. Guy felt no alarm whatever, less if possible than if the man hadn't been a policeman, he thought. When the policeman had passed, Guy walked fifteen paces beside the wall, sprang up and gripped its cornice across the top, and scrambled astride it. Almost directly below him, he saw the pale form of the milk crate Bruno had said he had flung near the wall. He bent to peer through the cherry tree branches at the house. He could see two of the five big windows on the first floor, and part of the rectangle of the swimming pond projecting towards him. There was no light. He jumped down.

Now he could see the start of the six white-sided steps at the back, and the misty frill of blossomless dogwood trees that surrounded the whole house. As he had suspected from Bruno's drawings, the house was too small for its ten double gables, obviously built because the client wanted gables and that was that. He moved along the inner side of the wall until crackling twigs frightened him. *Cut cattycornered across the lawn*, Bruno had said, and the twigs were why.

When he moved towards the house, a limb took his hat off. He rammed the hat in the front of his overcoat, and put his hand back in the pocket where the key was. When had he put the gloves on? He took a breath and moved across the lawn in a gait between running and walking, light and quick as a cat. I have done this many times before, he thought, this is only one of the times. He hesitated at the edge of the grass, glanced at the familiar garage towards which the gravel road curved, then went up the six back steps. The back door opened, heavy and smooth, and he caught the knob on the other side. But the second door with the Yale lock resisted, and a flush of something like embarrassment passed over him before he pushed harder and it yielded. He heard a clock on the kitchen table to his left. He knew it was a table, though he could see only blackness with less black forms of things, the big white stove, the servants' table and chairs left, the cabinets. He moved diagonally towards the back stairs, counting off his steps. *I would have you use the main stairway but the whole stairway creaks.* He walked slowly and stiffly, stretching his eyes, skirting the vegetable bins he did not really see. A sudden thought that he must resemble an insane somnambulist brought a start of panic.

Twelve steps up first, skip seven. Then two little flights after the turn . . . Skip four, skip three, step wide at the top. You can remember it, it's got a syncopated rhythm. He skipped the fourth step in the first little flight. There was a round window just at the turn before the last flight. Guy remembered from some essay, *As a house is built so the pattern of activity of those will be who live in it . . . Shall the child pause at the window for the view before he climbs fifteen steps to his playroom?* Ten feet ahead on his left was the butler's door. *This is the closest you'll come to anyone*, said Bruno in a crescendo as he passed the door's dark column.

The floor gave the tiniest wail of complaint, and Guy resiliently withdrew his foot, waited, and stepped around the spot. Delicately his hand closed on the knob of the hall door. As he opened it, the clock's tick on the landing of the main stairway came louder, and he realized he had been hearing it for several seconds. He heard a sigh.

A sigh on the main stairs!

A chime rang out. The knob rattled, and he squeezed it hard enough to break it, he thought. *Three. Four.* Close the door before the butler hears it! Was this why Bruno had said between eleven and midnight? Damn him! And now he didn't have the Luger! Guy closed the door with a *bump-bump.* While he sweated, feeling heat rise from his overcoat collar into his face, the clock kept on and on. And a last one.

Then he listened, and there was nothing but the deaf and blind *tick-tock* again, and he opened the door and went into the main hall. *My father's door is just to the right.* The tracks were back under him again. And surely he had been here before, in the empty hall that he could feel as he stared at Bruno's father's door, with the grey carpet, the panelled creamy walls, the marble table at the head of the stairs. The hall had a smell and even the smell was familiar. A sharp tickling sensation came at his temples. Suddenly he was sure the old man stood just the other side of the door, holding his breath just as he did, awaiting him. Guy held his own breath so long the old man must have died if he too had not breathed. Nonsense! Open the door!

He took the knob in his left hand, and his right moved automatically to the gun in his pocket. He felt like a machine, beyond danger and invulnerable. He had been here many, many times before, had killed him many times before, and this was only one of the times. He stared at the inch-wide crack in the door, sensing an infinite space opening out beyond, waiting until a feeling of vertigo passed. Suppose he couldn't *see* him when he got inside? Suppose the old man saw him first? *The night light on the front porch lights the room a little bit,* but the bed was over in the opposite corner. He opened the door wider, listened, and stepped too hastily in. But the room was still, the bed a big vague thing in the dark corner, with a lighter strip at the head. He closed the door, *the wind might blow the door*, then faced the corner.

The gun was in his hand already, aimed at the bed that looked empty however he peered at it.

He glanced at the window over his right shoulder. It was open only about a foot, and Bruno had said it would be open *all the way*. Because of the drizzle. He frowned at the bed, and then with a terrible thrill made out the form of the head lying rather near the wall side, tipped sideways as if it regarded him with a kind of gay disdain. The face was darker than the hair which blended with the pillow. The gun was looking straight at it as he was.

One should shoot the chest. Obediently the gun looked at the chest. Guy slid his feet nearer the bed and glanced again at the window behind him. There was no sound of breathing. One would really not think he were alive. That was what he had told himself he must think, that the figure was merely a target. And that, because he did not know the target, it was like killing in war. Now?

'Ha-ha-ha-a!' from the window.

Guy trembled and the gun trembled.

The laugh had come from a distance, a girl's laugh, distant but clear and straight as a shot. Guy wet his lips. The aliveness of the laugh had swept away everything of the scene for a moment, left nothing in its place, and now slowly the vacuum was filling with his standing here about to kill. It had happened in the time of a heartbeat. Life. The young girl walking in the street. With a young man, perhaps. And the man asleep in the bed, living. *No, don't think! You do it for Anne, remember? For Anne and for yourself! It is like killing in war, like killing –*

He pulled the trigger. It made a mere click. He pulled again and it clicked. It was a trick! It was all false and didn't even exist! Not even his standing here! He pulled the trigger again.

The room tore up with a roar. His fingers tightened in terror. The roar came again, as if the crust of the world burst.

'Kagh!' said the figure on the bed. The grey face moved upward, showing the line of head and shoulders.

Guy was on the porch roof, falling. The sensation awakened him like the fall at the end of a nightmare. By a miracle an awning bar slid into one of his hands, and he fell downward again, on to hands and knees. He jumped off the porch edge, ran along the side of the house, then cut across the lawn, straight for the place where the milk crate was. He awakened to the clinging earth, to the hopelessness of his pumping arms that tried to hurry his race against the lawn. This is how it feels, how it is, he thought – *life*, like the laugh upstairs. The truth was that it is like a nightmare when one is paralysed, against impossible odds.

'Hey!' a voice called.

The butler was after him, just as he had anticipated. He felt the butler was right behind him. The nightmare!

'Hey! Hey, there!'

Guy turned under the cherry trees and stood with his fist drawn back. The butler was not just behind him. He was a long way off, but he had seen him. The crazily running figure in white pyjamas wavered like leaping smoke, then curved towards him. Guy stood, paralysed, waiting.

'Hey!'

Guy's fist shot out for the oncoming chin, and the white wraith collapsed.

Guy jumped for the wall.

Darkness ran up higher and higher about him. He dodged a little tree, leapt what looked like a ditch, and ran on. Then suddenly he was lying face down and pain was spreading from the middle of him in all directions, rooting him to the ground. His body trembled violently, and he thought he must gather up the trembling and use it to run, that this wasn't where Bruno had said to go at all, but he could not move. You just take the little dirt road (no lights there) eastward off Newhope south of the house and keep going across two bigger streets to Columbia Street and walk south (right) . . . To the bus line that went to another railroad station. All very well for Bruno to write his damned instructions on paper. Damn him! He knew where he was now, in the field west of the house that never in any of the plans was to be used! He looked behind him. Which way was north now? What had happened to the street light? Maybe he wouldn't be able to find the little road in the dark. He didn't know whether the house lay behind him or to his left. A mysterious pain throbbed the length of his right forearm so sharp he thought it should have glowed in the dark.

He felt as if he had been shattered apart with the explosion of the gun, that he could never gather the energy to move again, and that he really didn't care. He remembered his being hit in the football game in high school, when he had lain face down like this, speechless with pain. He remembered the supper, the very supper and the hot-water bottle his mother had brought to him in bed, and the touch of her hands adjusting the covers under his chin. His trembling hand was sawing itself raw on a half-buried rock. He bit his lip and kept thinking vacuously, as one thinks when only half awake on an exhausted morning, that he must get up in the next moment regardless of the agony because he wasn't safe. He was still so close to the house. And suddenly his arms and legs scrambled under him as if statics had built up a charge abruptly released, and he was running again across the field.

A strange sound made him stop – a low musical moan that seemed to come from all sides.

Police sirens, of course. And like an idiot he had thought first of an airplane! He ran on, knowing he was only running blindly and directly away from the sirens that were over his left shoulder now, and that he should veer left to find the little road. He must have run far beyond the long plaster wall. He started to cut left to cross the main road that surely lay in that direction, when he realized the sirens were coming up the road. He would either have to wait – He couldn't wait. He ran on, parallel to the cars. Then something caught his foot, and cursing, he fell again. He lay in a kind of ditch with his arms outspread, the right bent up on higher ground. Frustration maddened him to a petulant sob.

His left hand felt odd. It was in water up to the wrist. It'll wet my wristwatch, he thought. But the more he intended to pull it out the more impossible it seemed to move it. He felt two forces, one that would move the arm and another that would not, balancing themselves so perfectly his arm was not even tense. Incredibly, he felt he might have slept now. *The police will surround me,* he thought out of nowhere, and was up again, running.

Close on his right, a siren shrieked in triumph as if it had found him.

A rectangle of light sprang up in front of him, and he turned and fled it. A window. He had nearly run into a house. The whole world was awake! And he *had* to cross the road!

The police car passed thirty feet before him on the road, with a blink of headlights through bushes. Another siren moaned to his left, where the house must be, and droned away to silence. Stooping, Guy crossed the road not far behind the car and entered deeper darkness. No matter where the little road was now, he could run farther from the house in this direction. *There's sort of unlighted woods all around to the south, easy to hide in in case you have to get off the little road . . . Do not try to get rid of the Luger no matter what happens between my house and the RR station.* His hand moved to his pocket and felt the cold of the little revolver through the holes in his gloves. He didn't remember putting the gun back in his pocket. It might have been lying on the blue carpet for all he knew! And suppose he had dropped it? A fine time to think of it!

Something had caught him and was holding him. He fought it automatically with his fists, and found it was bushes, twigs, briars, and kept fighting and hurling his body through it, because the sirens were still behind him and this was the only direction to go. He concentrated on the enemy ahead of him, and on both sides and even behind him, that caught at him with thousands of sharp tiny hands whose crackling began to drown out even the sirens. He spent his strength joyfully against them, relishing their clean, straight battle against him.

He awakened at the edge of a woods, face down on a downward

sloping hill. Had he awakened, or had he fallen only a moment ago? But there was greyness in the sky in front of him, the beginning of dawn, and when he stood up, his flickering vision told him he had been unconscious. His fingers moved directly to the mass of hair and wetness that stood out from the side of his head. Maybe my head is broken, he thought in terror, and stood for a moment dully, expecting himself to drop dead.

Below, the sparse lights of a little town glowed like stars at dusk. Mechanically, Guy got out a handkerchief and wrapped it tight around the base of his thumb where a cut had oozed black-looking blood. He moved towards a tree and leaned against it. His eyes searched the town and the road below. There was not a moving thing. Was this he? Standing against the tree with the memory of the gun's explosion, the sirens, the fight against the woods? He wanted water. On the dirt road that edged the town, he saw a filling station. He made his way down towards it.

There was an old-fashioned pump beside the filling station. He held his head under it. His face stung like a mask of cuts. Slowly his mind grew clearer. He couldn't be more than two miles from Great Neck. He removed his right glove that hung by one finger and the wrist, and put it in his pocket. Where was the other? Had he left it in the woods where he tied his thumb? A rush of panic comforted him with its familiarity. He'd have to go back for it. He searched his overcoat pockets, opened his overcoat and searched his trousers pockets. His hat fell at his feet. He had forgotten about the hat, and suppose he had dropped that somewhere? Then he found the glove inside his left sleeve, no more than the seam of the top that still circled his wrist, and a tatter, and pocketed it with an abstract relief like happiness. He turned up a trousers cuff that had been torn down. He decided to walk in the direction he knew was southward, catch any bus farther southward, and ride until he came to a railroad station.

As soon as he realized his objective, pain set in. How could he walk the length of this road with these knees? Yet he kept walking, holding his head high to urge himself along. It was a time of dubious balance between night and day, still dark, though a low iridescence lay everywhere. The dark might still overcome the light, it seemed, because the dark was bigger. If the night could only hold this much until he got home and locked his door!

Then daylight made a sudden thrust at the night, and cracked the whole horizon on his left. A silver line ran around the top of a hill, and the hill became mauve and green and tan, as if it were opening its eyes. A little yellow house stood under a tree on the hill. On his right, a dark field had become high grass of green and tan, gently moving like a sea. As he looked, a bird flew out of the grass with a cry and wrote a fast, jagged, exuberant message with its sharp-pointed wings across the sky. Guy stopped and watched it until it disappeared.

24

For the hundredth time, he examined his face in the bathroom mirror, patiently touched every scratch with the styptic pencil, and repowdered them. He ministered to his face and hands objectively, as if they were not a part of himself. When his eyes met the staring eyes in the mirror, they slipped away as they must have slipped away, Guy thought, that first afternoon on the train, when he had tried to avoid Bruno's eyes.

He went back and fell down on his bed. There was the rest of today, and tomorrow, Sunday. He needn't see anyone. He could go to Chicago for a couple of weeks and say he was away on a job. But it might seem suspicious if he left town the day after. *Yesterday. Last night.* Except for his scratched hands, he might have believed it one of his dreams that he had done it. Because he had not wanted to do it, he thought. It had not been his will. It had been Bruno's will, working through him. He wanted to curse Bruno, curse him aloud, but he simply had not the energy now. The curious thing was that he felt no guilt, and it seemed to him now that the fact Bruno's will had motivated him was the explanation. But what was this thing, guilt, that he had felt more after Miriam's death than now? Now he was merely tired, and unconcerned about anything. Or was this how anyone would feel after killing? He tried to sleep, and his mind retraced the moments on the Long Island bus, the two workmen who had stared at him, his pretence of sleep with the newspaper over his face. He had felt more shame with the workmen . . .

His knees buckled on the front steps and he almost fell. He did not look to see if he were being observed. It seemed an ordinary thing he did, to go down and buy a paper. But he knew also he hadn't the strength to look to see if he were being observed, the strength even to care, and he dreaded the time when the strength would come, as a sick or wounded man dreads the next inevitable operation.

The *Journal-American* had the longest account, with a silhouette of the murderer, composed from the butler's description, of a man six feet one, weighing about one hundred and seventy to eighty pounds, wearing a dark overcoat and hat. Guy read it with mild surprise, as if it might not have been about him: he was only five nine and weighed about a hundred and forty. And he had not been wearing a hat. He skipped the part of the story that told who Samuel Bruno was, and read with greatest interest the speculation about the murderer's flight. North along Newhope Road, it said, where it was believed he lost himself in the town of Great Neck; perhaps taking the 12.18 a.m. train out. Actually, he had gone south-east. He felt suddenly relieved, safe. It was an illusion, he warned himself, safety. He stood up, for the first time as panicked as he had been when he floundered in the lot beside the house. The paper was several hours old. They could have found their mistake by now. They could be coming for him, right outside his door, by now. He waited, and there was no sound anywhere, and feeling tired again, he sat down. He forced himself to concentrate on the rest of the long column. The coolness of the murderer was stressed, and the fact it seemed to be an inside job. No fingerprints, no clue except some shoe prints, size nine and a half, and the smudge of a black shoe on the white plaster wall. His clothes, he thought, he must get rid of his clothes and immediately, but when would he find the energy to do it? It was odd they overestimated his shoe size, Guy thought, with the ground so wet. '. . . an unusually small calibre of bullet,' the paper said. He must get rid of his revolver, too. He felt a little wrench of grief. He would hate that, how he would hate the instant he parted from his revolver! He pulled himself up and went to get more ice for the towel he was holding against his head.

Anne telephoned him in the late afternoon to ask him to go to a party with her Sunday night in Manhattan.

'Helen Heyburn's party. You know, I told you about it!'

'Yes,' Guy said, not remembering at all. His voice came evenly, 'I guess I don't quite feel like a party, Anne.'

For the last hour or so, he had felt numb. It made Anne's words distant, irrelevant. He listened to himself saying the right things, not even anticipating, or perhaps not even caring, that Anne might notice any difference. Anne said she might get Chris Nelson to go with her, and Guy said all right, and thought how happy Nelson would be to go with her because Nelson, who had used to see a great deal of Anne before she met Guy, was still in love with her, Guy thought.

'Why don't I bring in some delicatessen Sunday evening,' Anne said, 'and we'll have a snack together? I could have Chris meet me later.'

'I thought I might go out Sunday, Anne. Sketching.'

'Oh. I'm sorry. I had something to tell you.'

'What?'

'Something I think you'll like. Well – some other time.'

Guy crept up the stairs, alert for Mrs McCausland. Anne was cool to him, he thought monotonously, Anne was cool. The next time she saw him, she would know and she would hate him. Anne was through, Anne was through. He kept chanting it until he fell asleep.

He slept until the following noon, then lay in bed the rest of the day in a torpor that made it agony even to cross the room to refill his towel with ice. He felt he would never sleep enough to get back his strength. Retracing, he thought. His body and mind retracing the long road they had travelled. Coming back to what? He lay rigid and afraid, sweating and shivering with fear. Then he had to get up to go to the bathroom. He had a slight case of diarrhoea. From fear, he thought. As on a battlefield.

He dreamt in half-sleep that he crossed the lawn towards the house. The house was soft and white and unresisting as a cloud. And he stood there unwilling to shoot, determined to fight it to prove he could conquer it. The gunshot awakened him. He opened his eyes to the dawn in his room. He saw himself standing by his work table, exactly as he stood in the dream, pointing the gun at a bed in the corner, where Samuel Bruno struggled to sit up. The gun roared again. Guy screamed.

He sprang out of bed, staggering. The figure vanished. At his window was the same struggling light he had seen that dawn, the same mingling of life and death. The same light would come every dawn that he lived, would always reveal that room, and the room would grow more distinct with repetition, his horror sharper. Suppose he awakened every dawn that he lived?

The doorbell rang in the kitchenette.

The police are downstairs, he thought. This was just the time they *would* catch him, at dawn. And he didn't care, didn't care at all. He would make a complete confession. He would blurt it all out at once!

He leaned on the release button, then went to his door and listened.

Light quick steps ran up. Anne's steps. Rather the police than Anne! He turned completely around, stupidly drew his shade. He thrust his hair back with both hands and felt the knot on his head.

'Me,' Anne whispered as she slipped in. 'I walked over from Helen's. It's a wonderful morning!' She saw his bandage, and the elation left her face. 'What happened to your hand?'

He stepped back in the shadow near his bureau. 'I got into a fight.'

'When? Last night? And your face, Guy!'

'Yes.' He had to have her, had to keep her with him, he thought. He would perish without her. He started to put his arms around her, but she pushed him back, peering at him in the half light.

'Where, Guy? Who was it?'

'A man I don't even know,' he said tonelessly, hardly realizing even that he lied, because it was so desperately necessary that he keep her with him. 'In a bar. Don't turn on the light,' he said quickly. 'Please, Anne.'

'In a bar?'

'I don't know how it happened. Suddenly.'

'Someone you'd never seen before?'

'Yes.'

'I don't believe you.'

She spoke slowly, and Guy was all at once terrified, realizing she was a separate person from himself, a person with a different mind, different reactions.

'How can I?' she went on. 'And why should I believe you about the letter, about not knowing who sent it?'

'Because it's true.'

'Or the man you fought with on the lawn. Was it the same one?'

'No.'

'You're keeping something from me, Guy.' Then she softened, but each simple word seemed to attack him: 'What is it, darling? You know I want to help you. But you've got to tell me.'

'I've told you,' he said, and set his teeth. Behind him, the light was changing already. If he could keep Anne now, he thought, he could survive every dawn. He looked at the straight, pale curtain of her hair, and put out his hand to touch it, but she drew back.

'I don't see how we can go on like this, Guy. We can't.'

'It won't go on. It's over. I swear to you, Anne. Please believe me.' The moment seemed a test, as if it were now or never again. He should take her in his arms, he thought, hold her fiercely until she stopped struggling against him. But he could not make himself move.

'How do you know?'

He hesitated. 'Because it was a state of mind.'

'That letter was a state of mind?'

'The letter contributed to it. I felt tied in a knot. It was my work, Anne!' He bowed his head. Nailing his sins to his work!

'You once said I made you happy,' she said slowly, 'or that I could in spite of anything. I don't see it any more.'

Certainly he did not make her happy, she meant to say. But if she could still love him now, how he would try to make her happy! How he would worship and serve her! 'You do, Anne. I have nothing else.' He bent lower with sudden sobs, shameless, wracking sobs that did not cease the long moment before Anne touched his shoulder. And though he was grateful, he felt like twisting away from the touch, too, because he felt it was only pity, only humanity that made her touch him at all.

'Shall I fix you some breakfast?'

Even in the note of exasperated patience he heard in her voice, there was a hint of forgiveness that meant total forgiveness, he knew. For fighting in a bar. Never, he thought, would she penetrate to Friday night, because it was already buried too deep for her or for any other person to go.

25

'I don't give a damn what you think!' Bruno said, his foot planted in his chair. His thin blond eyebrows almost met with his frown, and rose up at the ends like the whiskers of a cat. He looked at Gerard like a golden, thin-haired tiger driven to madness.

'Didn't say I thought anything,' Gerard replied with a shrug of hunched shoulders, 'did I?'

'You implied.'

'I did not imply.' The round shoulders shook twice with his laugh. 'You mistake me, Charles. I didn't mean you told anyone on purpose you were leaving. You let it drop by accident.'

Bruno stared at him. Gerard had just implied that if it was an inside job, Bruno and his mother must have had something to do with it, and it certainly was an inside job. Gerard knew that he and his mother had decided only Thursday afternoon to leave Friday. The idea of getting him all the way down here in Wall Street to tell him that! Gerard didn't have anything, and he couldn't fool him by pretending that he had. It was another perfect murder.

'Mind if I shove off?' Bruno asked. Gerard was fooling around with papers on his desk as if he had something else to keep him here for.

'In a minute. Have a drink.' Gerard nodded towards the bottle of bourbon on the shelf across the office.

'No, thanks.' Bruno was dying for a drink, but not from Gerard.

'How's your mother?'

'You asked me that.' His mother wasn't well, wasn't sleeping, and that was the main reason he wanted to get home. A hot resentment came over him again at Gerard's friend-of-the-family attitude. A friend of his father's maybe! 'By the way, we're not hiring you for this, you know.'

Gerard looked up with a smile on his round, faintly pink-and-purple mottled face. 'I'd work on this case for nothing, Charles. That's how interesting I think it is.' He lighted another of the cigars that were shaped something like his fat fingers, and Bruno noticed once more, with disgust, the gravy stains on the lapels of his fuzzy, light-brown suit and the ghastly marble-patterned tie. Every single thing about Gerard annoyed Bruno. His slow speech annoyed him. Memories of the only other times he had seen Gerard, with his father, annoyed him. Arthur Gerard didn't even look like the kind of a detective who was not supposed to look like a detective. In spite of his record, Bruno found it impossible to believe that Gerard was a top-notch detective. 'Your father was a very fine man, Charles. A pity you didn't know him better.'

'I knew him well,' said Bruno.

Gerard's small, speckled tan eyes looked at him gravely. 'I think he knew you better than you knew him. He left me several letters concerning you, your character, what he hoped to make of you.'

'He didn't know me at all.' Bruno reached for a cigarette. 'I don't know why we're talking about this. It's beside the point and it's morbid.' He sat down coolly.

'You hated your father, didn't you?'

'He hated me.'

'But he didn't. That's where you didn't know him.'

Bruno pushed his hand off the chair arm and it squeaked with sweat. 'Are we getting anywhere or what're you keeping me here for? My mother's not feeling well and I want to get home.'

'I hope she'll be feeling better soon, because I want to ask her some questions. Maybe tomorrow.'

Heat rose up the sides of Bruno's neck. The next few weeks would be terrible on his mother, and Gerard would make it worse because he was an enemy of both of them. Bruno stood up and tossed his raincoat over one arm.

'Now I want you to try to think once more,' Gerard wagged a finger at him as casually as if he still sat in the chair, 'just where you went and whom you saw Thursday night. You left your mother and Mr Templeton and Mr Russo in front of the Blue Angel at 2.45 that morning. Where did you go?'

'Hamburger Hearth,' Bruno sighed.

'Didn't see anyone you knew there?'

'Who should I know there, the cat?'

'Then where'd you go?' Gerard checked on his notes.

'Clarke's on Third Avenue.'

'See anyone there?'

'Sure, the bartender.'

'The bartender said he didn't see you,' Gerard smiled.

Bruno frowned. Gerard hadn't said that a half an hour ago. 'So what? The place was crowded. Maybe I didn't see the bartender either.'

'All the barmen know you in there. They said you weren't in

Thursday night. Furthermore, the place wasn't crowded. Thursday night? Three or 3.30? – I'm just trying to help you remember, Charles.'

Bruno compressed his lips in exasperation. 'Maybe I wasn't in Clarke's. I usually go over for a nightcap, but maybe I didn't. Maybe I went straight home, I don't know. What about all the people my mother and I talked to Friday morning? We called up a lot of people to say good-bye.'

'Oh, we're covering those. But seriously, Charles –' Gerard leaned back, crossed a stubby leg, and concentrated on puffing his cigar to life – 'you wouldn't leave your mother and her friends just to get a hamburger and go straight home by yourself, would you?'

'Maybe. Maybe it sobered me up.'

'Why're you so vague?' Gerard's Iowan accent made his 'r' a snarl.

'So what if I'm vague? I've got a right to be vague if I was tight!'

'The point is – and of course it doesn't matter whether you were at Clarke's or some other place – *who* you ran into and told you were leaving for Maine the next day. You must think yourself it's funny your father was killed the night of the same day you left.'

'I didn't see anyone. I invite you to check up on everyone I know and ask them.'

'You just wandered around by yourself until after five in the morning.'

'Who said I got home after five?'

'Herbert. Herbert said so yesterday.'

Bruno sighed. 'Why didn't he remember all that Saturday?'

'Well, as I say, that's how the memory works. Gone – and then it comes. Yours'll come, too. Meanwhile, I'll be around. Yes, you can go now, Charles.' Gerard made a careless gesture.

Bruno lingered a moment, trying to think of something to say, and not being able to, went out and tried to slam the door but the air pressure retarded it. He walked back through the shabby,

151

depressing corridor of the Confidential Detective Bureau, where the typewriter that had been pecking thoughtfully throughout the interview came louder – 'We,' Gerard was always saying, and here they all were, grubbing away back of the doors – nodded good-bye to Miss Graham, the receptionist-secretary who had expressed her sympathies to him an hour ago when he had come in. How gaily he had come in an hour ago, determined not to let Gerard rile him, and now – He could never control his temper when Gerard made cracks about him and his mother, and he might as well admit it. So what? So what did they have on him? So what clues did they have on the murderer? Wrong ones.

Guy! Bruno smiled going down in the elevator. Not once had Guy crossed his mind in Gerard's office! Not one flicker even when Gerard had hammered at him about where he went Thursday night! Guy! Guy and himself! Who else was like them?

Who else was their equal? He longed for Guy to be with him now. He would clasp Guy's hand, and to hell with the rest of the world! Their feats were unparalleled! Like a sweep across the sky! Like two streaks of red fire that came and disappeared so fast, everybody stood wondering if they really had seen them. He remembered a poem he had read once that said something of what he meant. He thought he still had it in a pocket of his address case. He hurried into a bar off Wall Street, ordered a drink, and pulled the tiny paper out of the address-book pocket. It was torn out of a poetry book he had had in college.

THE LEADEN-EYED
by *Vachel Lindsay*

Let not young souls be
    smothered out before
They do quaint deeds and fully
    flaunt their pride.
It is the world's one crime its

> babes grow dull,
> Its poor are ox-like, limp and leaden-eyed.
>
> Not that they starve, but starve
>   so dreamlessly,
> Not that they sow, but that they
>   seldom reap,
> Not that they serve, but have no
>   gods to serve,
> Not that they die, but that they
>   die like sheep.

He and Guy were not leaden-eyed. He and Guy would not die like sheep now. He and Guy would reap. He would give Guy money, too, if he would take it.

26

At about the same time the next day, Bruno was sitting in a beach chair on the terrace of his house in Great Neck, in a mood of complaisance and halcyon content quite new and pleasant to him. Gerard had been prowling around that morning, but Bruno had been very calm and courteous, had seen that he and his little stooge got some lunch, and now Gerard was gone and he felt very proud of his behaviour. He must never let Gerard get him down again like yesterday, because that was the way to get rattled and make mistakes. Gerard, of course, was the dumb one. If he'd just been nicer yesterday, he might have co-operated. Co-operated? Bruno laughed out loud. What did he mean co-operated? What was he doing, kidding himself?

Overhead a bird kept singing, 'Tweedledee?' and answering itself, 'Tweedle*dum*!' Bruno cocked his head. His mother would know what kind of a bird it was. He gazed off at the russet-tinged lawn, the white plaster wall, the dogwoods that were beginning to bud. This afternoon, he found himself quite interested in nature. This afternoon, a cheque had arrived for twenty thousand for his mother. There would be a lot more when the insurance people stopped yapping and the lawyers got all the red tape cut. At lunch, he and his mother had talked about going to Capri, talked sketchily, but he knew they would go. And tonight, they were going out to dinner for the first time, at a little *intime* place that was their favourite restaurant, off the highway not far from Great Neck. No wonder he hadn't liked nature before. Now that he owned the grass and the trees, it meant something.

Casually, he turned the pages of the address book in his lap. He had found it this morning, couldn't remember if he had had it with him in Santa Fe or not, and wanted to make sure there wasn't anything about Guy in it before Gerard found it. There certainly were a lot of people he wanted to look up again, now that he had the wherewithal. An idea came to him, and he took a pencil from his pocket. Under the P's he wrote:

Tommy Pandini
232 W. 76 Street

and under the S's:

'Slitch'
Life Guard Station
Hell Gate Bridge

Give Gerard a few mysterious people to look up.

Dan 8.15 Hotel Astor, he found in the memos at the back of the book. He didn't even remember Dan. *Get $ from Capt. by June I.* The next page sent a little chill down him: *Item for Guy $25.* He tore the perforated page out. That Santa Fe belt for Guy. Why had he even put it down? In some dull moment –

Gerard's big black car purred into the driveway.

Bruno forced himself to sit there and finish checking the memos. Then he slipped the address book in his pocket, and poked the torn-out page into his mouth.

Gerard strolled on to the flagstones with a cigar in his mouth and his arms hanging.

'Anything new?' Bruno asked.

'Few things.' Gerard let his eyes sweep from the corner of the house diagonally across the lawn to the plaster wall, as though he reappraised the distance the murderer had run.

Bruno's jaw moved casually on the little wad of paper, as if he chewed gum. 'Such as what?' he asked. Past Gerard's shoulder he saw his little stooge sitting in the driver's seat of the car, staring at them fixedly from under a grey hatbrim. Of all the sinister-looking guys, Bruno thought.

'Such as the fact the murderer didn't cut back to town. He kept going in this general direction.' Gerard gestured like a country-store proprietor pointing out a road, bringing his whole arm down. 'Cut through those woods over there and must have had a pretty rough time. We found these.'

Bruno got up and looked at a piece of the purple gloves and a shred of dark blue material, like Guy's overcoat. 'Gosh. You sure they're off the murderer?'

'Reasonably sure. One's off an overcoat. The other – probably a glove.'

'Or a muffler.'

'No, there's a little seam.' Gerard poked it with a fat freckled forefinger.

'Pretty fancy gloves.'

'Ladies' gloves.' Gerard looked up with a twinkle.

Bruno gave an amused smirk, and stopped contritely.

'I first thought he was a professional killer,' Gerard said with a sigh. 'He certainly knew the house. But I don't think a professional killer would have lost his head and tried to get through those woods at the point he did.'

'Hm-m,' said Bruno with interest.

'He knew the right road to take, too. The right road was only ten yards away.'

'How do you know that?'

'Because this whole thing was carefully planned, Charles. The broken lock on the back door, the milk crate out there by the wall –'

Bruno was silent. Herbert had told Gerard that he, Bruno, broke the lock. Herbert had probably also told him he put the milk crate there.

'Purple gloves!' Gerard chuckled, as gaily as Bruno had ever heard him chuckle. 'What does the colour matter as long as they keep fingerprints off things, eh?'

'Yeah,' Bruno said.

Gerard entered the house through the terrace door.

Bruno followed him after a moment. Gerard went back to the kitchen, and Bruno climbed the stairs. He tossed the address book on his bed, then went down the hall. The open door of his father's room gave him a funny feeling, as if he were just realizing his father were dead. It was the door's hanging open that made him feel it, he thought, like a shirt-tail hanging out, like a guard let down, that never would have been if the Captain were alive. Bruno frowned, then went and closed the door quickly on the carpet scuffled by detectives' feet, by Guy's feet, on the desk with the looted pigeon-holes and the cheque-book that lay open as if awaiting his father's signatures. He opened his mother's door carefully. She was lying on her bed with the pink satin comforter drawn up to her chin, her head turned towards the inside of the room and her eyes open, as she had lain since Saturday night.

'You didn't sleep, Mom?'

'No.'

'Gerard's here again.'

'I know.'

'If you don't want to be disturbed, I'll tell him.'

'Darling, don't be silly.'

Bruno sat down on the bed and bent close to her. 'I wish you could sleep, Mom.' She had purple wrinkled shadows under her eyes, and she held her mouth in a way he had never seen before, that drew its corners long and thin.

'Darling, are you sure Sam never mentioned anything to you – never mentioned anyone?'

'Can you imagine him saying anything like that to me?' Bruno wandered about the room. Gerard's presence in the house irked him. It was Gerard's manner that was so obnoxious, as if he had something up his sleeve against everyone, even Herbert who he knew had idolized his father, who was saying everything against him short of plain accusation. But Herbert hadn't seen him measuring the grounds, Bruno knew, or Gerard would have let him know by now. He had wandered all over the grounds, and the house while his mother was sick, and anyone seeing him wouldn't have known when he was counting his paces or not. He wanted to sound off about Gerard now, but his mother wouldn't understand. She insisted on their continuing to hire him, because he was supposed to be the best. They were not working together, his mother and he. His mother might say something else to Gerard – like the fact they'd decided only Thursday to leave Friday – of terrible importance and not mention it to him at all!

'You know you're getting fat, Charley?' his mother said with a smile.

Bruno smiled, too, she sounded so like herself. She was putting on her shower cap at her dressing-table now. 'Appetite's not bad,' he said. But his appetite was worse and so was his digestion. He was getting fatter anyway.

Gerard knocked just after his mother had closed the bathroom door.

'She'll be quite a long time,' Bruno told him.

'Tell her I'll be in the hall, will you?'

Bruno knocked on the bathroom door and told her, then went down to his own room. He could tell by the position of the address book on his bed that Gerard had found it and looked at it. Slowly Bruno mixed himself a short highball, drank it, then went softly down the hall and heard Gerard already talking to his mother.

'– didn't seem in high or low spirits, eh?'

'He's a very moody boy, you know. I doubt if I'd have noticed,' his mother said.

'Oh – people pick up psychic feelings sometimes. Don't you agree, Elsie?'

His mother did not answer.

'– too bad, because I'd like more co-operation from him.'

'Do you think he's withholding anything?'

'I don't know,' with his disgusting smile, and Bruno could tell from his tone that Gerard expected him to be listening, too. 'Do you?'

'Of course, I don't think he is. What're you getting at, Arthur?'

She was standing up to him. She wouldn't think so much of Gerard after this, Bruno thought. He was being dumb again, a dumb Iowan.

'You want me to get at the truth, don't you, Elsie?' Gerard asked, like a radio detective. 'He's hazy about what he did Thursday night after leaving you. He's got some pretty shady acquaintances. One might have been a hireling of a business enemy's of Sam's, a spy or something like that. And Charles could have mentioned that you and he were leaving the next day –'

'What're you getting at, Arthur, that Charles knows something about this?'

'Elsie, I wouldn't be surprised. Would you, really?'

'Damn him!' Bruno murmured. Damn him for saying that to his *mother*!

'I'll certainly tell you everything he tells me.'

Bruno drifted towards the stairway. Her submissiveness shocked him. Suppose she began to suspect? Murder was something she wouldn't be able to take. Hadn't he realized it in Santa Fe? And if she remembered Guy, remembered that he had talked about him in Los Angeles? If Gerard found Guy in the next two weeks, he might have scratches on him from getting through those woods, or a bruise or a cut that might raise suspicion. Bruno heard Herbert's soft tread in the downstairs hall, saw him come into view with his mother's afternoon drink on a tray, and retreated up the stairs again. His heart beat as if he were in a battle, a strange many-sided battle. He hurried back to his own room, took a big drink, then lay down and tried to fall asleep.

He awakened with a jerk and rolled from under Gerard's hand on his shoulder.

'Bye-bye,' Gerard said, his smile showing his tobacco-stained lower teeth. 'Just leaving and thought I'd say good-bye.'

'Is it worth waking somebody up for?' Bruno said.

Gerard chuckled and waddled from the room before Bruno could think of some mitigating phrase he really wanted to say. He plunged back on the pillow and tried to resume his nap, but when he closed his eyes, he saw Gerard's stocky figure in the light-brown suit going down the halls, slipping wraithlike through closed doors, bending to look into drawers, to read letters, to make notes, turning to point a finger at him, tormenting his mother so it was impossible not to fight back.

27

'What else can you make of it? He's accusing me!' Bruno shouted across the table.

'Darling, he's not. He's attending to his business.'

Bruno pushed his hair back. 'Want to dance, Mom?'

'You're in no condition to dance.'

He wasn't and he knew it. 'Then I want another drink.'

'Darling, the food's coming right away.'

Her patience with it all, the purple circles under her eyes, pained him so he could not look in front of him. Bruno glanced around for a waiter. The place was so crowded tonight, it was hard to tell a waiter from any other guy. His eyes stopped on a man at a table across the dance floor who looked like Gerard. He couldn't see the man he was with, but he certainly looked like Gerard, the bald head and light brown hair, except this man wore a black jacket. Bruno closed one eye to stop the rhythmic splitting of the image.

'Charley, do sit down. The waiter's coming.'

It *was* Gerard, and he was laughing now, as if the other fellow had told him he was watching them. For one suspended, furious second, Bruno wondered whether to tell his mother. Then he sat down and said with vehemence: 'Gerard's over there!'

'Is he? Where?'

'Over left of the orchestra. Under the blue lamp.'

'I don't see him.' His mother stretched up. 'Darling, you're imagining.'

'I am not imagining!' Bruno shouted and threw his napkin in his roast beef au jus.

'I see the one you mean, and it's not Gerard,' she said patiently.

'You can't see him as good as I can! It's him and I don't feel like eating in the same room with him!'

'Charles,' she sighed. 'Do you want another drink? Have another drink. Here's a waiter.'

'I don't even feel like drinkin' with him! Want me to prove it's him?'

'What does it matter? He's not going to bother us. He's guarding us probably.'

'You admit it's him! He's spying on us and he's in a dark suit so he can follow us anywhere else we go!'

'It's not Arthur anyway,' she said quietly, squeezing lemon over her broiled fish. 'You're having hallucinations.'

Bruno stared at her with his mouth open. 'What do you *mean* saying things like that to me, Mom?' His voice cracked.

'Sweetie, everybody's looking at us.'

'I don't care!'

'Darling, let me tell you something. You're making too much out of this.' She interrupted him. 'You are, because you want to. You want excitement. I've seen it before.'

Bruno was absolutely speechless. His mother was turning against him. He had seen her look at the Captain the way she looked at him now.

'You've probably said something to Gerard,' she went on, 'in anger, and he thinks you're behaving most peculiarly. Well, you are.'

'Is that any reason for him to tail me day and night?'

'Darling, I don't think that's Gerard,' she said firmly.

Bruno pushed himself up and staggered away towards the table where Gerard sat. He'd prove to her it was Gerard, and prove to Gerard he wasn't afraid of him. A couple of tables blocked him at the edge of the dance floor, but he could see it was Gerard now.

Gerard looked up at him and waved a hand familiarly, and his little stooge stared at him. And *he*, he and his mother were paying for it! Bruno opened his mouth, not knowing exactly what he wanted to say, then teetered around. He knew what he wanted to do, call up Guy. Right here and now. Right in the same room with Gerard. He struggled across the dance floor towards the telephone booth by the bar. The slow, crazily revolving figures pressed him back like a sea wave, baffling him. The wave floated towards him again, buoyant but insuperable, sweeping him yet farther back, and a similar moment at a party in his house when he was a little boy, when he tried to get through the dancing couples to his mother across the living-room, came back to him.

Bruno woke up early in the morning, in bed, and lay perfectly still, retracing the last moments he could remember. He knew he had passed out. Had he called Guy before he passed out? If he had, could Gerard trace it? He surely hadn't talked to Guy or he'd remember it, but maybe he'd called his house. He got up to go ask his mother if he had passed out in the telephone booth. Then the shakes came on and he went into the bathroom. The Scotch and water splashed up in his face when he lifted the glass. He braced himself against the bathroom door. It was getting him at both ends now, the shakes, early and late, waking him earlier and earlier, and he had to take more and more at night to get to sleep.

And in between was Gerard.

28

Momentarily, and faintly, as one re-experiences a remembered sensation, Guy felt secure and self-sufficient as he sat down at his work table where he had his hospital books and notes carefully arranged.

In the last month, he had washed and repainted all his bookshelves, had his carpet and curtains cleaned, and had scrubbed his kitchenette until its porcelain and aluminium gleamed. All guilt, he had thought as he poured the pans of dirty water down the sink, but since he could sleep no more than two or three hours a night, and then only after physical exercise, he reasoned that cleaning one's house was a more profitable manner of tiring oneself than walking the streets of the city.

He looked at the unopened newspaper on his bed, then got up and glanced through all its pages. But the papers had stopped mentioning the murder six weeks ago. He had taken care of every clue – the purple gloves cut up and flushed down the toilet, the overcoat (a good overcoat, and he had thought of giving it to a beggar, but who would be so base as to give even a beggar a murderer's overcoat?) and the trousers torn in pieces and disposed of gradually in the garbage. And the Luger dropped off the Manhattan Bridge. And his shoes off another. The only thing he had not disposed of was the little revolver.

He went to his bureau to look at it. Its hardness under his fingertips soothed him. The one clue he had not disposed of, and all the clue they needed if they found him. He knew exactly why he kept the revolver: it was *his*, a part of himself, the third hand that had done the murder. It was himself at fifteen when he had bought it, himself when he had loved Miriam and had kept it in their room in Chicago, looking at it now and then in his most contented, most inward moments. The best of himself, with its mechanical, absolute logic. Like him, he thought now, in its power to kill.

If Bruno dared to contact him again, he would kill him, too.

Guy was sure that he could. Bruno would know it, too. Bruno had always been able to read him. The silence from Bruno now brought more relief than the silence from the police. In fact, he was not anxious at all lest the police find him, had never been. The anxiety had always been within himself, a battle of himself against himself, so torturous he might have welcomed the law's intervention. Society's law was lax compared to the law of conscience. He might go to the law and confess, but confession seemed a minor point, a mere gesture, even an easy way out, an avoidance of truth. If the law executed him, it would be a mere gesture.

'I have no great respect for the law,' he remembered he had said to Peter Wriggs in Metcalf two years ago. Why should he have respect for a statute that called him and Miriam man and wife? 'I have no great respect for the church,' he had said sophomorishly to Peter at fifteen. Then, of course, he had meant the Metcalf Baptists. At seventeen, he had discovered God by himself. He had discovered God through his own awakening talents, and through a sense of unity of all the arts, and then of nature, finally of science – of all the creating and ordering forces in the world. He believed he could not have done his work without a belief in God. And where had his belief been when he murdered?

Awkwardly, he turned and faced his work table. A gasp hissed between his teeth, and nervously, impatiently, he passed his hand hard across his mouth. And yet, he felt, there was *something* still to come, still to be grasped, some severer punishment, some bitterer realization.

'I don't suffer enough!' burst from him suddenly in a whisper. But why had he whispered? Was he ashamed? 'I don't suffer enough,' he said in a normal voice, glancing about him as if he expected some ear to hear him. And he would have shouted it, if he had not felt some element of pleading in it, and considered himself unworthy of pleading for anything, from anyone.

His new books, for instance, the beautiful new books he had bought today – he could still think about them, love them. Yet he felt he had left them there long ago on his work table, like his own youth. He must go immediately and work, he thought. He had been commissioned to plan a hospital. He frowned at the little stack of notes he had already taken, spotlighted under his gooseneck lamp. Somehow it did not seem real that he had been commissioned. He would awaken soon and find that all these weeks had been a fantasy, a wishful dream. A hospital. Wasn't a hospital more fitting than even a prison? He frowned puzzledly, knowing his mind had strayed wildly, that two weeks ago when he had begun the hospital interior he had not thought once of death, that the positive requisites of health and healing alone had occupied him. He hadn't told Anne about the hospital, he remembered suddenly, that was why it seemed unreal. She was his glass of reality, not his work. But on the other hand, why hadn't he told her?

He must go immediately and work, but he could feel in his legs now that frenzied energy that came every evening, that sent him out in the streets finally in a vain effort to spend it. The energy frightened him because he could find no task that would absorb it, and because he felt at times that the task might be his suicide. Yet very deep inside him, and very much against his own will, his roots still clung to life.

He thought of his mother, and felt he could never let her embrace him again. He remembered her telling him that all men were equally good, because all men had souls and the soul was entirely good. Evil, she said, always came from externals. And so he had believed even months after Miriam, when he had wanted to murder her lover Steve. So he had believed even on the train, reading his Plato. In himself, the second horse of the charioteer had always been obedient as the first. But love and hate, he thought now, good and evil, lived side by side in the human heart, and not merely in differing proportions in one man and the next, but all good and all evil. One had merely to look for a little of either to find it all, one had merely to scratch the surface. All things had opposites close by, every decision a reason against it, every animal an animal that destroys it, the male the female, the positive the negative. The splitting of the atom was the only true destruction, the breaking of the universal law of oneness. Nothing could be without its opposite that was bound up with it. Could space exist in a building without objects that stopped it? Could energy exist without matter, or matter without energy? Matter and energy, the inert and the active, once considered opposites, were now known to be one.

And Bruno, he and Bruno. Each was what the other had not chosen to be, the cast-off self, what he thought he hated but perhaps in reality loved.

For a moment, he felt as if he might be mad. He thought, madness and genius often overlapped, too. But what mediocre lives most people lived! In middle waters, like most fish!

No, there was that duality permeating nature down to the tiny proton and electron within the tiniest atom. Science was now at work trying to split the electron, and perhaps it couldn't because perhaps only an idea was behind it: the one and only truth, that the opposite is always present. Who knew whether an electron was matter or energy? Perhaps God and the Devil danced hand in hand around every single electron!

He threw his cigarette at the waste-basket and missed.

When he put out the stub in the basket, he saw a crumpled page on which he had written last night one of his guilt-crazed confessions. It dragged him up sickeningly to a present that assaulted him from all sides – Bruno, Anne, this room, this night, the conference with the Department of Hospitals tomorrow.

Towards midnight, when he felt drowsy, he left his work table and lay down carefully on his bed, not daring to undress lest he awaken himself again.

He dreamed that he woke up in the night to the sound of the slow, watchful breathing that he heard every night in his room as he tried to fall asleep. It came from outside his window now. Someone was climbing the house. A tall figure in a great cape like a bat's wing sprang suddenly into the room.

'I'm here,' said the figure matter-of-factly.

Guy jumped from his bed to fight him. 'Who are you?' He saw it was Bruno.

Bruno resisted him rather than fought back. If Guy used his utmost strength, he could just pin Bruno's shoulders to the floor, and always in the recurrent dream, Guy had to use his utmost strength. Guy held Bruno to the floor with his knees and strangled him, but Bruno kept grinning up at him as if he felt nothing.

'You,' Bruno answered finally.

Guy awakened heavy-headed and perspiring. He sat up higher, vigilantly guarding his empty room. There were slimily wet sounds in the room now, as of a snake crawling through the cement court below, slapping its moist coils against the walls. Then suddenly he recognized the sound as that of rain, a gentle, silvery summer rain, and sank back again on his pillow. He began to cry softly. He thought of the rain, rushing at a slant to the earth. It seemed to say: Where are the spring plants to water? Where is the new life that depends on me? *Where is the green vine, Anne, as we saw love in our youth?* he had written last night on the crumpled paper. The rain would find the new life awaiting it, depending on it. What fell in his court was only its excess. *Where is the green vine, Anne . . .*

He lay with his eyes open until the dawn eased its fingertips on to the sill, like the stranger who had sprung in. Like Bruno. Then he got up and turned on his lights, drew the shades, and went back to his work.

29

Guy slammed his foot on the brake pedal, but the car leapt, screaming towards the child. There was a tinny clatter of the bicycle falling. Guy got out and ran around the car, banged his knee excruciatingly on the front bumper, and dragged the child up by his shoulders.

'I'm okay,' the little boy said.

'Is he all right, Guy?' Anne ran up, white as the child.

'I think so.' Guy gripped the bicycle's front wheel with his knees and straightened the handlebars, feeling the child's curious eyes on his own violently trembling hands.

'Thanks,' said the boy.

Guy watched him mount the bicycle and pedal off as if he watched a miracle. He looked at Anne and said quietly, with a shuddering sigh, 'I can't drive any more today.'

'All right,' she replied, as quietly as he, but there was a suspicion in her eyes, Guy knew, as she turned to go around to the driver's seat.

Guy apologized to the Faulkners as he got back into the car, and they murmured something about such things happening to every driver now and then. But Guy felt their real silence behind him, a silence of shock and horror. He had seen the boy coming down the side road. The boy had stopped for him, but Guy had swerved the car towards him as if he had intended to hit him. Had he? Tremulously, he lighted a cigarette. Nothing but bad co-ordination, he told himself, he had seen it a hundred times in the past two weeks – collisions with revolving doors, his inability even to hold a pen against a ruler, and so often the feeling he wasn't *here*, doing what he was doing. Grimly he re-established what he was doing now, driving in Anne's car up to Alton to see the new house. The house was done. Anne and her mother had put the drapes up last week. It was Sunday, nearly noon. Anne had told him she had got a nice letter from his mother yesterday, and his mother had sent her three crocheted aprons and a lot of home-made preserves to start their kitchen shelves. Could he remember all that? All he seemed to remember was the sketch of the Bronx hospital in his pocket, that he hadn't told Anne about yet. He wished he could go away somewhere and do nothing but work, see no one, not even Anne. He stole a glance at her, at her coolly lifted face with the faint arch in the bridge of the nose. Her thin strong hands swung the wheel expertly into a curve and out. Suddenly he was sure she loved her car more than she loved him.

'If anybody's hungry, speak up now,' Anne said. 'This little store's the last place for miles.'

But no one was hungry.

'I expect to be asked for dinner at least once a year, Anne,' her father said. 'Maybe a brace of ducks or some quail. I hear there's some good hunting around here. Any good with a gun, Guy?'

Anne turned the car into the road that led to the house.

'Fair, sir,' Guy said finally, stammering twice. His heart was flogging him to run, he could still it only by running, he was sure.

'Guy!' Anne smiled at him. Stopping the car, she whispered to him, 'Have a nip when you get in the house. There's a bottle of brandy in the kitchen.' She touched his wrist, and Guy jerked his hand back, involuntarily.

He must, he thought, have a brandy or something. But he knew also that he would not take anything.

Mrs Faulkner walked beside him across the new lawn. 'It's simply beautiful, Guy. I hope you're proud of it!'

Guy nodded. It was finished, he didn't have to imagine it any more as he had in the brown bureau of the hotel room in Mexico. Anne had wanted Mexican tiles in the kitchen. So many things she wore from time to time were Mexican. A belt, a handbag, huarachas. The long embroidered skirt that showed now below her tweed coat was Mexican. He felt he must have chosen the Hotel Montecarlo so that dismal pink-and-brown room and Bruno's face in the brown bureau would haunt him the rest of his life.

It was only a month until their marriage now. Four more Friday nights, and Anne would sit in the big square green chair by the fireplace, her voice would call to him from the Mexican kitchen, they would work together in the studio upstairs. What right had he to imprison her with himself? He stood staring at their bedroom, vaguely aware that it seemed cluttered, because Anne had said she wanted their bedroom 'not modern'.

'Don't forget to thank Mother for the furniture, will you?' she whispered to him. 'Mother gave it to us, you know.'

The cherry bedroom set, of course. He remembered her telling him that morning at breakfast, remembered his bandaged hand,

and Anne in the black dress she had worn to Helen's party. But when he should have said something about the furniture, he didn't, and then it seemed too late. They must know something is the matter, he felt. Everyone in the world must know. He was only somehow being reprieved, being saved for some weight to fall upon him and annihilate him.

'Thinking about a new job, Guy?' Mr Faulkner asked, offering him a cigarette.

Guy had not seen his figure there when he stepped on to the side porch. With a sense of justifying himself, he pulled the folded paper from his pocket and showed it to him, explained it to him. Mr Faulkner's bushy, grey and brown eyebrows came down thoughtfully. But he's not listening to me at all, Guy thought. He's bending closer only to see my guilt that is like a circle of darkness about me.

'Funny Anne didn't say anything to me about it,' Mr Faulkner said.

'I'm saving it.'

'Oh,' Mr Faulkner chuckled. 'A wedding present?'

Later, the Faulkners took the car and went back for sandwiches from the little store. Guy was tired of the house. He wanted Anne to walk with him up the rock hill.

'In a minute,' she said. 'Come here.' She stood in front of the tall stone fireplace. She put her hands on his shoulders and looked into his face, a little apprehensive, but still glowing with her pride in their new house. 'Those are getting deeper, you know,' she told him, drawing her fingertips down the hollow in his cheek. 'I'm going to make you eat.'

'Maybe need a little sleep,' he murmured. He had told her that lately his work demanded long hours. He had told her, of all things, that he was doing some agency jobs, hack jobs, as Myers did, in order to earn some money.

'Darling, we're – we're well off. What on earth's troubling you?'

And she had asked him half a dozen times if it was the wedding, if he wanted not to marry her. If she asked him again, he might say yes, but he knew she would not ask it now, in front of their fireplace. 'Nothing's troubling me,' he said quickly.

'Then will you please not work so hard?' she begged him, then spontaneously, out of her own joy and anticipation, hugged him to her.

Automatically – as if it were nothing at all, he thought – he kissed her, because he knew she expected him to. She will notice, he thought, she always notices the slightest difference in a kiss, and it had been so long since he had kissed her. When she said nothing, it seemed to him only that the change in him was simply too enormous to mention.

30

Guy crossed the kitchen and turned at the back door. 'Awfully thoughtless of me to invite myself on the cook's night out.'

'What's thoughtless about it? You'll just fare as we do on Thursday nights, that's all.' Mrs Faulkner brought him a piece of the celery she was washing at the sink. 'But Hazel's going to be disappointed she wasn't here to make the shortcake herself. You'll have to do with Anne's tonight.'

Guy went out. The afternoon was still bright with sun, though the picket fence cast long oblique bars of shadow over the crocus and iris beds. He could just see Anne's tied-back hair and the pale green of her sweater beyond a crest in the rolling sea of lawn. Many times he had gathered mint and watercress there with Anne, from the stream that flowed out of the woods where he had fought Bruno. Bruno is past, he reminded himself, gone, vanished. Whatever method Gerard had used, he had made Bruno afraid to contact him.

He watched Mr Faulkner's neat black car enter the driveway and roll slowly into the open garage. What was he doing here, he asked himself suddenly, where he deceived everyone, even the coloured cook who liked to make shortcake for him because, once perhaps, he had praised her dessert? He moved into the shelter of the pear tree, where neither Anne nor her father would easily see him. If he should step out of Anne's life, he thought, what difference would it make to her? She had not given up all her old friends, hers and Teddy's set, the eligible young men, the handsome young men who played at polo and, rather harmlessly, at the night clubs before they entered their father's business and married one of the beautiful young girls who decorated their country clubs. Anne was different, of course, or she wouldn't have been attracted to him in the first place. She was not one of the beautiful young girls who worked at a career for a couple of years just to say they had done it, before they married one of the eligible young men. But wouldn't she have been just the same herself, without him? She had often told him he was her inspiration, he and his own ambition, but she had had the same talent, the same drive the day he met her, and wouldn't she have gone on? And wouldn't another man, like himself but worthy of her, have found her? He began to walk towards her.

'I'm almost done,' she called to him. 'Why didn't you come sooner?'

'I hurried,' he said awkwardly.

'You've been leaning against the house ten minutes.'

A sprig of watercress was floating away on the stream, and he sprang to rescue it. He felt like a possum, scooping it up. 'I think I'll take a job soon, Anne.'

She looked up, astoundedly. 'A job? You mean with a firm?'

It was a phrase to be used about other architects, 'a job with a firm'. He nodded, not looking at her. 'I feel like it. Something steady with a good salary.'

'Steady?' She laughed a little. 'With a year's work ahead of you at the hospital?'

'I won't need to be in the drafting room all the time.'

She stood up. 'Is it because of money? Because you're not taking the hospital money?'

He turned away from her and took a big step up the moist bank. 'Not exactly,' he said through his teeth. 'Maybe partly.' He had decided weeks ago to give his fee back to the Department of Hospitals after he paid his staff.

'But you said it wouldn't matter, Guy. We both agreed we – you could afford it.'

The world seemed silent all at once, listening. He watched her push a strand of her hair back and leave a smudge of wet earth on her forehead. 'It won't be for long. Maybe six months, maybe a lot less.'

'But why at all?'

'I feel like it!'

'Why do you feel like it? Why do you want to be a martyr, Guy?'

He said nothing.

The setting sun dropped free of the trees and poured on to them suddenly. Guy frowned deeper, shading his eye with the brow that bore the white scar from the woods – the scar that would always show, he thought. He kicked at a stone in the ground, without being able to dislodge it. Let her think the job was still part of his depression after the Palmyra. Let her think anything.

'Guy, I'm sorry,' she said.

Guy looked at her. 'Sorry?'

She came closer to him. 'Sorry. I think I know what it is.'

He still kept his hands in his pockets. 'What do you mean?'

She waited a long while. 'I thought all this, all your uneasiness after the Palmyra – even without your knowing it, I mean – goes back to Miriam.'

He twisted away abruptly. 'No. No, that's not it at all!' He said it so honestly, yet it sounded so like a lie! He thrust his fingers in his hair and shoved it back.

'Listen, Guy,' Anne said softly and clearly, 'maybe you don't want the wedding as much as you think you do. If you think that's part of it, say it, because I can take that a lot easier than this job idea. If you want to wait – still – or if you want to break it off entirely, I can bear it.'

Her mind was made up, and had been for a long while. He

could feel it at the very centre of her calmness. He could give her up at this moment. The pain of that would cancel out the pain of guilt.

'Hey, there, Anne!' her father called from the back door. 'Coming in soon? I need that mint!'

'Minute, Dad!' she shouted back. 'What do you say, Guy?'

His tongue pressed the top of his mouth. He thought, she is the sun in my dark forest. But he couldn't say it. He could only say, 'I can't say –'

'Well – I want you now more than ever, because you need me now more than ever.' She pressed the mint and watercress into his hand. 'Do you want to take this to Dad? And have a drink with him. I have to change my clothes.' She turned and went off towards the house, not fast, but much too fast for Guy to try to follow her.

Guy drank several of the mint juleps. Anne's father made them the old-fashioned way, letting the sugar and bourbon and mint stand in a dozen glasses all day, getting colder and more frosted, and he liked to ask Guy if he had ever tasted better ones anywhere. Guy could feel the precise degree to which his tension lessened, but it was impossible for him to become drunk. He had tried a few times and made himself sick, without becoming drunk.

There was a moment after dusk, on the terrace with Anne, when he imagined he might not have known her any better than he had the first evening he visited her, when he suddenly felt a tremendous, joyous longing to make her love him. Then he remembered the house in Alton awaiting them after the wedding Sunday, and all the happiness he had known already with Anne rushed back to him. He wanted to protect her, to achieve some impossible goal, which would please her. It seemed most positive, the happiest ambition he had ever known. There was a way out, then, if he could feel like this. It was only a part of himself he had to cope with, not his whole self, not Bruno, or his work. He had merely to crush the other part of himself, and live in the self he was now.

31

But there were too many points at which the other self could invade the self he wanted to preserve, and there were too many forms of invasion: certain words, sounds, lights, actions his hands or feet performed, and if he did nothing at all, heard and saw nothing, the shouting of some triumphant inner voice that shocked him and cowed him. The wedding so elaborately prepared for, so festive, so pure with white lace and linen, so happily awaited by everyone, seemed the worst act of treachery he could commit, and the closer it drew, the more frantically and vainly he debated cancelling it. Up to the last hour, he wanted simply to flee.

Robert Treacher, the friend of his Chicago days, telephoned his good wishes and asked if he might come to the wedding. Guy put him off with some feeble excuse. It was the Faulkners' affair, he felt, their friends, their family church, and the presence of a friend would put a hole in his armour. He had invited only Myers, who didn't matter – since the hospital commission, he no longer shared an office with him – Tim O'Flaherty, who couldn't come, and two or three architects from the Deems Academy, who knew his work better than they knew him. But half an hour after Treacher's call from Montreal, Guy telephoned back and asked Bob if he would be his best man.

Guy realized he had not even thought of Treacher in nearly a year, had not answered his last letter. He had not thought of Peter Wriggs, or Vic De Poyster and Gunther Hall. He had used to call on Vic and his wife in their Bleecker Street apartment, had once taken Anne there. Vic was a painter, and had sent him an invitation to his exhibit last winter, Guy remembered. He hadn't even answered. Vaguely now, he remembered that Tim had been in New York and had called him to have lunch during the period when Bruno had been haunting him by telephone, and that he had refused. The Theological Germanica, Guy recalled, said that the ancient Germans had judged an accused man innocent or guilty by the number of friends who came forth to vouch for his character. How many would vouch for him now? He had never given a great deal of time to his friends, because they were not the kind of people who expected it, but now he felt his friends were shunning him in turn, as if they sensed without seeing him that he had become unworthy of friendship.

The Sunday morning of the wedding, walking in slow circles around Bob Treacher in the vestry of the church, Guy clung to his memory of the hospital drawings as to a single last shred of hope, the single proof that he still existed. He had done an excellent job. Bob Treacher, his friend, had praised him. He had proven to himself that he could still create.

Bob had given up trying to make conversation with him. He sat with his arms folded, with a pleasant but rather absent expression on his chubby face. Bob thought he was simply nervous. Bob didn't know how he felt, Guy knew, because however much he thought it showed, it didn't. And that was the hell, that one's life could so easily be total hypocrisy. This was the essence, his wedding and his friend, Bob Treacher, who no longer knew him. And the little stone vestry with the high grilled window, like a prison cell. And the murmur of voices outside, like the self-righteous murmurings of a mob impatient to storm the prison and wreak justice.

'You didn't by any chance bring a bottle.'

Bob jumped up. 'I certainly did. It's weighing me down and I completely forgot it.' He set the bottle on the table and waited for Guy to take it. Bob was about forty-five, a man of modest but sanguine temperament, with an indelible stamp of contented bachelorhood and of complete absorption and authority in his profession. 'After you,' he prompted Guy. 'I want to drink a private toast to Anne. She's very beautiful, Guy.' He added softly, with a smile, 'As beautiful as a white bridge.'

Guy stood looking at the opened pint bottle. The hubbub out the window seemed to poke fun at him now, at him and Anne. The bottle on the table was part of it, the jaded, half-humorous concomitant of the traditional wedding. He had drunk whisky at his wedding with Miriam. Guy hurled the bottle into the corner. Its solid crack and spatter ended the hooting horns, the voices, the silly tremolo of the organ only for a second, and they began to seep back again.

'Sorry, Bob. I'm very sorry.'

Bob had not taken his eyes from him. 'I don't blame you a bit,' he smiled.

'But I blame myself!'

'Listen, old man –'

Guy could see that Bob did not know whether to laugh or be serious.

'Wait,' Treacher said. 'I'll get us some more.'

The door opened just as Bob reached for it, and Peter Wriggs' thin figure slipped in. Guy introduced him to Treacher. Peter had come all the way up from New Orleans to be at his wedding. He wouldn't have come to his wedding with Miriam, Guy thought. Peter had hated Miriam. There was grey at Peter's temples now, though his lean face still grinned like a sixteen-year-old's. Guy returned his quick embrace, feeling that he moved automatically now, on rails as he had the Friday night.

'It's time, Guy,' Bob said, opening the door.

Guy walked beside him. It was twelve steps to the altar. The accusing faces, Guy thought. They were silent with horror, as the Faulkners had been in the back of the car. When were they going to interfere and stop it all? How much longer was everyone going to wait?

'Guy!' somebody whispered.

Six, Guy counted, seven.

'Guy!' faint and direct, from among the faces, and Guy glanced left, followed the gaze of two women who looked over their shoulders, and saw Bruno's face and no other.

Guy looked straight again. Was it Bruno or a vision? The face had been smiling eagerly, the grey eyes sharp as pins. Ten, eleven, he counted. *Twelve steps up, skip seven . . . You can remember it. It's got a syncopated rhythm.* His scalp tingled. Wasn't that a proof it was a vision and not Bruno? He prayed, Lord, don't let me faint. Better you fainted than married, the inner voice shouted back.

He was standing beside Anne, and Bruno was here with them, not an event, not a moment, but a condition, something that had always been and always would be. Bruno, himself, Anne. And the moving on the tracks. And the lifetime of moving on the tracks until death do us part, for that was the punishment. What more punishment was he looking for?

Faces bobbed and smiled all around him, and Guy felt himself aping them like an idiot. It was the Sail and Racquet Club. There was a buffet breakfast, and everyone had a champagne glass, even himself. And Bruno was not here. There was really no one here but wrinkled, harmless, perfumed old women in hats. Then Mrs Faulkner put an arm around his neck and kissed his cheek, and over her shoulder he saw Bruno thrusting himself through the door with the same smile, the same pinlike eyes that had already found him. Bruno came straight towards him and stopped, rocking on his feet.

'My best – best wishes, Guy. You didn't mind if I looked in, did you? It's a happy occasion!'

'Get out. Get out of here fast.'

Bruno's smile faded hesitantly. 'I just got back from Capri,' he said in the same hoarse voice. He wore a new dark royal-blue gabardine suit with lapels broad as an evening suit's lapels. 'How've you been, Guy?'

An aunt of Anne's babbled a perfumed message into Guy's ear, and he murmured something back. Turning, Guy started to move off.

'I just wanted to wish you well,' Bruno declared. 'There it is.'

'Get out,' Guy said. 'The door's behind you.' But he mustn't say any more, he thought. He would lose control.

'Call a truce, Guy. I want to meet the bride.'

Guy let himself be drawn away by two middle-aged women, one on either arm. Though he did not see him, he knew that Bruno had retreated, with a hurt, impatient smile, to the buffet table.

'Bearing up, Guy?' Mr Faulkner took his half-empty glass from his hand. 'Let's get something better at the bar.'

Guy had half a glassful of Scotch. He talked without knowing what he was saying. He was sure he had said, Stop it all, tell everyone to go. But he hadn't, or Mr Faulkner wouldn't be roaring with laughter. Or would he?

Bruno watched from down the table as they cut the cake, watched Anne mostly, Guy noticed. Bruno's mouth was a thin, insanely smiling line, his eyes glinted like the diamond pin on his dark blue tie, and in his face Guy saw that same combination of wistfulness, awe, determination, and humour that he had seen the first moment he met him.

Bruno came up to Anne. 'I think I met you somewhere before. Are you any relation to Teddy Faulkner?'

Guy watched their hands meet. He had thought he wouldn't be able to bear it, but he was bearing it, without making a move.

'He's my cousin,' Anne said with her easy smile, the same smile she had given someone a moment before.

Bruno nodded. 'I played golf with him a couple of times.' Guy felt a hand on his shoulder.

'Got a minute, Guy? I'd –' It was Peter Wriggs.

'I haven't.' Guy started after Bruno and Anne. He closed his fingers around Anne's left hand.

Bruno sauntered on the other side of her, very erect, very much at ease, bearing his untouched piece of wedding cake on a plate in front of him. 'I'm an old friend of Guy's. An old acquaintance.' Bruno winked at him behind Anne's head.

'Really? Where'd you two know each other?'

'In school. Old school friends.' Bruno grinned. 'You know, you're the most beautiful bride I've seen in years, Mrs Haines. I'm certainly glad to have met you,' he said, not with finality but an emphatic conviction that made Anne smile again.

'Very glad to have met you,' she replied.

'I hope I'll be seeing you both. Where're you going to live?'

'In Connecticut,' Anne said.

'Nice state, Connecticut,' Bruno said with another wink at Guy, and left them with a graceful bow.

'He's a friend of Teddy's?' Guy asked Anne. 'Did Teddy invite him?'

'Don't look so worried, darling!' Anne laughed at him. 'We'll leave soon.'

'Where is Teddy?' But what was the use finding Teddy, what was the sense in making an issue of it, he asked himself at the same time.

'I saw him two minutes ago up at the head of the table,' Anne told him. 'There's Chris. I've got to say hello to him.'

Guy turned, looking for Bruno, and saw him helping himself to shirred eggs, talking gaily to two young men who smiled at him as if under the spell of a devil.

The ironic thing, Guy thought bitterly in the car a few moments later, the ironic thing was that Anne had never had time to know him. When they first met, he had been melancholic. Now his efforts, because he so rarely made efforts, had come to seem real. There had been, perhaps, those few days in Mexico City when he had been himself.

'Did the man in the blue suit go to Deems?' Anne asked.

They were driving out to Montauk Point. One of Anne's relatives had lent them her cottage for their three-day honeymoon. The honeymoon was only three days, because he had pledged to start work at Horton, Horton and Keese, Architects, in less than a month, and he would have to work on the double to get the detailed drawings for the hospital under way before he began. 'No, the Institute. For a while.' But why did he fall in with Bruno's lie?

'Interesting face he has,' Anne said, straightening her dress about her ankles before she put her feet on the jump seat.

'Interesting?' Guy asked.

'I don't mean attractive. Just intense.'

Guy set his teeth. Intense? Couldn't she see he was insane? Morbidly insane? Couldn't anyone see it?

32

The receptionist at Horton, Horton and Keese, Architects, handed him a message that Charles Bruno had called and left his number. It was the Great Neck number.

'Thank you,' Guy said, and went on across the lobby.

Suppose the firm kept records of telephone messages. They didn't, but suppose they did. Suppose Bruno dropped in one day. But Horton, Horton and Keese were so rotten themselves, Bruno wouldn't make much of a contrast. And wasn't that exactly why he was here, steeping himself in it, under some illusion that revulsion was atonement and that he would begin to feel better here?

Guy went into the big skylighted, leather-upholstered lounge, and lighted a cigarette. Mainwaring and Williams, two of the firm's first-string architects, sat in big leather armchairs, reading company reports. Guy felt their eyes on him as he stared out the window. They were always watching him, because he was supposed to be something special, a genius, the junior Horton had assured everybody, so what was he doing here? He might be broker than everybody thought, of course, and he had just got married, but quite apart from that and from the Bronx hospital, he was obviously nervous, had lost his grip. The best lost their grip sometimes, they would say to themselves, so why should they scruple about taking a comfortable job? Guy gazed down on to the dirty jumble of Manhattan roofs and streets that looked like a floor model of how a city should not be built. When he turned around, Mainwaring dropped his eyes like a schoolboy.

He spent the morning dawdling over a job that he had been on for several days. Take your time, they told him. All he had to do was give the client what he wanted and sign his name to it. Now, this job was a department store for an opulent little community in Westchester, and the client wanted something like an old mansion, in keeping with the town, only sort of modern, too, see? And he had asked especially for Guy Daniel Haines. By adjusting his brain to the level of the trick, the cartoon, Guy could have tossed it off, but the fact it was really going to be a department store kept intruding certain functional demands. He erased and sharpened pencils all morning, and figured it would take him four or five more days, well into next week, until he got anything down as even a rough idea to show the client.

'Charley Bruno's coming tonight, too,' Anne called that evening from the kitchen.

'What?' Guy came around the partition.

'Isn't that his name? The young man we saw at the wedding.' Anne was cutting chives on a wooden board.

'You invited him?'

'He seems to have heard about it, so he called up and sort of invited himself,' Anne replied so casually that a wild suspicion she might be testing him sent a faint chill up his spine. 'Hazel – not milk, Angel, there's plenty of cream in the refrigerator.'

Guy watched Hazel set the cream container down by the bowl of crumbled gorgonzola cheese.

'Do you mind his coming, Guy?' Anne asked him.

'Not at all, but he's no friend of mine, you know.' He moved awkwardly towards the cabinets and got out the shoe-polish box. How could he stop him? There had to be a way, yet even as he racked his brain, he knew that the way would elude him.

'You do mind,' Anne said, with a smile.

'I think he's sort of a bounder, that's all.'

'It's bad luck to turn anyone away from a housewarming. Don't you know that?'

Bruno was pink-eyed when he arrived. Everyone else had made some comment about the new house, but Bruno stepped down into the brick-red and forest-green living-room as if he had been here a hundred times before. Or as if he lived here, Guy thought as he introduced Bruno around the room. Bruno focused a grinning, excited attention on Guy and Anne, hardly acknowledging the greetings of the others – two or three looked as if they knew him, Guy thought – except for that of a Mrs Chester Boltinoff of Muncey Park, Long Island, whose hand

Bruno shook in both his as if he had found an ally. And Guy watched with horror as Mrs Boltinoff looked up at Bruno with a wide, friendly smile.

'How's every little thing?' Bruno asked Guy after he had got himself a drink.

'Fine. Very fine.' Guy was determined to be calm, even if he had to anaesthetize himself. He had already had two or three straight shots in the kitchen. But he found himself walking away, retreating, towards the perpendicular spiral stairway in the corner of the living-room. Just for a moment, he thought, just to get his bearings. He ran upstairs and into the bedroom, laid his cold hand against his forehead, and brought it slowly down his face.

'Pardon me, I'm still exploring,' said a voice from the other side of the room. 'It's such a terrific house, Guy, I had to retreat to the nineteenth century for a while.'

Helen Heyburn, Anne's friend from the Bermuda schooldays, was standing by the bureau. Where the little revolver was, Guy thought.

'Make yourself at home. I just came up for a handkerchief. How's your drink holding up?' Guy slid out the right top drawer where lay both the gun he didn't want and the handkerchief he didn't need.

'Well – better than I am.'

Helen was in another 'manic' period, Guy supposed. She was a commercial artist, a good one, Anne thought, but she worked only when her quarterly allowance gave out and she slipped into a depressive period. And she didn't like him, he felt, since the Sunday evening when he hadn't gone with Anne to her party. She was suspicious of him. What was she doing now in their bedroom, pretending to feel her drinks more than she did?

'Are you always so serious, Guy? You know what I said to Anne when she told me she was going to marry you?'

'You told her she was insane.'

'I said, "But he's so serious. Very attractive and maybe a genius, but he's so serious, how can you stand it?" ' She lifted her squarish, pretty blonde face. 'You don't even defend yourself. I'll bet you're too serious to kiss me, aren't you?'

He forced himself towards her, and kissed her.

'That's no kiss.'

'But I deliberately wasn't being serious!'

He went out. She would tell Anne, he thought, she would tell her that she had found him in the bedroom looking pained at ten o'clock. She might look into the drawer and find the gun, too. But he didn't believe any of it. Helen was silly, and he hadn't the slightest idea why Anne liked her, but she wasn't a trouble-maker. And she wasn't a snooper any more than Anne was. My God, hadn't he left the revolver there in the drawer next to Anne's all the time they had been living here? He was no more afraid Anne would investigate his half of the bureau than he was that she would open his mail.

Bruno and Anne were on the right-angled sofa by the fireplace when he came down. The glass Bruno wobbled casually on the sofa back had made dark green splotches on the cloth.

'He's telling me all about the new Capri, Guy,' Anne looked up at him. 'I've always wanted us to go there.'

'The thing to do is to take a whole house,' Bruno went on, ignoring Guy, 'take a castle, the bigger the better. My mother and I lived in a castle so big we never walked to the other end of it until one night I couldn't find the right door. There was a whole Italian family having dinner at the other end of the veranda, and the same night they all come over, about twelve of them, and ask if they can work for us for nothing, just if we let them stay there. So of course we did.'

'And you never learned any Italian?'

'No need to!' Bruno shrugged, his voice hoarse again, exactly as Guy always heard it in his mind.

Guy busied himself with a cigarette, feeling Bruno's avid, shyly flirtatious gaze at Anne boring into his back, deeper than the numbing tingle of the alcohol. No doubt Bruno had already complimented the dress she was wearing, his favourite dress of grey taffeta with the tiny blue pattern like peacocks' eyes. Bruno always noticed women's clothes.

'Guy and I,' Bruno's voice said distinctly behind him as if he had turned his head, 'Guy and I once talked about travelling.'

Guy jabbed his cigarette into an ashtray, put out every spark, then went towards the sofa. 'How about seeing our game room upstairs?' he said to Bruno.

'Sure.' Bruno got up. 'What kind of games you play?'

Guy pushed him into a small room lined with red, and closed the door behind them. 'How far are you going?'

'Guy! You're tight!'

'What's the idea of telling everyone we're old friends?'

'Didn't tell everyone. I told Anne.'

'What's the idea of telling her or anyone? What's the idea of coming here?'

'Quiet, Guy! Sh - sh - sh-h-h!' Bruno swung his drink casually in one hand.

'The police are still watching your friends, aren't they?'

'Not enough to worry me.'

'Get out. Get out now.' His voice shook with his effort to control it. And why should he control himself? The revolver with the one bullet was just across the hall.

Bruno looked at him boredly and sighed. The breath against his upper lip was like the breathing Guy heard in his room at night.

Guy staggered slightly, and the stagger enraged him.

'I think Anne's beautiful,' Bruno remarked pleasantly.

'If I see you talking with her again, I'll kill you.'

Bruno's smile went slack, then came back even broader. 'Is that a threat, Guy?'

'That's a promise.'

Half an hour later, Bruno passed out back of the sofa where he and Anne had been sitting. He looked extremely long on the floor, and his head tiny on the big hearthstone. Three men picked him up, then didn't know what to do with him.

'Take him – I suppose to the guest room,' Anne said.

'That's a good omen, Anne,' Helen laughed. 'Somebody's supposed to stay overnight at every housewarming, you know. First guest?'

Christopher Nelson came over to Guy. 'Where'd you dig him up? He used to pass out so often at the Great Neck Club, he can't get in any more.'

Guy had checked with Teddy after the wedding. Teddy hadn't invited Bruno, didn't know anything about him, except that he didn't like him.

Guy climbed the steps to the studio, and closed the door. On his work table lay the unfinished sketch of the cockeyed department store that conscience had made him take home to complete this week-end. The familiar lines, blurred now with drinking, almost made him sick. He took a blank sheet of paper and began to draw the building they wanted. He knew exactly what they wanted. He hoped he could finish before he became sick, and after he finished be as sick as a dog. But he wasn't sick when he finished. He only sat back in his chair, and finally went and opened a window.

33

The department store was accepted and highly praised, first by the Hortons and then by the client, Mr Howard Wyndham of New Rochelle, who came into the office early Monday afternoon to see the drawing. Guy rewarded himself by spending the rest of the day smoking in his office and thumbing through a morocco-bound copy of *Religio Medici* he had just bought at Brentano's to give Anne on her birthday. What assignment would they give him next, he wondered. He skipped through the book, remembering the passages he and Peter had used to like . . . *the man without a navel yet lives in me* . . . What atrocity would he be asked to do next? He had already fulfilled an assignment. Hadn't he done enough? Another thing like the department store would be unbearable. It wasn't self-pity, only *life*. He was still alive, if he wanted to blame himself for that. He got up from the drawing-table, went to his typewriter, and began his letter of resignation.

Anne insisted they go out and celebrate that evening. She was so glad, so overflowing with gladness, Guy felt his own spirits lifting a little, uncertainly, as a kite tries to lift itself from the ground on a still day. He watched her quick, slender fingers draw her hair tight back at the sides and close the bar pin over it in back.

'And, Guy, can't we make the cruise now?' she asked as they came down into the living-room.

Anne still had her heart set on the cruise down the coast in the *India*, the honeymoon trip they had put off. Guy had intended to give all his time to the drafting rooms that were doing his hospital drawings, but he couldn't refuse Anne now.

'How soon do you think we can leave? Five days? A week?'

'Maybe five days.'

'Oh, I just remember,' she sighed. 'I've got to stay till the twenty-third. There's a man coming in from California who's interested in all our cotton stuff.'

'And isn't there a fashion show the end of this month?'

'Oh, Lillian can take care of that.' She smiled. 'How wonderful of you to remember!'

He waited while she pulled the hood of her leopard coat up about her head, amused at the thought of her driving a hard bargain with the man from California next week. She wouldn't leave that to Lillian. Anne was the business half of the shop. He saw the long-stemmed orange flowers on the coffee table for the first time. 'Where'd these come from?' he asked.

'Charley Bruno. With a note apologizing for passing out Friday night.' She laughed. 'I think it's rather sweet.'

Guy stared at them. 'What kind are they?'

'African daisies.' She held the front door open for him, and they went on out to the car.

She was flattered by the flowers, Guy thought. But her opinion of Bruno, he also knew, had gone down since the night of the party. Guy thought again of how bound up they were now, he and Bruno, by the score of people at the party. The police might investigate him any day. They *would* investigate him, he warned himself. And why wasn't he more concerned? What state of mind was he in that he could no longer say even what state it was? Resignation? Suicide? Or simply a torpor of stupidity?

During the next idle days he was compelled to spend at Horton, Horton and Keese to launch the drawings of the department store interior, he even asked himself whether he could be mentally deranged, if some subtle madness had not taken possession of him. He remembered the week or so after the Friday night, when his safety, his existence, had seemed to hang in a delicate balance that a failure of nerve might upset in a second. Now he felt none of that. Yet he still dreamt of Bruno invading his room. If he woke at dawn, he could still see himself standing in the room with the gun. He still felt that he must, and very soon, find some atonement for what he had done, some atonement for which no service or sacrifice he could yet envisage sufficed. He felt rather like two people, one of whom could create and feel in harmony with God when he created, and the other who could murder. 'Any kind of person can murder,' Bruno had said on the train. The man who had explained the cantilever principle to Bobbie Cartwright two years ago in Metcalf? No, nor the man who had designed the hospital, or even the department store, or debated half an hour with himself over the colour he would paint a metal chair on the back lawn last week, but the man who had glanced into the mirror just last night and had seen for one instant the murderer, like a secret brother.

And how could he sit at his desk thinking of murder, when in less than ten days he would be with Anne on a white ship? Why had he been given Anne, or the power to love her? And had he agreed so readily to the cruise only because he wanted to be free of Bruno for three weeks? Bruno, if he wanted to, could take Anne from him. He had always admitted that to himself, always tried to face it. But he realized that since he had seen them together, since the day of the wedding, the possibility had become a specific terror.

He got up and put on his hat to go out to lunch. He heard the switchboard buzz as he crossed the lobby. Then the girl called to him.

'Take it from here if you like, Mr Haines.'

Guy picked up the telephone, knowing it was Bruno, knowing he would agree to Bruno's seeing him some time today. Bruno asked him to have lunch, and Guy promised to meet him at Mario's Villa d'Este in ten minutes.

There were pink and white patterned drapes in the restaurant's window. Guy had a feeling that Bruno had laid a trap, that detectives would be behind the pink and white curtain, but not Bruno. And he didn't care, he felt, didn't care at all.

Bruno spotted him from the bar and slid off his stool with a grin. Guy walking around with his head in the air again, he thought, walking right by him. Bruno laid his hand on Guy's shoulder.

'Hi, Guy. I've got a table the end of this row.'

Bruno was wearing his old rust-brown suit. Guy thought of the first time he had followed the long legs, down the swaying train to the compartment, but the memory brought no remorse now. He felt, in fact, well-disposed towards Bruno, as he sometimes did by night, but never until now by day. He did not even resent Bruno's evident gratification that he had come to lunch with him.

Bruno ordered the cocktails and the lunch. He ordered broiled liver for himself, because of his new diet, he said, and eggs Benedict for Guy, because he knew Guy liked them. Guy was inspecting the table nearest them. He felt a puzzled suspicion of the four smartly dressed, fortyish women, all of whom were smiling with their eyes almost closed, all of whom lifted cocktail glasses. Beyond them, a well-fed, European-looking man hurled a smile across the table at his invisible companion. Waiters scurried zealously. Could it all be a show created and enacted by madmen, he and Bruno the main characters, and the maddest of all? For every movement he saw, every word he heard, seemed wrapped in the heroic gloom of predestination.

'Like 'em?' Bruno was saying. 'I got 'em at Clyde's this morning. Best selection in town. For summer anyway.'

Guy looked down at the four tie boxes Bruno had opened in their laps. There were knitted, silk and linen ties, and a pale lavender bow-tie of heavy linen. There was a shantung silk tie of aqua, like a dress of Anne's.

Bruno was disappointed. Guy didn't seem to like them. 'Too loud? They're summer ties.'

'They're nice,' Guy said.

'This is my favourite. I never saw anything like this.' Bruno held up the white knitted tie with the thin red stripe down the centre. 'Started to get one for myself, but I wanted you to have it. Just you, I mean. They're for you, Guy.'

'Thanks.' Guy felt an unpleasant twitch in his upper lip. He might have been Bruno's lover, he thought suddenly, to whom Bruno had brought a present, a peace offering.

'Here's to the trip,' Bruno said, lifting his glass.

Bruno had spoken to Anne this morning on the telephone, and Anne had mentioned the cruise, he said. Bruno kept telling him, wistfully, how wonderful he thought Anne was.

'She's so pure-looking. You certainly don't see a – a *kind*-looking girl like that very often. You must be awfully happy, Guy.' He hoped Guy might say something, a phrase or a word, that would somehow explain just why he was happy. But Guy didn't say anything, and Bruno felt rebuffed, felt the choking lump travelling from his chest up to his throat. What could Guy take offence at about that? Bruno wanted very much to put his hand over Guy's fist, that rested lightly on the edge of the table, just for a moment as a brother might, but he restrained himself. 'Did she like you right away or did you have to know her a long time? Guy?'

Guy heard him repeat the question. It seemed ages old. 'How can you ask me about time? It's a fact.' He glanced at Bruno's narrow, plumpening face, at the cowlick that still gave his forehead a tentative expression, but Bruno's eyes were vastly more confident than when he had seen them first, and less sensitive. Because he had his money now, Guy thought.

'Yeah. I know what you mean.' But Bruno didn't quite. Guy was happy with Anne even though the murder still haunted him. Guy would be happy with her even if he were broke. Bruno winced now for even having thought once that he might offer Guy money. He could hear the way Guy would say 'No,' with that look of drawing back in his eyes, of being miles away from him in a second. Bruno knew he would never have the things Guy had no matter how much money he had or what he did with it. Having his mother to himself was no guarantee of happiness, he had found out. Bruno made himself smile. 'You think Anne likes me all right?'

'All right.'

'What does she like to do outside of designing? Does she like to cook? Things like that?' Bruno watched Guy pick up his martini and drain it in three swallows. 'You know. I just like to know the kind of things you do together. Like take walks or work crossword puzzles.'

'We do things like that.'

'What do you do in the evenings?'

'Anne sometimes works in the evenings.' His mind slid easily, as it never had before with Bruno, to the upstairs studio where he and Anne often worked in the evenings, Anne talking to him from time to time, or holding something up for him to comment on, as if her work were effortless. When she dabbled her paintbrush fast in a glass of water, the sound was like laughter.

'I saw her picture in *Harper's Bazaar* a couple of months ago with some other designers. She's pretty good, isn't she?'

'Very good.'

'I –' Bruno laid his forearms one above the other on the table. 'I sure am glad you're happy with her.'

Of course he was. Guy felt his shoulders relax, and his breathing grow easier. Yet at this moment, it was hard to believe she was his. She was like a goddess who descended to pluck him from battles that would certainly have killed him, like the goddesses in mythology who saved the heroes, yet introduced an element at the end of the stories that had always struck him, when he read them as a child, as extraneous and unfair. In the nights when he could not sleep, when he stole out of the house and walked up the rock hill in pyjamas and overcoat, in the unchallenging, indifferent summer nights, he did not permit himself to think of Anne. '*Dea ex machina*,' Guy murmured.

'What?'

Why was he sitting here with Bruno, eating at the same table with him? He wanted to fight Bruno and he wanted to weep. But all at once he felt his curses dissolve in a flood of pity. Bruno did not know how to love, and that was all he needed. Bruno was too lost, too blind to love or to inspire love. It seemed all at once tragic.

'You've never even been in love, Bruno?' Guy watched a restive, unfamiliar expression come into Bruno's eyes.

Bruno signalled for another drink. 'No, not really in love, I guess.' He moistened his lips. Not only hadn't he ever fallen in love, but he didn't care too much about sleeping with women. He had never been able to stop thinking it was a silly business, that he was standing off somewhere and watching himself. Once, one terrible time, he had started giggling. Bruno squirmed. That was the most painful difference he felt separating him and Guy, that Guy could forget himself in women, had practically killed himself for Miriam.

Guy looked at Bruno, and Bruno lowered his eyes. Bruno was waiting, as if for him to tell him how to fall in love. 'Do you know the greatest wisdom in the world, Bruno?'

'I know a lot of wisdoms,' Bruno smirked. 'Which one do you mean?'

'That everything has its opposite close beside it.'

'Opposites attract?'

'That's too simple. I mean – you give me ties. But it also occurred to me you might have the police waiting for me here.'

'F' Christ's sake, Guy, you're my *friend*!' Bruno said quickly, suddenly frantic. 'I like you!'

I like you, I don't hate you, Guy thought. But Bruno wouldn't say that, because he did hate him. Just as he would never say to Bruno, I like you, but instead, I hate you, because he did like him. Guy set his jaw, and rubbed his fingers back and forth across his forehead. He could foresee a balance of positive and negative will that would paralyse every action before he began it. Such as that, for instance, that kept him sitting here. He jumped up, and the new drinks splashed on the cloth.

Bruno stared at him in terrified surprise. 'Guy, what's the matter?' Bruno followed him. 'Guy, wait! You don't think I'd do a thing like that, do you? I wouldn't in a million years!'

'Don't touch me!'

'*Guy!*' Bruno was almost crying. Why did people do these things to him? *Why?* He shouted on the sidewalk: 'Not in a million years! Not for a million dollars! Trust me, Guy!'

Guy pushed his hand into Bruno's chest and closed the taxi door. Bruno would not in a million years betray him, he knew. But if everything were as ambiguous as he believed, how could he really be sure?

34

'What's your connection with Mrs Guy Haines?'

Bruno had expected it. Gerard had his latest charge accounts, and this was the flowers he had sent Anne. 'Friend. Friend of her husband.'

'Oh. Friend?'

'Acquaintance.' Bruno shrugged, knowing Gerard would think he was trying to brag because Guy was famous.

'Known him long?'

'Not long.' From his horizontal slump in his easy chair, Bruno reached for his lighter.

'How'd you happen to send flowers?'

'Feeling good, I guess. I was going to a party there that night.'

'Do you know him that well?'

Bruno shrugged again. 'Ordinary party. He was one of the architects we thought of when we were talking about building a house.' That had just popped out, and it was rather good, Bruno thought.

'Matt Levine. Let's get back to him.'

Bruno sighed. Skipping Guy, maybe because he was out of town, maybe just skipping him. Now Matt Levine – they didn't come any shadier, and without realizing it might be useful, he had seen a lot of Matt before the murder. 'What about him?'

'How is it you saw him the twenty-fourth, twenty-eighth, and thirtieth of April, the second, fifth, sixth, seventh of March, and two days before the murder?'

'Did I?' he smiled. Gerard had had only three dates the last time. Matt didn't like him either. Matt had probably said the worst. 'He was interested in buying my car.'

'And you were interested in selling it? Why, because you thought you'd get a new one soon?'

'Wanted to sell it to get a little car,' Bruno said obliviously. 'The one in the garage now. Crosley.'

Gerard smiled. 'How long have you known Mark Lev?'

'Since he was Mark Levitski,' Bruno retorted. 'Go back a little farther and you'll find he killed his own father in Russia.' Bruno glared at Gerard. The 'own' sounded funny, he shouldn't have said it, but Gerard trying to be smart with the aliases!

'Matt doesn't care for you either. What's the matter, couldn't you two come to terms?'

'About the car?'

'Charles,' Gerard said patiently.

'I'm not saying anything.' Bruno looked at his bitten nails, and thought again how well Matt matched Herbert's description of the murderer.

'You haven't seen Ernie Schroeder much lately.'

Bruno opened his mouth boredly to answer.

35

Barefoot, in white duck trousers, Guy sat cross-legged on the *India*'s forward deck. Long Island had just come in sight but he did not want to look at it yet. The gently rolling movement of the ship rocked him pleasantly and familiarly, like something he had always known. The day he had last seen Bruno, in the restaurant, seemed a day of madness. Surely he had been going insane. Surely Anne must have seen it.

He flexed his arm and pinched up the thin brown skin that covered its muscles. He was brown as Eagon, the half-Portuguese ship's boy they had hired from the Long Island dock at the start of the cruise. Only the little scar in his right eyebrow remained white.

The three weeks at sea had given him a peace and resignation he had never known before, and that a month ago he would have declared foreign to him. He had come to feel that his atonement, whatever it might be, was a part of his destiny, and like the rest of his destiny would find him without his seeking. He had always trusted his sense of destiny. As a boy with Peter, he had known that he would not merely dream, as he had somehow known, too, that Peter would do nothing but dream, that he would create famous buildings, that his name would take its proper place in architecture, and finally – it had always seemed to him the crowning achievement – that he would build a bridge. It would be a white bridge with a span like an angel's wing, he had thought as a boy, like the curving white bridge of Robert Maillart in his architecture books. It was a kind of arrogance, perhaps, to believe so in one's destiny. But, on the other hand, who could be more genuinely humble than one who felt compelled to obey the laws of his own fate? The murder that had seemed an outrageous departure, a sin against himself, he believed now might have been a part of his destiny, too. It was impossible to think otherwise. And if it were so, he would be given a way to make his atonement, and given the strength to make it. And if death by law overtook him first, he would be given the strength to meet that also, and strength besides sufficient for Anne to meet it. In a strange way, he felt humbler than the smallest minnows of the sea, and stronger than the greatest mountain on earth. But he was not arrogant. His arrogance had been a defence, reaching its height at the time of the break with Miriam. And hadn't he known even then, obsessed by her, wretchedly poor, that he would find another woman whom he could love and who would love him always? And what better proof did he need that all this was so than that he and Anne had never been closer, their lives never more like one harmonious life, than during these three weeks at sea?

He turned himself with a movement of his feet, so he could see her as she leaned against the mainmast. There was a faint smile on her lips as she gazed down at him, a half-repressed, prideful smile like that of a mother, Guy thought, who had brought her child safely through an illness, and smiling back at her, Guy marvelled that he could put such trust in her infallibility and rightness and that she could still be merely a human being. Most of all, he marvelled that she could be his. Then he looked down at his locked hands and thought of the work he would begin tomorrow on the hospital, of all the work to come, and the events of his destiny that lay ahead.

Bruno telephoned a few evenings later. He was in the neighbourhood, he said, and wanted to come by. He sounded very sober, and a little dejected.

Guy told him no. He told him calmly and firmly that neither he nor Anne wanted to see him again, but even as he spoke, he felt the sands of his patience running out fast, and the sanity of the past weeks crumbling under the madness of their conversing at all.

Bruno knew that Gerard had not spoken to Guy yet. He did not think Gerard would question Guy more than a few minutes. But Guy sounded so cold, Bruno could not bring himself to tell him now that Gerard had got his name, that he might be interviewed, or that he intended to see Guy strictly secretly from now on – no more parties or even lunches – if Guy would only let him.

'Okay,' Bruno said mutedly, and hung up.

Then the telephone rang again. Frowning, Guy put out the cigarette he had just lighted relievedly, and answered it.

'Hello. This is Arthur Gerard of the Confidential Detective Bureau . . .' Gerard asked if he could come over.

Guy turned around, glancing warily over the living-room, trying to reason away a feeling that Gerard had just heard his and Bruno's conversation over tapped wires, that Gerard had just captured Bruno. He went upstairs to tell Anne.

'A private detective?' Anne asked, surprised. 'What's it about?'

Guy hesitated an instant. There were so many, many places where he might hesitate too long! Damn Bruno! Damn him for dogging him! 'I don't know.'

Gerard arrived promptly. He fairly bowed over Anne's hand, and after apologizing for intruding on their evening, made polite conversation about the house and the strip of garden in front. Guy stared at him in some astonishment. Gerard looked dull, tired, and vaguely untidy. Perhaps Bruno wasn't entirely wrong about him. Even his absent air, heightened by his slow speech, did not suggest the absent-mindedness of a brilliant detective. Then as Gerard settled himself with a cigar and a highball, Guy caught the shrewdness in the light hazel eyes and the energy in the chunky hands. Guy felt uneasy then. Gerard looked unpredictable.

'You're a friend of Charles Bruno, Mr Haines?'

'Yes. I know him.'

'His father was murdered last March as you probably know, and the murderer has not been found.'

'I didn't know that!' Anne said.

Gerard's eyes moved slowly from her back to Guy.

'I didn't know either,' said Guy.

'You don't know him that well?'

'I know him very slightly.'

'When and where did you meet?'

'At –' Guy glanced at Anne – 'the Parker Art Institute, I think around last December.' Guy felt he had walked into a trap. He had repeated Bruno's flippant reply at the wedding, simply because Anne had heard Bruno say it, and Anne had probably forgotten. Gerard regarded him, Guy thought, as if he didn't believe a word of it. Why hadn't Bruno warned him about Gerard? Why hadn't they *settled* on the story Bruno had once proposed about their having met at the rail of a certain midtown bar?

'And when did you see him again?' Gerard asked finally.

'Well – not until my wedding in June.' He felt himself assuming the puzzled expression of a man who does not yet know his inquisitor's object. Fortunately, he thought, fortunately, he had already assured Anne that Bruno's assertion they were old friends was only Bruno's style of humour. 'We didn't invite him,' Guy added.

'He just came?' Gerard looked as if he understood. 'But you did invite him to the party you gave in July?' He glanced at Anne also.

'He called up,' Anne told him, 'and asked if he could come, so – I said yes.'

Gerard then asked if Bruno knew about the party through any friends of his who were coming, and Guy said possibly, and gave the name of the blonde woman who had smiled so horrifically at Bruno that evening. Guy had no other names to give. He had never seen Bruno with anyone.

Gerard leaned back. 'Do you like him?' he smiled.

'Well enough,' Anne replied finally, politely.

'All right,' Guy said, because Gerard was waiting. 'He seems a bit pushing.' The right side of his face was in shadow. Guy wondered if Gerard were scanning his face now for scars.

'A hero-worshipper. Power-worshipper, in a sense.' Gerard

smiled, but the smile no longer looked genuine, or perhaps it never had. 'Sorry to bother you with these questions, Mr Haines.'

Five minutes later, he was gone.

'What does it mean?' Anne asked. 'Does he suspect Charles Bruno?'

Guy bolted the door, then came back. 'He probably suspects one of his acquaintances. He might think Charles knows something, because he hated his father so. Or so Charles told me.'

'Do you think Charles might know?'

'There's no telling. Is there?' Guy took a cigarette.

'Good Lord.' Anne stood looking at the corner of the sofa, as if she still saw Bruno where he had sat the night of the party. She whispered, 'Amazing what goes on in people's lives!'

36

'Listen,' Guy said tensely into the receiver. 'Listen, Bruno!' Bruno was drunker than Guy had ever heard him, but he was determined to penetrate to the muddled brain. Then he thought suddenly that Gerard might be with him, and his voice grew even softer, cowardly with caution. He found out Bruno was in a telephone booth, alone. 'Did you tell Gerard we met at the Art Institute?'

Bruno said he had. It came through the drunken mumblings that he had. Bruno wanted to come over. Guy couldn't make it register that Gerard had already come to question him. Guy banged the telephone down, and tore open his collar. Bruno calling him now! Gerard had externalized his danger. Guy felt it was more imperative to break completely with Bruno even than to arrange a story with him that would tally. What annoyed him most was that he couldn't tell from Bruno's drivelling what had happened to him, or even what kind of mood he was in.

Guy was upstairs in the studio with Anne when the door chime rang.

He opened the door only slightly, but Bruno bumped it wide,

stumbled across the living-room, and collapsed on the sofa. Guy stopped short in front of him, speechless first with anger, then disgust. Bruno's fat, flushed neck bulged over his collar. He seemed more bloated than drunk, as if an oedema of death had inflated his entire body, filling even the deep eye-sockets so the red-grey eyes were thrust unnaturally forward. Bruno stared up at him. Guy went to the telephone to call a taxi.

'Guy, who it is?' Anne whispered down the stairway.

'Charles Bruno. He's drunk.'

'Not drunk!' Bruno protested suddenly.

Anne came halfway down the stairs, and saw him. 'Shouldn't we just put him upstairs?'

'I don't want him here.' Guy was looking in the telephone book, trying to find a taxi company's number.

'Yess-s!' Bruno hissed, like a deflating tyre.

Guy turned. Bruno was staring at him out of one eye, the eye the only living point in the sprawled, corpse-like body. He was muttering something, rhythmically.

'What's he saying?' Anne stood closer to Guy.

Guy went to Bruno and caught him by the shirt-front. The muttered, imbecile chant infuriated him. Bruno drooled on to his hand as he tried to pull him upright. 'Get up and get out!' Then he heard it:

'I'll *tell* her, I'll *tell* her – I'll *tell* her, I'll *tell* her,' Bruno chanted, and the wild red eye stared up. 'Don't send me away, I'll tell her – I'll –'

Guy released him in abhorrence.

'What's the matter, Guy? What's he saying?'

'I'll put him upstairs,' Guy said.

Guy tried with all his strength to get Bruno over his shoulder, but the flaccid, dead weight defeated him. Finally, Guy stretched him out across the sofa. He went to the front window. There was no car outside. Bruno might have dropped out of the sky. Bruno slept noiselessly, and Guy sat up watching him, smoking.

Bruno awakened about three in the morning, and had a couple of drinks to steady himself. After a few moments, except for the bloatedness, he looked almost normal. He was very happy at finding himself in Guy's house, and had no recollection of arriving. 'I had another round with Gerard,' he smiled. 'Three days. Been seeing the papers?'

'No.'

'You're a fine one, don't even look at the papers!' Bruno said softly. 'Gerard's hot on a bum scent. This crook friend of mine, Matt Levine. He doesn't have an alibi for that night. Herbert thinks it could be him. I been talking with all three of them for three days. Matt might get it.'

'Might die for it?'

Bruno hesitated, still smiling. 'Not die, just take the rap. He's got two or three killings on him now. The cops're glad to have him.' Bruno shuddered, and drank the rest in his glass.

Guy wanted to pick up the big ashtray in front of him and smash Bruno's bloated head, burn out the tension he felt would grow and grow until he did kill Bruno, or himself. He caught Bruno's shoulders hard in both hands. 'Will you get out? I swear this is the last time!'

'No,' Bruno said quietly, without any movement of resistance, and Guy saw the old indifference to pain, to death, that he had seen when he had fought him in the woods.

Guy put his hands over his own face, and felt its contortion against his palms. 'If this Matt gets blamed,' he whispered, 'I'll tell them the whole story.'

'Oh, he won't. They won't have enough. It's a joke, son!' Bruno grinned. 'Matt's the right character with the wrong evidence. You'd be the wrong character with the right evidence. You're an important guy, f' Christ's sake!' He pulled something out of his pocket and handed it to Guy. 'I found this last week. Very nice, Guy.'

Guy looked at the photograph of 'The Pittsburgh Store', funereally backgrounded by black. It was a booklet from the Modern Museum. He read: 'Guy Daniel Haines, hardly thirty, follows the Wright tradition. He has achieved a distinctive, uncompromising style noted for a rigorous simplicity without starkness, for the grace he calls "singingness" . . .' Guy closed it nervously, disgusted by the last word that was an invention of the Museum's.

Bruno repocketed the booklet. 'You're one of the tops. If you kept your nerve up, they could turn you inside out and never suspect.'

Guy looked down at him. 'That's still no reason for you to see me. Why do you do it?' But he knew. Because his life with Anne fascinated Bruno. Because he himself derived something from seeing Bruno, some torture that perversely eased.

Bruno watched him as if he knew everything that passed through his mind. 'I like you, Guy, but remember – they've got a lot more against you than against me. I could wriggle out if you turned me in, but you couldn't. There's the fact Herbert might remember you. And Anne might remember you were acting funny around that time. And the scratches and the scar. And all the little clues they'd shove in front of you, like the revolver, and glove pieces –' Bruno recited them slowly and fondly, like old memories. 'With me against you you'd crack up. I bet.'

37

Guy knew as soon as Anne called to him that she had seen the dent. He had meant to get it fixed, and had forgotten. He said first that he didn't know how it got there, then that he did. He had taken the boat out last week, he said, and it had bumped a buoy.

'Don't be terribly sorry,' she mocked him, 'it isn't worth it.' She took his hand as she stood up. 'Egon said you had the boat out one afternoon. Is that why you didn't say anything about it?'

'I suppose.'

'Did you take it out by yourself?' Anne smiled a little, because he wasn't a good-enough sailor to take the boat out by himself.

Bruno had called up and insisted they go out for a sail.

Gerard had come to a new dead-end with Matt Levine, dead-ends everywhere, and Bruno had insisted that they celebrate. 'I took it out with Charles Bruno one afternoon,' he said. And he had brought the revolver with him that day, too.

'It's all right, Guy. Only why'd you see him again? I thought you disliked him so.'

'A whim,' he murmured. 'It was the two days I was doing that work at home.' It wasn't all right, Guy knew. Anne kept the *India's* brass and white-painted wood gleaming and spotless, like something of chryselephantine, And Bruno! She mistrusted Bruno now.

'Guy he's not the man we saw that night in front of your apartment, is he? The one who spoke to us in the snow?'

'Yes. He's the same one.' Guy's fingers, supporting the weight of the revolver in his pocket, tightened helplessly.

'What's his interest in you?' Anne followed him casually down the deck. 'He isn't interested in architecture particularly. I talked with him the night of the party.'

'He's got no interest in me. Just doesn't know what to do with himself.' When he got rid of the revolver, he thought, he could talk.

'You met him at school?'

'Yes. He was wandering around a corridor.' How easy it was to lie when one *had* to lie! But it was wrapping tendrils around his feet, his body, his brain. He would say the wrong thing one day. He was doomed to lose Anne. Perhaps he had already lost her, at this moment when he lighted a cigarette and she stood leaning against the mainmast, watching him. The revolver seemed to weight him to the spot, and determinedly he turned and walked towards the prow. Behind him, he heard Anne's step on to the deck, and her soft tread in her tennis shoes, going back towards the cockpit.

It was a sullen day, promising rain. The *India* rocked slowly on the choppy surface, and seemed no farther from the grey shore than it had been an hour ago. Guy leaned on the bow-sprit and looked down at his white-clad legs, the blue gilt-buttoned jacket he had taken from the *India*'s locker, that perhaps had belonged to Anne's father. He might have been a sailor instead of an architect, he thought. He had been wild to go to sea at fourteen. What had stopped him? How different his life might have been without – what? Without Miriam, of course. He straightened impatiently and pulled the revolver from the pocket of the jacket.

He held the gun in both hands over the water, his elbow on the bowsprit. How intelligent a jewel, he thought, and how innocent it looked now. Himself – He let it drop. The gun turned once head-over, in perfect balance, with its familiar look of willingness, and disappeared.

'What was that?'

Guy turned and saw her standing on the deck near the cabin. He measured the ten or twelve feet between them. He could think of nothing, absolutely nothing to say to her.

38

Bruno hesitated about the drink. The bathroom walls had that look of breaking up in little pieces, as if the walls might not really have been there, or he might not really have been here.

'Ma!' But the frightened bleat shamed him, and he drank his drink.

He tiptoed into his mother's room and awakened her with a press of the button by her bed, which signalled to Herbert in the kitchen that she was ready for her breakfast.

'Oh-h,' she yawned, then smiled. 'And how are you?' She patted his arm, slid up from the covers, and went into the bathroom to wash.

Bruno sat quietly on her bed until she came out and got back under the cover again.

'We're supposed to see that trip man this afternoon. What's his name, Saunders? You'd better feel like going in with me.'

Bruno nodded. It was about their trip to Europe, that they

might make into a round-the-world trip. It didn't have any charm this morning. He might like to go around the world with Guy. Bruno stood up, wondering whether to go get another drink.

'How're you feeling?'

His mother always asked him at the wrong times. 'Okay,' he said, sitting down again.

There was a knock on the door, and Herbert came in. 'Good morning, madam. Good morning, sir,' Herbert said without looking at either of them.

With his chin in his hand, Bruno frowned down at Herbert's silent, polished, turned-out shoes. Herbert's insolence lately was intolerable! Gerard had made him think he was the key to the whole case, if they just produced the right man. Everyone said how brave he was to have chased the murderer. And his father had left him twenty thousand in his will. Herbert *might* take a vacation!

'Does madam know if there'll be six or seven for dinner?'

As Herbert spoke, Bruno looked up at his pink, pointed chin and thought, Guy whammed him there and knocked him right out.

'Oh, dear, I haven't called yet, Herbert, but I think seven.'

'Very good, madam.'

Rutledge Overbeck II, Bruno thought. He had known his mother would end up having him, though she pretended to be doubtful because he would make an odd number. Rutledge Overbeck was madly in love with his mother, or pretending to be. Bruno wanted to tell his mother Herbert hadn't sent his clothes to be pressed in six weeks, but he felt too sickish to begin.

'You know, I'm dying to see Australia,' she said through a bite of toast. She had propped a map up against her coffee pot.

A tingling, naked sensation spread over his buttocks. He stood up. 'Ma, I don't feel so hot.'

She frowned at him concernedly, which frightened him more, because he realized there was nothing in the world she could do to help him. 'What's the matter, darling? What do you want?'

He hurried from the room, feeling he might have to be sick. The bathroom went black. He staggered out, and let the still-corked Scotch bottle topple on to his bed.

'What, Charley? What is it?'

'I wanna lie down.' He flopped down, but that wasn't it. He motioned his mother away so he could get up, but when he sat up he wanted to lie down again, so he stood up. 'Feel like I'm dying!'

'Lie down, darling. How about some – some hot tea?'

Bruno tore off his smoking jacket, then his pyjama top. He was suffocating. He had to pant to breathe. He *did* feel like he was dying!

She hurried to him with a wet towel. 'What is it, your stomach?'

'Everything.' He kicked off his slippers. He went to the window to open it, but it was already open. He turned, sweating. 'Ma, maybe I'm dying. You think I'm dying?'

'I'll get you a drink!'

'No, get the doctor!' he shrieked. 'Get me a drink, too!' Feebly he pulled his pyjama string and let the pants drop. What was it? Not just the shakes. He was too weak to shake. Even his hands were weak and tingly. He held up his hands. The fingers were curved inward. He couldn't open them. 'Ma, somp'n's the matter with my hands! Look, Ma, what is it, what is it?'

'Drink this!'

He heard the bottle chatter on the rim of the glass. He couldn't wait for it. He trotted into the hall, stooped with terror, staring at his limp, curling hands. It was the two middle fingers on each hand. They were curving in, almost touching the palm.

'Darling, put your robe on!' she whispered.

'*Get the doctor!*' A robe! She talked about a robe! What did it matter if he was stark naked? 'Ma, but don't let 'em take me away!' He plucked at her as she stood at the telephone. 'Lock all the doors! You know what they do?' He spoke fast and confidentially, because the numbness was working up and he knew what was the matter now. He was a case! He was going to be like this all his life! 'Know what they do, Ma, they put you in a strait-jacket without a drop and it'll kill me!'

'Dr Packer? This is Mrs Bruno. Could you recommend a doctor in the neighbourhood?'

Bruno screamed. How would a doctor get out here in the Connecticut sticks? 'Massom –' He gasped. He couldn't talk, couldn't move his tongue. It had gone into his vocal cords! 'Aaaaagh!' He wriggled from under the smoking jacket his mother was trying to throw over him. Let Herbert stand there gaping at him if he wanted to!

'Charles!'

He gestured towards his mouth with his crazy hands. He trotted to the closet mirror. His face was white, flat around the mouth as if someone had hit him with a board, his lips drawn horribly back from his teeth. And his hands! He wouldn't be able to hold a glass any more, or light a cigarette. He wouldn't be able to drive a car. He wouldn't even be able to go to the john by himself!

'*Drink* this!'

Yes, liquor, liquor. He tried to catch it all in his stiff lips. It burnt his face and ran down his chest. He motioned for more. He tried to remind her to lock the doors. Oh, Christ, if it went away, he would be grateful all his life! He let Herbert and his mother push him on to the bed.

'Tehmeh!' he choked. He twisted his mother's dressing-gown and nearly pulled her down on top of him. But at least he could hold to something now. 'Dome tehmeh way!' he said with his breath, and she assured him she wouldn't. She told him she would lock all the doors.

Gerard, he thought, Gerard was still working against him, and he would keep on and on and on. Not only Gerard but a whole army of people, checking and snooping and visiting people, hammering typewriters, running out and running back with more pieces, pieces from Santa Fe now, and one day Gerard might put them together right. One day Gerard might come in and find him like this morning, and ask him and he would tell everything. He had killed someone. They killed *you* for killing someone. Maybe he couldn't cope. He stared up at the light fixture in the centre of the ceiling. It reminded him of the round chromium drainstop in the basin at his grandmother's house in Los Angeles. Why did he think of that?

The cruel jab of the hypodermic needle shocked him to sharper consciousness.

The young, jumpy-looking doctor was talking to his mother in a corner of the darkened room. But he felt. They wouldn't take him away now. It was okay now. He had just been panicky. Cautiously, just under the top of the sheet, he watched his fingers flex. 'Guy,' he whispered. His tongue was still thick, but he could talk. Then he saw the doctor go out.

'Ma, I don't want to go to Europe!' he said in a monotone as his mother came over.

'All right, darling, we won't go.' She sat down gently on the side of the bed, and he felt immediately better.

'The doctor didn't say I couldn't go, did he?' As if he wouldn't go if he wanted to! What was he afraid of? Not even of another attack like this! He touched the puffed shoulder of his mother's dressing-gown, but he thought of Rutledge Overbeck at dinner tonight, and let his hand drop. He was sure his mother was having an affair with him. She went to see him too much at his studio in Silver Springs, and she stayed too long. He didn't want to admit it, but why shouldn't he when it was under his nose? It was the first affair, and his father was dead so why shouldn't she, but why did she have to pick such a jerk? Her eyes looked darker now, in the shaded room. She hadn't improved since the days after his father's death. She was going to be like this, Bruno realized now, stay like this, never be young again the way he liked her. 'Don't look so sad, Mom.'

'Darling, will you promise me you'll cut down? The doctor said this is the beginning of the end. This morning was a warning, don't you see? Nature's warning.' She moistened her lips, and the sudden softness of the rouged, lined underlip so close to him was more than Bruno could bear.

He closed his eyes tight shut. If he promised, he would be lying. 'Hell, I didn't get the D.T.s, did I? I never had 'em!'

'But this is worse. I talked with the doctor. It's destroying your nerve tissues, he said, and it can kill you. Doesn't that mean anything to you?'

'Yes, Ma.'

'Promise me?' She watched his eyelids flutter shut again, and heard him sigh. The tragedy was not this morning, she thought, but years ago when he had taken his first drink by himself. The tragedy was not even the first drink, because the first drink was not the first resort but the last. There'd had to be first the failure of everything else – of her and Sam, of his friends, of his hope, of his interests, really. And hard as she tried, she could never discover why or where it might have begun, because Charley had always been given everything, and both she and Sam had done their best to encourage him in everything and anything he had ever shown interest in. If she could only discover the place in the past where it might have begun – She got up, needing a drink herself.

Bruno opened his eyes tentatively. He felt deliciously heavy with sleep. He saw himself halfway across the room, as if he watched himself on a screen. He was in his red-brown suit. It was the island in Metcalf. He saw his younger, slimmer body arc towards Miriam and fling her to the earth, those few short moments separate from time before and time after. He felt he had made special movements, thought special brilliant thoughts in those moments, and that such an interval would never come again. Like Guy had talked about himself, the other day on the boat, when he built the Palmyra. Bruno was glad those special moments for both of them had come so near the same time. Sometimes he thought he could die without regrets, because what else could he ever do that would measure up to the night in Metcalf? What else wouldn't be an anticlimax? Sometimes, like now, he felt his energy might be winding down, and something, maybe his curiosity, dying down. But he didn't mind, because he felt so wise now somehow, and really so content. Only yesterday he wanted to go around the world. And why? To say he had been? To say to whom? Last month he had written to William Beebe, volunteering to go down in the new superbathysphere that they were testing first without a man inside. Why? Everything was silly compared to the night in Metcalf. Every person he knew was silly compared to Guy. Silliest of all to think he'd wanted to see a lot of European women! Maybe the Captain's whores had soured him, so what? Lots of people thought sex was overrated. No love lasts forever, the psychologists said. But he really shouldn't say that about Guy and Anne. He had a feeling theirs might last, but just why he didn't know. It wasn't only that Guy was so wrapped up in her he was blind to all the rest. It wasn't just that Guy had enough money now. It was something invisible that he hadn't even thought of yet. Sometimes he felt he was right on the brink of thinking of it. No, he didn't want the answer for himself. Purely in the spirit of scientific inquiry.

He turned on his side, smiling, clicking and unclicking the top of his gold Dunhill lighter. That trip man wouldn't see them today or any other day. Home was a hell of a lot more comfortable than Europe. And Guy was here.

39

Gerard was chasing him through a forest, waving all the clues at him – the glove scraps, the shred of overcoat, even the revolver, because Gerard already had Guy. Guy was tied up back in the forest, and his right hand was bleeding fast. If he couldn't circle around and get to him, Guy would bleed to death. Gerard giggled as he ran, as if it were a good joke, a good trick they'd played, but he'd guessed it after all. In a minute, Gerard would touch him with those ugly hands!

'Guy!' But his voice sounded feeble. And Gerard was almost touching him. That was the game, when Gerard *touched* him!

With all his power, Bruno struggled to sit up. The nightmare slid from his brain like heavy slabs of rock.

Gerard! There he was!

'What's the matter? Bad dream?'

The pink-purply hands touched him, and Bruno whirled himself off the bed on to the floor.

'Woke you just in time, eh?' Gerard laughed.

Bruno set his teeth hard enough to break them. He bolted to the bathroom and took a drink with the door wide open. In the mirror, his face looked like a battlefield in hell.

'Sorry to intrude, but I found something new,' Gerard said in the tense, high-pitched voice that meant he had scored a little victory. 'About your friend Guy Haines. The one you were just dreaming about, weren't you?'

The glass cracked in Bruno's hand, and meticulously he gathered up the pieces from the basin and put them in the jagged bottom of the glass. He staggered boredly back to his bed.

'When did you meet him, Charles? Not last December.' Gerard leaned against the chest of drawers, lighting a cigar. 'Did you meet him about a year and a half ago? Did you go with him on the train down to Santa Fe?' Gerard waited. He pulled something from under his arm and tossed it on the bed. 'Remember that?'

It was Guy's Plato book from Santa Fe, still wrapped and with its address half rubbed off. 'Sure, I remember it.' Bruno pushed it away. 'I lost it going to the post office.'

'Hotel La Fonda had it right on the shelf. How'd you happen to borrow a book of Plato?'

'I found it on the train.' Bruno looked up. 'It had Guy's address in it, so I meant to mail it. Found it in the dining-car, matter of fact.' He looked straight at Gerard, who was watching him with his sharp, steady little eyes that didn't always have anything behind them.

'When did you meet him, Charley?' Gerard asked again, with the patient air of one questioning a child he knows is lying.

'In December.'

'You know about his wife's murder, of course.'

'Sure, I read about it. Then I read about him building the Palmyra Club.'

'And you thought, how interesting, because you had found a book six months before that belonged to him.'

Bruno hesitated. 'Yeah.'

Gerard grunted, and looked down with a little smile of disgust.

Bruno felt odd, uncomfortable. When had he seen it before, a smile like that after a grunt? Once when he had lied to his father about something, very obviously lied and clung to it, and his father's grunt, the disbelief in the smile, had shamed him. Bruno realized that his eyes pled with Gerard to forgive him, so he deliberately looked off at the window.

'And you made all those calls to Metcalf not even knowing Guy Haines.' Gerard picked up the book.

'What calls?'

'Several calls.'

'Maybe one when I was tight.'

'Several. About what?'

'About the damned book!' If Gerard knew him so well, he should know that was exactly the kind of thing he would do. 'Maybe I called when I heard his wife got murdered.'

Gerard shook his head. 'You called before she was murdered.'

'So what? Maybe I did.'

'So what? I'll have to ask Mr Haines. Considering your interest in murder, it's remarkable you didn't call him after the murder, isn't it?'

'I'm sick of murder!' Bruno shouted.

'Oh, I believe it, Charley, I believe it!' Gerard sauntered out, and down the hall towards his mother's room.

Bruno showered and dressed with slow care. Gerard had been much, much more excited about Matt Levine, he remembered. As far as he knew, he had made only two calls to Metcalf from Hotel La Fonda where Gerard must have picked up the bills. He could say Guy's mother was mistaken about the others, that it hadn't been he.

'What'd Gerard want?' Bruno asked his mother.

'Nothing much. Wanted to know if I knew a friend of yours. Guy Haines.' She was brushing her hair with upward strokes, so it stood out wildly around the calm, tired face. 'He's an architect, isn't he?'

'Uh-huh, I don't know him very well.' He strolled along the floor behind her. She had forgotten the clippings in Los Angeles, just as he had thought she would. Thank Christ, he hadn't reminded her he knew Guy when all the Palmyra pictures came out! The back of his mind must have known he was going to get Guy to do it.

'Gerard was talking about your calling him last summer. What was all that?'

'Oh, Mom, I get so damn sick of Gerard's dumb steers!'

40

A few moments later that morning, Guy stepped out of the director's office at Hanson and Knapp Drafters, happier than he had felt in weeks. The firm was copying the last of the hospital drawings, the most complex Guy had ever supervised, the last okays had come through on the building materials, and he had got a telegram early that morning from Bob Treacher that made Guy rejoice for his old friend. Bob had been appointed to an advisory committee of engineers for the new Alberta Dam in Canada, a job he had been looking forward to for the last five years.

Here and there at one of the long tables that fanned out on either side of him, a draftsman looked up and watched him as he walked towards the outer door. Guy nodded a greeting to a smiling foreman. He detected the smallest glow of self-esteem. Or maybe it was nothing but his new suit, he thought, only the third suit in his life he had ever had made for him. Anne had chosen the grey-blue glen plaid material. Anne had chosen the tomato-coloured woollen tie this morning to go with it, an old tie but one that he liked. He tightened its knot in the mirror between the elevators. There was a wild grey hair sticking up from one black, heavy eyebrow. The brows went up a little in surprise. He smoothed the hair down. It was the first grey hair he had ever noticed on himself.

A draftsman opened the office door. 'Mr Haines? Lucky I caught you. There's a telephone call.'

Guy went back, hoping it wouldn't be long, because he was to meet Anne for lunch in ten minutes. He took the call in an empty office off the drafting room.

'Hello, Guy? Listen, Gerard found that Plato book . . . Yeah, in Santa Fe. Now, listen, it doesn't change anything . . .'

Five minutes had passed before Guy was back at the elevators. He had always known the Plato might be found. Not a chance, Bruno had said. Bruno could be wrong. Bruno could be caught, therefore. Guy scowled as if it were incredible, the idea Bruno could be caught. And somehow it had been incredible, until now.

Momentarily, as he came out into the sunlight, he was conscious again of the new suit, and he clenched his fist in frustrated anger with himself. 'I found the book on the train, see?' Bruno had said. 'If I called you in Metcalf, it was on account of the book. But I didn't meet you until December . . .' The voice more clipped and anxious than Guy had ever heard it before, so alert, so harried, it hardly seemed Bruno's voice. Guy went over the fabrication Bruno had just given him as if it were something that didn't belong to him, as if it were a swatch of material he indifferently considered for a suit, he thought. No, there were no holes in it, but it wouldn't necessarily wear. Not if someone remembered seeing them on the train. The waiter, for instance, who had served them in Bruno's compartment.

He tried to slow his breathing, tried to slow his pace. He looked up at the small disc of the winter sun. His black brows with the grey hair, with the white scar, his brows that were growing shaggier lately, Anne said, broke the glare into particles and protected him. If one looks directly into the sun for fifteen seconds, one can burn through the cornea, he remembered from somewhere. Anne protected him, too. His work protected him. *The new suit, the stupid new suit.* He felt suddenly inadequate and dull-witted, helpless. Death had insinuated itself into his brain. It enwrapped him. He had breathed its air so long, perhaps, he had grown quite used to it. Well, then, he was not afraid. He squared his shoulders superfluously.

Anne had not arrived when he got to the restaurant. Then he remembered she had said she was going to pick up the snapshots they had made Sunday at the house. Guy pulled Bob Treacher's telegram from his pocket and read it again and again:

JUST APPOINTED TO ALBERTA COMMITTEE. HAVE RECOMMENDED YOU. THIS IS A BRIDGE, GUY. GET FREE SOON AS POSSIBLE. ACCEPTANCE GUARANTEED. LETTER COMING.

Acceptance guaranteed. Regardless of how he engineered his life, his ability to engineer a bridge was beyond question. Guy sipped his martini thoughtfully, holding the surface perfectly steady.

41

'I've wandered into another case,' Gerard murmured pleasantly, gazing at the typewritten report on his desk. He had not looked at Bruno since the young man had come in. 'Murder of Guy Haines' first wife. Never been solved.'

'Yeah, I know.'

'I thought you'd know quite a lot about it. Now tell me everything you know.' Gerard settled himself.

Bruno could tell he had gone all the way into it since Monday when he had the Plato book. 'Nothing,' Bruno said. 'Nobody knows. Do they?'

'What do you think? You must have talked a great deal with Guy about it.'

'Not particularly. Not at all. Why?'

'Because murder interests you so much.'

'What do you mean, murder interests me so much?'

'Oh, come, Charles, if I didn't know from you, I'd know that much from your father!' Gerard said in a rare burst of impatience.

Bruno started to reach for a cigarette and stopped. 'I talked with him about it,' he said quietly, respectfully. 'He doesn't know anything. He didn't even know his wife very well then.'

'Who do you think did it? Did you ever think Mr Haines might have arranged it? Were you interested maybe in how he'd done it and got away with it?' At his ease again, Gerard leaned back with his hands behind his head, as if they were talking about the good weather that day.

'Of course I don't think he arranged it,' Bruno replied. 'You don't seem to realize the calibre of the person you're talking about.'

'The only calibre ever worth considering is the gun's, Charles.' Gerard picked up his telephone. 'As you'd be the first to tell me probably. – Have Mr Haines come in, will you?'

Bruno jumped a little, and Gerard saw it. Gerard watched him in silence as they listened to Guy's footsteps coming closer in the hall. He had expected Gerard would do this, Bruno told himself. So what, so what, so what?

Guy looked nervous, Bruno thought, but his usual air of being nervous and in a hurry covered it. He spoke to Gerard, and nodded to Bruno.

Gerard offered him his remaining chair, a straight one. 'My whole purpose in asking you to come down here, Mr Haines, is to ask you a very simple question. What does Charles talk with you about most of the time?' Gerard offered Guy a cigarette from a pack that must have been years old, Bruno thought, and Guy took it.

Bruno saw Guy's eyebrows draw together with the look of irritation that was exactly appropriate. 'He's talked to me now and then about the Palmyra Club,' Guy replied.

'And what else?'

Guy looked at Bruno. Bruno was nibbling, so casually the action seemed nonchalant, at a fingernail of the hand that propped his cheek. 'Can't really say,' Guy answered.

'Talked to you about your wife's murder?'

'Yes.'

'How does he talk to you about the murder?' Gerard asked kindly. 'I mean your wife's murder.'

Guy felt his face flush. He glanced again at Bruno, as anybody might, he thought, as anybody might in the presence of a discussed party who is being ignored. 'He often asked me if I knew who might have done it.'

'And do you?'

'No.'

'Do you like Charles?' Gerard's fat fingers trembled slightly, incongruously. They began playing with a match cover on his desk blotter.

Guy thought of Bruno's fingers on the train, playing with the match cover, dropping it on to the steak. 'Yes, I like him,' Guy answered puzzledly.

'Hasn't he annoyed you? Hasn't he thrust himself on you many times?'

'I don't think so,' Guy said.

'Were you annoyed when he came to your wedding?'

'No.'

'Did Charles ever tell you that he hated his father?'

'Yes, he did.'

'Did he ever tell you he'd like to kill him?'

'No,' he replied in the same matter-of-fact tone.

Gerard got the brown paper-wrapped book from a drawer in his desk. 'Here's the book Charles meant to mail you. Sorry I can't let you have it just now, because I may need it. How did Charles happen to have your book?'

'He told me he found it on the train.' Guy studied Gerard's sleepy, enigmatic smile. He had seen a trace of it the night Gerard called at the house, but not like this. This smile was calculated to inspire dislike. This smile was a professional weapon. What it must be, Guy thought, facing that smile day after day. Involuntarily, he looked over at Bruno.

'And you didn't see each other on the train?' Gerard looked from Guy to Bruno.

'No,' said Guy.

'I spoke with the waiter who served you two dinner in Charles' compartment.'

Guy kept his eyes on Gerard. This naked shame, he thought, was more annihilating than guilt. This was annihilation he was feeling, even as he sat upright, looking straight at Gerard.

'So what?' Bruno said shrilly.

'So I'm interested in why you two take such elaborate trouble,' Gerard wagged his head amusedly, 'to say you met months later.' He waited, letting the passing seconds eat at them. 'You won't tell me the answer. Well, the answer is obvious. That is, one answer, as a speculation.'

All three of them were thinking of the answer, Guy thought. It was visible in the air now, linking him and Bruno, Bruno and Gerard, Gerard and himself. The answer Bruno had declared beyond thought, the eternally missing ingredient.

'Will you tell me, Charles, you who read so many detective stories?'

'I don't know what you're getting at.'

'Within a few days, your wife was killed, Mr Haines. Within a few months, Charles' father. My obvious and first speculation is that you both knew those murders were going to happen –'

'Oh, crap!' Bruno said.

'– and discussed them. Pure speculation, of course. That's assuming you met on the train. Where did you meet?' Gerard smiled. 'Mr Haines?'

'Yes,' Guy said, 'we met on the train.'

'And why've you been so afraid of admitting it?' Gerard jabbed one of his freckled fingers at him, and again Guy felt in Gerard's prosaicness his power to terrify.

'I don't know,' Guy said.

'Wasn't it because Charles told you he would like to have his father killed? And you were uneasy then, Mr Haines, because you knew?'

Was that Gerard's trump? Guy said slowly, 'Charles said nothing about killing his father.'

Gerard's eyes slid over in time to catch Bruno's tight smirk of satisfaction. 'Pure speculation, of course,' Gerard said.

Guy and Bruno left the building together. Gerard had dismissed them together, and they walked together down the long block towards the little park where the subways were, and the taxicabs. Bruno looked back at the tall narrow building they had left.

'All right, he still hasn't anything,' Bruno said. 'Any way you look at it, he hasn't anything.'

Bruno was sullen, but calm. Suddenly Guy realized how cool Bruno had been under Gerard's attack. Guy was continually imagining Bruno hysterical under pressure. He glanced quickly at Bruno's tall hunched figure beside him, feeling that wild, reckless comradeship of the day in the restaurant. But he had nothing to say. Surely, he thought, Bruno must know that Gerard wasn't going to tell them everything he had discovered.

'You know, the funny thing,' Bruno continued, 'Gerard's not looking for us, he's looking for other people.'

42

Gerard poked a finger between the bars and waggled it at the little bird that fluttered in terror against the opposite side of the cage. Gerard whistled a single soft note.

From the centre of the room, Anne watched him uneasily. She didn't like his having just told her Guy had been lying, then his strolling off to frighten the canary. She hadn't liked Gerard for the last quarter hour, and because she had thought she did like him on his first visit, her misjudgement annoyed her.

'What's his name?' Gerard asked.

'Sweetie,' Anne replied. She ducked her head a little, embarrassedly, and swung half around. Her new alligator pumps made her feel very tall and graceful, and she had thought, when she bought them that afternoon, that Guy would like them, that they would coax a smile from him as they sat having a cocktail before dinner. But Gerard's arrival had spoilt that.

'Do you have any idea why your husband didn't want to say he met Charles June before last?'

The month Miriam was murdered, Anne thought again. June before last meant nothing else to her. 'It was a difficult month for him,' she said. 'It was the month his wife died. He might have forgotten almost anything that happened that month.' She frowned, feeling Gerard was making too much of his little discovery, that it couldn't matter so very much, since Guy hadn't even seen Charles in the six months afterwards.

'Not in this case,' Gerard said casually, reseating himself. 'No, I think Charles talked with your husband on the train about his father, told him he wanted him dead, maybe even told him how he intended to go about –'

'I can't imagine Guy listening to that,' Anne interrupted him.

'I don't know,' Gerard went on blandly, 'I don't know, but I strongly suspect Charles knew about his father's murder and that he may have confided to your husband that night on the train. Charles is that kind of a young man. And I think the kind of man your husband is would have kept quiet about it, tried to avoid Charles from then on. Don't you?'

It would explain a great deal, Anne thought. But it would also make Guy a kind of accomplice. Gerard seemed to want to make Guy an accomplice. 'I'm sure my husband wouldn't have tolerated Charles even to this extent,' she said firmly, 'if Charles had told him anything like that.'

'A very good point. However –' Gerard stopped vaguely, as if lost in his own slow thoughts.

Anne did not like to look at the top of his bald freckled head, so she stared at the tile cigarette box on the coffee table, and finally took a cigarette.

'Do you think your husband has any suspicion who murdered his wife, Mrs Haines?'

Anne blew her smoke out defiantly. 'I certainly do not.'

'You see, if that night on the train, Charles went into the subject of murder, he went into it thoroughly. And if your husband did have some reason to think his wife's life was in danger, and if he mentioned it to Charles – why then they have a sort of mutual secret, a mutual peril even. It's only a speculation,' he hurried to add, 'but investigators always have to speculate.'

'I know my husband couldn't have said anything about his wife's being in danger. I was with him in Mexico City when the news came, and with him days before in New York.'

'How about March of this year?' Gerard asked in the same even tone. He reached for his empty highball glass, and submitted to Anne's taking it to refill.

Anne stood at the bar with her back to Gerard, remembering March, the month Charles' father was killed, remembering Guy's nervousness then. Had that fight been in February or March? And *hadn't* he fought with Charles Bruno?

'Do you think your husband could have been seeing Charles now and then around the month of March without your knowing about it?'

Of course, she thought, that might explain it: that Guy had known Charles intended to kill his father, and had tried to stop him, had fought with him, in a bar. 'He could have, I suppose,' she said uncertainly. 'I don't know.'

'How did your husband seem around the month of March, if you can remember, Mrs Haines?'

'He was nervous. I think I know the things he was nervous about.'

'What things?'

'His work –' Somehow she couldn't grant him a word more than that about Guy. Everything she said, she felt Gerard would incorporate in the misty picture he was composing, in which he was trying to see Guy. She waited, and Gerard waited, as if he vied with her not to break the silence first.

Finally, he tapped out his cigar and said, 'If anything does occur to you about that time in regard to Charles, will you be sure and tell me? Call me any time during the day or night. There'll be somebody there to take messages.' He wrote another name on his business card, and handed it to Anne.

Anne turned from the door and went directly to the coffee table to remove his glass. Through the front window, she saw him sitting in his car with his head bent forward, like a man asleep, while, she supposed, he made his notes. Then with a little stab, she thought of his writing that Guy might have seen Charles in March without her knowing about it. Why had she said it? She did know about it. Guy said he hadn't seen Charles, between December and the wedding.

When Guy came in about an hour later, Anne was in the kitchen, tending the casserole that was nearly done in the oven. She saw Guy put his head up, sniffing the air.

'Shrimp casserole,' Anne told him. 'I guess I should open a vent.'

'Was Gerard here?'

'Yes. You knew he was coming?'

'Cigars,' he said laconically. Gerard had told her about the meeting on the train, of course. 'What did he want this time?' he asked.

'He wanted to know more about Charles Bruno.' Anne glanced at him quickly from the front window. 'If you'd said anything to me about suspecting him of anything. And he wanted to know about March.'

'About March?' He stepped on to the raised portion of the floor where Anne stood.

He stopped in front of her, and Anne saw the pupils of his eyes contract suddenly. She could see a few of the hair-fine scars over his cheek-bone from that night in March, or February. 'Wanted to know if you suspected Charles was going to have his father killed that month.' But Guy only stared at her with his mouth in a familiar straight line, without alarm, and without guilt. She stepped aside, and went down into the living-room. 'It's terrible, isn't it,' she said, 'murder?'

Guy tapped a fresh cigarette on his watch face. It tortured him to hear her say 'murder'. He wished he could erase every memory of Bruno from her brain.

'You didn't know, did you, Guy – in March?'

'No, Anne. What did you tell Gerard?'

'Do you believe Charles had his father killed?'

'I don't know. I think it's possible. But it doesn't concern us.' And he did not realize for seconds that it was even a lie.

'That's right. It doesn't concern us.' She looked at him again. 'Gerard also said you met Charles June before last on the train.'

'Yes, I did.'

'Well – what does it matter?'

'I don't know.'

'Was it because of something Charles said on the train? Is that why you dislike him?'

Guy shoved his hands deeper in his jacket pockets. He wanted a brandy suddenly. He knew he showed what he felt, that he could not hide it from Anne now: 'Listen, Anne,' he said quickly. 'Bruno told me on the train he wished his father were dead. He didn't mention any plans, he didn't mention any names. I didn't like the way he said it, and after that I didn't like him. I refuse to tell Gerard all that, because I don't know if Bruno had his father killed or not. That's for the police to find out. Innocent men have been hanged because people reported their saying something like that.'

But whether she believed him or not, he thought, he was finished. It seemed the basest lie he had ever told, the basest thing he had ever done – the transferring of his guilt to another man. Even Bruno wouldn't have lied like this, wouldn't have lied against him like this. He felt himself totally false, totally a lie. He flung his cigarette into the fireplace and put his hands over his face.

'Guy, I do believe you're doing what you should,' Anne's voice said gently.

His face was a lie, his level eyes, the firm mouth, the sensitive hands. He whipped his hands down and put them in his pockets. 'I could use a brandy.'

'Wasn't it Charles you fought with in March?' she asked as she stood at the bar.

There was no reason not to lie about this also, but he could not. 'No, Anne.' He knew from the quick sidelong glance she gave him that she didn't believe him. She probably thought he had fought with Bruno to stop him. She was probably proud of him! Must there always be this protection, that he didn't even want? Must everything always be so easy for him? But Anne would not be satisfied with this. She would come back to it and back to it until he told her, he knew.

That evening, Guy lighted the first fire of the year, the first fire in their new house. Anne lay on the long hearthstone with her head on a sofa pillow. The thin nostalgic chill of autumn was in the air, filling Guy with melancholy and a restless energy. The energy was not buoyant as autumnal energy had been in his youth, but underlaid with frenzy and despair, as if his life were winding down and this might be his last spurt. What better proof did he need that his life was winding down than that he had no dread of what lay ahead? Couldn't Gerard guess it now, knowing that he and Bruno had met on the train? Wouldn't it dawn on him one day, one night, one instant as his fat fingers lifted a cigar to his mouth? What were they waiting for, Gerard and the police? He had sometimes the feeling that Gerard wanted to gather every tiniest contributing fact, every gramme of evidence against them both, then let it fall suddenly upon them and demolish them. But however they demolished him, Guy thought, they would not demolish his buildings. And he felt again the strange and lonely isolation of his spirit from his flesh, even from his mind.

But suppose his secret with Bruno were never found out? There were still those moments of mingled horror at what he had done, and of absolute despondency, when he felt that secret bore a charmed inviolability. Perhaps, he thought, that was why he was not afraid of Gerard or the police, because he still believed in its inviolability. If no one had guessed it so far, after all their carelessness, after all Bruno's hints, wasn't there something making it impregnable?

Anne had fallen asleep. He stared at the smooth curve of her forehead, paled to silver by the fire's light. Then he lowered his lips to her forehead and kissed her, so gently she would not awaken. The ache inside him translated itself into words: 'I forgive you.' He wanted Anne to say it, no one but Anne.

In his mind, the side of the scale that bore his guilt was hopelessly weighted, beyond the scale's measure, yet into the other side he continually threw the equally hopeless featherweight of self-defence. He had committed the crime in self-defence, he reasoned. But he vacillated in completely believing this. If he believed in the full complement of evil in himself, he had to believe also in a natural compulsion to express it. He found himself wondering, therefore, from time to time, if he might have enjoyed his crime in some way, derived some primal satisfaction from it – how else could one really explain in mankind the continued toleration of wars, the perennial enthusiasm for wars when they came, if not for some primal pleasure in killing? – and because the capacity to wonder came so often, he accepted it as true that he had.

43

District Attorney Phil Howland, immaculate and gaunt, as sharp of outline as Gerard was fuzzy, smiled tolerantly through his cigarette smoke. 'Why don't you let the kid alone? It was an angle at first, I grant you. We combed through his friends, too. There's nothing, Gerard. And you can't arrest a man on his personality.'

Gerard recrossed his legs and allowed himself a complaisant smile. This was his hour. His satisfaction was heightened by the fact that he sat here smiling in the same way during other less momentous interviews.

Howland pushed a typewritten sheet with his fingertips to the edge of the desk. 'Twelve new names here, if you're interested. Friends of the late Mr Samuel furnished us by the insurance companies,' Howland said in his calm, bored voice, and Gerard knew he pretended especial boredom now, because as District Attorney he had so many hundreds of men at his disposal, could throw so much finer nets so much farther.

'You can tear them up,' Gerard said.

Howland hid his surprise with a smile, but he couldn't hide the sudden curiosity in his dark, wide eyes. 'I suppose you've already got your man. Charles Bruno, of course.'

'Of course,' Gerard chuckled. 'Only I've got him for another murder.'

'Only one? You always said he was good for four or five.'

'I never said,' Gerard denied quietly. He was smoothing out a number of papers, folded in thirds like letters, on his knees.

'Who?'

'Curious? Don't you know?' Gerard smiled with his cigar between his teeth. He pulled a straight chair closer to him, and proceeded to cover its seat with his papers. He never used Howland's desk, however many papers he had, and Howland knew now not to bother offering it. Howland disliked him personally as well as professionally, Gerard knew. Howland accused him of not being co-operative with the police. The police had never been in the least co-operative with him, but with all their hindrance, Gerard in the last decade had solved an impressive number of cases the police hadn't even been warm on.

Howland got up and strolled slowly towards Gerard on his long thin legs, then hung back, leaning against the front of his desk. 'But does all this shed any light on the *case*?'

'The trouble with the police force is that it has a single-track mind,' Gerard announced. 'This case, like many others, took a double-track mind. Simply couldn't have been solved without a double-track mind.'

'Who and when?' Howland sighed.

'Ever hear of Guy Haines?'

'Certainly. We questioned him last week.'

'His wife. June eleventh of last year in Metcalf, Texas. Strangulation, remember? The police never solved it.'

'Charles Bruno?' Howland frowned.

'Did you know that Charles Bruno and Guy Haines were on the same train going South on June first? Ten days before the murder of Haines' wife. Now, what do you deduce from that?'

'You mean they knew each other before last June?'

'No, I mean they met each other on that train. Can you put the rest together? I'm giving you the missing link.'

The District Attorney smiled faintly. 'You're saying Charles Bruno killed Guy Haines' wife?'

'I certainly am.' Gerard looked up from his papers, finished. 'The next question is, what's my proof? There it is. All you want.' He gestured towards the papers that overlapped in a long row, like cards in a game of solitaire. 'Read from the bottom up.'

While Howland read, Gerard drew a cup of water from the tank in the corner and lighted another cigar from the one he had been smoking. The last statement, from Charles' taxi-driver in Metcalf, had come in this morning. He hadn't even had a drink on it yet, but he was going to have three or four as soon as he left Howland, in the lounge car of an Iowa-bound train.

The papers were signed statements from Hotel La Fonda bellhops, from one Edward Wilson who had seen Charles leaving the Santa Fe station on an eastbound train the day of Miriam Haines' murder, from the Metcalf taxi-driver who had driven Charles to the Kingdom of Fun Amusement Park at Lake Metcalf, from the barman in the roadhouse where Charles had tried to get hard liquor, plus telephone bills of long-distance calls to Metcalf.

'But no doubt you know that already,' Gerard remarked.

'Most of it, yes,' Howland answered calmly, still reading.

'You knew he made a twenty-four-hour trip to Metcalf that day, too, did you?' Gerard asked, but he was really in too good spirits for sarcasm. 'That taxi-driver was certainly hard to find. Had to trace him all the way up to Seattle, but once we found him, it didn't take any jostling for him to remember. People don't forget a young man like Charles Bruno.'

'So you're saying Charles Bruno is so fond of murder,' Howland remarked amusedly, 'that he murders the wife of a man he meets on a train the week before? A woman he's never even seen? Or had he seen her?'

Gerard chuckled again. 'Of course he hadn't. My Charles had a plan.' The 'my' slipped out, but Gerard didn't care. 'Can't you see it? Plain as the nose on your face? And this is only half.'

'Sit down, Gerard, you'll work yourself into a heart attack.'

'You can't see it. Because you didn't know and don't know Charles' personality. You weren't interested in the fact he spends most of his time planning perfect crimes of various sorts.'

'All right, what's the rest of your theory?'

'That Guy Haines killed Samuel Bruno.'

'Ow!' Howland groaned.

Gerard smiled back at the first grin Howland had given him since he, Gerard, had made a mistake in a certain case years ago. 'I haven't finished checking on Guy Haines yet,' Gerard said with deliberate ingenuousness, puffing away at the cigar. 'I want to take it easy, and that's the only reason I'm here, to get you to take it easy with me. I didn't know but what you'd grab Charles, you see, with all your information against him.'

Howland smoothed his black moustache. 'Everything you say confirms my belief you should have retired about fifteen years ago.'

'Oh, I've solved a few cases in the last fifteen years.'

'A man like Guy Haines?' Howland laughed again.

'Against a fellow like Charles? Mind you, I don't say Guy Haines did it of his own free will. He was made to do it for Charles' unsolicited favour of freeing him of his wife. Charles hates women,' he remarked in a parenthesis. 'That was Charles' plan. Exchange. No clues, you see. No motives. Oh, I can just hear him! But even Charles is human. He was too interested in Guy Haines to leave him alone afterwards. And Guy Haines was too frightened to do anything about it. Yes –' Gerard jerked his head for emphasis, and his jowls shook – 'Haines was coerced. How terribly probably no one will ever know.'

Howland's smile went away momentarily at Gerard's earnestness. The story had the barest possibility, but still a possibility. 'Hmm-m.'

'Unless he tells us,' Gerard added.

'And how do you propose to make him tell us?'

'Oh, he may yet confess. It's wearing him down. But otherwise, confront him with the facts. Which my men are busy gathering. One thing, Howland –' Gerard jabbed a finger at his papers on the chair seat. 'When you and your – your army of oxes go out checking these statements, don't question Guy Haines' mother. I don't want Haines forewarned.'

'Oh. Cat-and-mouse technique for Mr Haines,' Howland smiled. He turned to make a telephone call about an inconsequential matter, and Gerard waited, resenting that he had to turn his information over to Howland, that he had to leave the Charles-Guy Haines spectacle. 'Well –' Howland let his breath out in a long sigh – 'what do you want me to do, work over your little boy with this stuff? Think he'll break down and tell all about his brilliant plan with Guy Haines, architect?'

'No, I don't want him worked over. I like clean jobs. I want a few days more or maybe weeks to finish checking on Haines, then I'll confront them both. I'm giving you this on Charles, because from now on I'm out of the case personally, so far as they're to know. I'm going to Iowa for a vacation, I really am, and I'm going to let Charles know it.' Gerard's face lighted with a big smile.

'It's going to be hard to hold the boys back,' Howland said regretfully, 'especially for all the time it'll take you to get evidence against Guy Haines.'

'Incidentally –' Gerard picked up his hat and shook it at

Howland. 'You couldn't crack Charles with all that, but I could crack Guy Haines with what I've got this minute.'

'Oh, you mean *we* couldn't crack Guy Haines?'

Gerard looked at him with elaborate contempt. 'But you're not interested in cracking him, are you? You don't think he's the man.'

'Take that vacation, Gerard!'

Methodically, Gerard gathered his papers and started to pocket them.

'I thought you were going to leave those.'

'Oh, if you think you'll need them.' Gerard presented the papers courteously, and turned towards the door.

'Mind telling me what you've got that'll crack Guy Haines?'

Gerard made a disdainful sound in his throat. 'The man is tortured with guilt,' he said, and went out.

44

'You know, in the whole world,' Bruno said, and tears started in his eyes so he had to look down at the long hearthstone under his feet, 'I wouldn't want to be anywhere else but here tonight, Anne.' He leaned his elbow jauntily on the high mantel.

'Very nice of you to say,' Anne smiled, and set the plate of melted cheese and anchovy canapés on the sawbuck table. 'Have one of these while they're hot.'

Bruno took one, though he knew he wouldn't be able to get it down. The table looked beautiful, set for two with grey linen and big grey plates. Gerard was off on a vacation. They had beaten him, Guy and he, and the lid was off his brains! He might have tried to kiss Anne, he thought, if she didn't belong to Guy. Bruno stood taller and adjusted his cuffs. He took great pride in being a perfect gentleman with Anne. 'So Guy thinks he's going to like it up there?' Bruno asked. Guy was in Canada now, working on the big Alberta dam. 'I'm glad all this dumb questioning is over, so he won't have to worry about it when he's working. You can imagine how I feel. Like celebrating!' He laughed, mainly at his understatement.

Anne stared at his tall restless figure by the mantel, and wondered if Guy, despite his hatred, felt the same fascination she did. She still didn't know, though, whether Charles Bruno would have been capable of arranging his father's murder, and she had spent the whole day with him in order to make up her mind. He slid away from certain questions with joking answers, he was serious and careful about answering others. He hated Miriam as if he had known her. It rather surprised Anne that Guy had told him so much about Miriam.

'Why didn't you want to tell anyone you'd met Guy on the train?' Anne asked.

'I didn't mind. I just made the mistake of kidding around about it first, said we'd met in school. Then all those questions came up, and Gerard started making a lot out of it. I guess because it looked bad, frankly. Miriam killed so soon after, you know. I think it was quite nice of Guy at the inquest on Miriam not to drag in anybody he'd just met by accident.' He laughed, a single loud clap, and dropped into the armchair. 'Not that I'm a suspicious character, by any means!'

'But that didn't have anything to do with the questioning about your father's death.'

'Of course not. But Gerard doesn't pay any attention to logic. He should have been an inventor!'

Anne frowned. She couldn't believe that Guy would have fallen in with Charles' story simply because telling the truth would have looked bad, or even because Charles had told him on the train that he hated his father. She must ask Guy again. There was a great deal she had to ask him. About Charles' hostility to Miriam, for instance, though he had never seen her. Anne went into the kitchen.

Bruno strolled to the front window with his drink, and watched a plane alternating its red and green lights in the black sky. It looked like a person exercising, he thought, touching fingertips to shoulders and stretching arms out again. He wished Guy might be on that plane, coming home. He looked at the dusky pink face of his new wrist-watch, thinking again, before he read the time on its tall gold numerals, that Guy would probably like a watch like this, because of its modern design. In just three hours more, he would have been with Anne twenty-four hours, a whole day. He had driven by last evening instead of telephoning, and it had got so late, Anne had invited him to spend the night. He had slept up in the guest room where they had put him the night of the party, and Anne had brought him some hot bouillon before he went to sleep. Anne was terribly sweet to him, and he really loved her! He spun around on his heel, and saw her coming in from the kitchen with their plates.

'Guy's very fond of you, you know,' Anne said during the dinner.

Bruno looked at her, having already forgotten what they had been talking about. 'There's *nothing* I wouldn't do for him! I feel a tremendous tie with him, like a brother. I guess because everything started happening to him just after we met each other on the train.' And though he had started out to be gay, even funny, the seriousness of his real feeling for Guy got the better of him. He fingered the rack of Guy's pipes near him on an end table. His heart was pounding. The stuffed potato was beautiful, but he didn't dare eat another mouthful. Nor the red wine. He had an impulse to try to spend the night again. Couldn't he manage to stay again tonight, if he didn't feel well? On the other hand, the new house was closer than Anne thought. Saturday he was giving a big party. 'You're sure Guy'll be back this week-end?' he asked.

'So he said.' Anne ate her green salad thoughtfully. 'I don't know whether he'll feel like a party, though. When he's been working, he usually doesn't like anything more distracting than a sail.'

'I'd like a sail. If you wouldn't mind company.'

'Come along.' Then she remembered, Charles had already been out on the *India*, had invited himself with Guy, had dented the gunwale, and suddenly she felt puzzled, tricked, as if something had prevented her remembering until now. And she found herself thinking, Charles could probably do anything, atrocious things, and fool everyone with the same ingratiating naïveté, the same shy smile. Except Gerard. Yes, he could have arranged his father's murder. Gerard wouldn't be speculating in that direction if it weren't possible. She might be sitting opposite a murderer. She felt a little pluck of terror as she got up, a bit too abruptly as if she were fleeing, and removed the dinner plates. And his grim, merciless pleasure in talking of his loathing for Miriam. He would have enjoyed killing her, Anne thought. A fragile suspicion that he might have killed her crossed her mind like a dry leaf blown by the wind.

'So you went on to Santa Fe after you met Guy?' she almost stammered, from the kitchen.

'Uh-huh.' Bruno was deep in the big green armchair again.

Anne dropped a demitasse spoon and it made an outrageous clatter on the tiles. The odd thing, she thought, was that it didn't seem to matter what one said to Charles or asked him. Nothing would shock him. But instead of making it simpler to talk to him, this was the very quality that she felt rattling her and throwing her off.

'Have you ever been to Metcalf?' she heard her own voice call around the partition.

'No,' Bruno replied. 'No, I always wanted to. Have you?'

Bruno sipped his coffee at the mantel. Anne was on the sofa, her head tipped back so the curve of her throat above the tiny ruffled collar of her dress was the lightest thing about her. *Anne is like light to me*, Bruno remembered Guy once saying. If he could strangle Anne, too, then Guy and he could really be together. Bruno frowned at himself, then laughed and shifted on his feet.

'What's funny?'

'Just thinking,' he smiled. 'I was thinking of what Guy always says, about the doubleness of everything. You know, the positive and negative, side by side. Every decision has a reason against it.' He noticed suddenly he was breathing hard.

'You mean two sides to everything?'

'Oh, no, that's too simple!' Women were really so crude sometimes! 'People, feelings, everything! Double! Two people in each person. There's also a person exactly the opposite of you, like the unseen part of you, somewhere in the world, and he waits in ambush.' It thrilled him to say Guy's words, though he hadn't liked hearing them, he remembered, because Guy had said the two people were mortal enemies, too, and Guy had meant him and himself.

Anne brought her head up slowly from the sofa back. It sounded so like Guy, yet he had never said it to her. Anne thought of the unsigned letter last spring. Charles must have written it. Guy must have meant Charles when he talked of ambush. There was no one else besides Charles to whom Guy reacted so violently. Surely it was Charles who alternated hatred with devotion.

'It's not all good and evil either, but that's how it shows itself best, in action,' Bruno went on cheerfully. 'By the way, I mustn't forget to tell Guy about giving the thousand dollars to a beggar. I always said when I had my own money, I'd give a thousand to a beggar. Well, I did, but you think he thanked me? It took me twenty minutes to prove to him the money was real! I had to take a hundred in a bank and break it for him! Then he acted as if he thought I was crazy!' Bruno looked down and shook his head. He had counted on its being a memorable experience, and then to have the bastard look practically *sore* at him the next time he saw him – still begging on the same street corner, too – because he hadn't brought him *another* thousand! 'As I was saying anyway –'

'About good and evil,' Anne said. She loathed him. She knew all that Guy felt now about him. But she didn't yet know why Guy tolerated him.

'Oh. Well, these things come out in actions. But for instance, murderers. Punishing them in the law courts won't make them any better, Guy says. Every man is his own law court and punishes himself enough. In fact, every man is just about everything to Guy!' He laughed. He was so tight, he could hardly see her face now, but he wanted to tell her everything that he and Guy had ever talked about, right up to the last little secret that he couldn't tell her.

'People without consciences don't punish themselves, do they?' Anne asked.

Bruno looked at the ceiling. 'That's true. Some people are too dumb to have consciences, other people too evil. Generally the dumb ones get caught. But take the two murderers of Guy's wife and my father.' Bruno tried to look serious. 'Both of them must have been pretty brilliant people, don't you think.'

'So they have consciences and don't deserve to get caught?'

'Oh, I don't say that. Of course not! But don't think they aren't suffering a little. In their fashion!' He laughed again, because he was really too tight to know just where he was going. 'They weren't just madmen, like they said the murderer of Guy's wife was. Shows how little the authorities know about real criminology. A crime like that took planning.' Out of the blue, he remembered he hadn't planned that one at all, but he certainly had planned his father's, which illustrated his point well enough. 'What's the matter?'

Anne laid her cold fingers against her forehead. 'Nothing.'

Bruno fixed her a highball at the bar Guy had built into the side of the fireplace. Bruno wanted a bar just like it for his own house.

'Where did Guy get those scratches on his face last March?'

'What scratches?' Bruno turned to her. Guy had told him she didn't know about the scratches.

'More than scratches. Cuts. And a bruise on his head!'

'I didn't see them.'

'He fought with you, didn't he?' Charles stared at her with a strange pinkish glint in his eyes. She was not deceitful enough to smile now. She was sure. She felt Charles was about to rush across the room and strike her, but she kept her eyes fixed on his. If she told Gerard, she thought, the fight would be proof of Charles' knowledge of the murder. Then she saw Charles' smile waver back.

'No!' he laughed. He sat down. 'Where did he say he got the scratches? I didn't see him anyway in March. I was out of town then.' He stood up. He suddenly didn't feel well in the stomach, and it wasn't the questions, it was his stomach. Suppose he was in for another attack now. Or tomorrow morning. He mustn't pass out, mustn't let Anne see *that* in the morning! 'I'd better go soon,' he murmured.

'What's the matter? You're not feeling well? You're a little pale.'

She wasn't sympathetic. He could tell by her voice. What woman ever was, except his mother? 'Thank you very much, Anne, for – for all day.'

She handed him his coat, and he stumbled out the door, gritting his teeth as he started the long walk towards his car at the kerb.

The house was dark when Guy came home a few hours later. He prowled the living-room, saw the cigarette stub ground on the hearth, the pipe rack askew on the end table, the depression in a small pillow on the sofa. There was a peculiar disorder that couldn't have been created by Anne and Teddy, or by Chris, or by Helen Heyburn. Hadn't he known?

He ran up to the guest room. Bruno wasn't there, but he saw a tortured roll of newspaper on the bed table and a dime and two pennies domestically beside it. At the window, the dawn was coming in like that dawn. He turned his back on the window, and his held breath came out like a sob. What did Anne mean by doing this to him? Now of all times when it was intolerable – when half of himself was in Canada and the other half here, caught in the tightening grip of Bruno, Bruno with the police off his trail. The police had given him a little insulation! But he had overreached now. There was no enduring much longer.

He went into the bedroom and knelt beside Anne and kissed her awake, frightenedly, harshly, until he felt her arms close around him. He buried his face in the soft muss of the sheets over her breast. It seemed there was a rocking, roaring storm all around him, all around both of them, and that Anne was the only point of stillness, at its centre, and the rhythm of her breathing the only sign of a normal pulse in a sane world. He got his clothes off with his eyes shut.

'I've missed you,' were the first words Anne said.

Guy stood near the foot of the bed with his hands in the pockets of his robe, clenched. The tension was still in him, and all the storm seemed gathered in his own core now. 'I'll be here three days. Have you missed me?'

Anne slid up a few inches in the bed. 'Why do you look at me like that?'

Guy did not answer.

'I've seen him only once, Guy.'

'Why did you see him at all?'

'Because –' Her cheeks flushed as pink as the spot on her shoulder, Guy noticed. His beard had scratched her shoulder. He had never spoken to her like this before. And the fact she was going to answer him reasonably seemed only to give more reason to his anger. 'Because he came by –'

'He always comes by. He always telephones.'

'Why?'

'He slept here!' Guy burst out, then he saw Anne's recoil in the subtle lift of her head, the flicker of her lashes.

'Yes. Night before last,' her steady voice challenged him. 'He came by late, and I asked him to stay over.'

It had crossed his mind in Canada that Bruno might make advances to Anne, simply because she belonged to him, and that Anne might encourage him, simply because she wanted to know what he had not told her. Not that Bruno would go very far, but the touch of his hand on Anne's, the thought of Anne permitting it, and the reason for which she would permit it, tormented him. 'And he was here last evening?'

'Why does it bother you so?'

'Because he's dangerous. He's half insane.'

'I don't think that's the reason he bothers you,' Anne said in the same slow steady voice. 'I don't know why you defend him,

Guy. I don't know why you don't admit he's the one who wrote that letter to me and the one who almost drove you insane in March.'

Guy stiffened with guilty defensiveness. Defence of Bruno, he thought, always defence of Bruno! Bruno hadn't admitted sending the letter to Anne, he knew. It was just that Anne, like Gerard, with different facts, was putting pieces together. Gerard had quit, but Anne would never quit. Anne worked with the intangible pieces, and the intangible pieces were the ones that would make the picture. But she didn't have the picture yet. It would take time, a little more time, and a little more time to torture him! He turned to the window with a tired leaden movement, too dead even to cover his face or bow his head. He did not care to ask Anne what she and Bruno had talked of yesterday. Somehow he could *feel* exactly what they had said, exactly how much more Anne had learned. There was some allotted period of time, he felt suddenly, in this agony of postponement. It had gone on beyond all logical expectation, as life sometimes did against a fatal disease, that was all.

'Tell me, Guy,' Anne said quietly, not pleading with him now, her voice merely like the tolling of a bell that marked another length of time. 'Tell me, will you?'

'I shall tell you,' he replied, still looking at the window, but hearing himself say it now, believing himself, such a lightness filled him, he was sure Anne must see it in the half of his face, in his whole being, and his first thought was to share it with her, though for a moment he could not take his eyes from the sunlight on the window-sill. *Lightness*, he thought, both a lifting of darkness and of weight, weightlessness. He would tell Anne.

'Guy, come here.' She held up her arms for him, and he sat beside her, slipped his arms around her, and held her tight against him. 'There's going to be a baby,' she said. 'Let's be happy. Will you be happy, Guy?'

He looked at her, feeling suddenly like laughing for happiness, for surprise, for her shyness. 'A baby!' he whispered.

'What'll we do these days you're here?'

'When, Anne?'

'Oh – not for ages. I guess in May. What'll we do tomorrow?'

'We'll definitely go out on the boat. If it's not too rough.' And the foolish, conspiratorial note in his voice made him laugh out loud now.

'Oh, Guy!'

'Crying?'

'It's so good to hear you laugh!'

45

Bruno telephoned Saturday morning to congratulate Guy on his appointment to the Alberta Committee, and to ask if he and Anne would come to his party that evening. Bruno's desperate, elated voice exhorted him to celebrate. 'Talking over my own private wires, Guy. Gerard's gone back to Iowa. Come on, I want you to see my new house.' Then, 'Let me talk to Anne.'

'Anne's out right now.'

Guy knew the investigations were over. The police had notified him and so had Gerard, with thanks.

Guy went back into the living-room where he and Bob Treacher were finishing their late breakfast. Bob had flown down to New York a day ahead of him, and Guy had invited him for the week-end. They were talking of Alberta and the men they worked with on the Committee, of the terrain, the trout fishing, and of whatever came into their heads. Guy laughed at a joke Bob told in French-Canadian dialect. It was a fresh, sunny November morning, and when Anne got back from her marketing, they were going to take the car to Long Island and go for a sail. Guy felt a boyish, holiday delight in having Bob with him. Bob symbolized Canada and the work there, the project in which Guy felt he had entered another vaster chamber of himself where Bruno could not follow. And the secret of the coming child gave him a sense of impartial benevolence, of magical advantage.

Just as Anne came in the door, the telephone rang again. Guy stood up, but Anne answered it. Vaguely, he thought, Bruno always knows exactly when to call. Then he listened, incredulously, to the conversation drifting towards the sail that afternoon.

'Come along then,' Anne said. 'Oh, I suppose some beer would be nice if you must bring something.'

Guy saw Bob staring at him quizzically.

'What's up?' Bob asked.

'Nothing.' Guy sat down again.

'That was Charles. You don't mind too much if he comes, do you, Guy?' Anne walked briskly across the room with her bag of groceries. 'He said Thursday he'd like to come sailing if we went, and I practically invited him.'

'I don't mind,' Guy said, still looking at her. She was in a gay, euphoric mood this morning, in which it would have been difficult to imagine her refusing anybody anything, but there was more than that, Guy knew, in her inviting Bruno. She wanted to see them together again. She couldn't wait, even today. Guy felt a rise of resentment, and said quickly to himself, she doesn't realize, she can't realize, and it's all your own fault anyway for the hopeless muddle you've made. So he put the resentment down, refused even to admit the odium Bruno would inspire that afternoon. He determined to keep himself under the same control all day.

'You could do worse than watch your nerves a bit, old man,' Bob told him. He lifted his coffee cup and drained it, contentedly. 'Well, at least you're not the coffee fiend you used to be. What was it, ten cups a day?'

'Something like that.' No, he had cut out coffee entirely, trying to sleep, and now he hated it.

They stopped for Helen Heyburn in Manhattan, then crossed the Triboro Bridge to Long Island. The winter sunlight had a frozen clarity at the shore, lay thin on the pale beach, and sparkled nervously on the choppy water. The *India* was like an iceberg at anchor, Guy thought, remembering when its whiteness had been the essence of summer. Automatically, as he rounded the corner of the parking lot, his eye fell on Bruno's long, bright blue convertible. The merry-go-round horse Bruno had ridden on, Guy remembered Bruno saying, had been royal blue, and that was why he had bought the car. He saw Bruno standing under the shed of the dockhouse, saw everything of him except his head, the long black overcoat and the small shoes, the arms with the hands in the pockets, the familiar anxiety of his waiting figure.

Bruno picked up the sack of beer and strolled towards the car with a shy smile, but even at a distance, Guy could see the pent elation, ready to explode. He wore a royal-blue muffler, the same colour as his car. 'Hello. Hello, Guy. Thought I'd try and see you while I could.' He glanced at Anne for help.

'Nice to see you!' Anne said. 'This is Mr Treacher. Mr Bruno.'

Bruno greeted him. 'You couldn't possibly make it to the party tonight, Guy? It's quite a big party. All of you?' His hopeful smile included Helen and Bob.

Helen said she was busy or she would love to. Glancing at her as he locked the car, Guy saw her leaning on Bruno's arm, changing into her moccasins. Bruno handed Anne the sack of beer with an air of departure.

Helen's blonde eyebrows fluted troubledly. 'You're coming with us, aren't you?'

'Not exactly dressed,' Bruno protested feebly.

'Oh, there's lots of slickers on board,' Anne said.

They had to take a rowboat from the dock. Guy and Bruno argued politely but stubbornly about who should row until Helen suggested they both row. Guy pulled in long strokes, and Bruno, beside him on the centre thwart, matched him carefully. Guy could feel Bruno's erratic excitement mounting as they drew near the *India*. Bruno's hat blew off twice, and at last he stood up and spun it spectacularly into the sea.

'I hate hats anyway!' he said with a glance at Guy.

Bruno refused to put on a slicker, though the spray dashed now and then over the cockpit. It was too gusty to raise sail. The *India* entered the Sound under engine power, with Bob steering.

'Here's to Guy!' Bruno shouted, but with the odd hitch of repression and inarticulateness Guy had noticed since he first spoke that morning. 'Congratulations, salutations!' He brought the beautiful, fruit-ornamented silver flask down suddenly and presented it to Anne. He was like some clumsy, powerful machine that could not catch its proper time beat to start. 'Napoleon brandy. Five-star.'

Anne declined, but Helen, who was already feeling the cold, drank some, and so did Bob. Under the tarpaulin, Guy held Anne's mittened hand and tried not to think about anything, not about Bruno, not about Alberta, not about the sea. He could not bear to look at Helen, who was encouraging Bruno, nor at Bob's polite, vaguely embarrassed smile as he faced front at the wheel.

'Anybody know "Foggy, Foggy Dew"?' Bruno asked, brushing spray fussily off a sleeve. His pull from the silver flask had pushed him over the line into drunkenness.

Bruno was nonplussed because no one wanted any more of his specially selected liquor, and because no one wanted to sing. It also crushed him that Helen said 'Foggy, Foggy Dew' was depressing. He loved 'Foggy, Foggy Dew'. He wanted to sing or shout or do *something*. When else would they all be together again like this? He and Guy. Anne. Helen. And Guy's friend. He twisted up in his corner seat and looked all around him, at the thin line of horizon that appeared and disappeared behind the swells of sea, at the diminishing land behind them. He tried to look at the pennant at the top of the mast, but the mast's swaying made him dizzy.

'Some day Guy and I are going to circle the world like an isinglass ball, and tie it up in a ribbon!' he announced, but no one paid any attention.

Helen was talking with Anne, making a gesture like a ball with her hands, and Guy was explaining something about the motor to Bob. Bruno noticed as Guy bent over that the creases in his forehead looked deeper, his eyes as sad as ever.

'Don't you realize anything!' Bruno shook Guy's arm. 'You have to be so serious *today*?'

Helen started to say something about Guy's always being serious, and Bruno roared her down, because she didn't know a damned thing about the way Guy was serious or why. Bruno returned Anne's smile gratefully, and produced the flask again.

But still Anne did not want any, and neither did Guy.

'I brought it specially for you, Guy. I thought you'd like it,' Bruno said, hurt.

'Have some, Guy,' Anne said.

Guy took it and drank a little.

'To Guy! Genius, friend, and partner!' Bruno said and drank after him. 'Guy *is* a genius. Do you all realize that?' He looked around at them, suddenly wanting to call them all a bunch of numbskulls.

'Certainly,' said Bob agreeably.

'As you're an old friend of Guy's,' Bruno raised his flask, 'I salute you also!'

'Thank you. A very old friend. One of the oldest.'

'How old?' Bruno challenged.

Bob glanced at Guy and smiled. 'Ten years or so.'

Bruno frowned. 'I've known Guy all his life,' he said softly, menacingly. 'Ask him.'

Guy felt Anne wriggle her hand from his tight hold. He saw Bob chuckling, not knowing what to make of it. Sweat made his forehead cold. Every shred of calm had left him, as it always did. Why did he always think he could endure Bruno, given one more chance?

'Go on and tell him I'm your closest friend, Guy.'

'Yes,' Guy said. He was conscious of Anne's small tense smile and of her silence. Didn't she know everything now? Wasn't she merely waiting for him and Bruno to put it into words in the next seconds? And suddenly it was like the moment in the coffee shop, the afternoon of the Friday night, when he felt he had already told Anne everything that he was going to do. He was going to tell her, he remembered. But the fact he hadn't quite yet told her, that Bruno was once more dancing around him, seemed the last good measure of excoriation for his delay.

'Sure I'm mad!' Bruno shouted to Helen, who was inching away from him on the seat. 'Mad enough to take on the whole world and whip it! Any man doesn't think I whipped it, I'll settle with him privately!' He laughed, and the laugh, he saw, only bewildered the blurred, stupid faces around him, tricked them into laughing with him. 'Monkeys!' he threw at them cheerfully.

'Who is he?' Bob whispered to Guy.

'Guy and I are superman!' Bruno said.

'You're a superman drinker,' Helen remarked.

'That's not true!' Bruno struggled on to one knee.

'Charles, calm *down*!' Anne told him, but she smiled, too, and Bruno only grinned back.

'I defy what she said about my drinking!'

'What's he talking about?' Helen demanded. 'Have you two made a killing on the stock market?'

'Stock market, cr—!' Bruno stopped, thinking of his father. 'Yee-hoo-oo! I'm a Texan! Ever ride the merry-go-round in Metcalf, Guy?'

Guy's feet jerked under him, but he did not get up and he did not look at Bruno.

'Awright, I'll sit down,' Bruno said to him. 'But you disappoint me. You disappoint me horribly!' Bruno shook his empty flask, then lobbed it overboard.

'He's crying,' Helen said.

Bruno stood up and stepped out of the cockpit on to the deck. He wanted to take a long walk away from all of them, even away from Guy.

'Where's he going?' Anne asked.

'Let him go,' Guy murmured, trying to light a cigarette.

Then there was a splash, and Guy knew Bruno had fallen overboard. Guy was out of the cockpit before any of them spoke.

Guy ran to the stern, trying to get his overcoat off. He felt his arms pinned behind him and, turning, hit Bob in the face with his fist and flung himself off the deck. Then the voices and the rolling stopped, and there was a moment of agonizing stillness before his body began to rise through the water. He shed the overcoat in slow motion, as if the water that was so cold it was merely a pain had frozen him already. He leapt high, and saw Bruno's head incredibly far away, like a mossy, half-submerged rock.

'You can't reach him!' Bob's voice blared, cut off by a burst of water against his ear.

'Guy!' Bruno called from the sea, a wail of dying.

Guy cursed. He could reach him. At the tenth stroke, he leapt up again. 'Bruno!' But he couldn't see him now.

'There, Guy!' Anne pointed from the stern of the *India*.

Guy couldn't see him, but he threshed towards the memory of his head, and went down at the place, groping with his arms wide, the farthest tips of his fingers searching. The water slowed him. As if he moved in a nightmare, he thought. As on the lawn. He came up under a wave and took a gasp of water. The *India* was in a different place, and turning. Why didn't they direct him? They didn't care, those others!

'Bruno!'

Perhaps behind one of the wallowing mountains. He threshed on, then realized he was directionless. A wave bashed the side of his head. He cursed the gigantic, ugly body of the sea. Where was his friend, his brother?

He went down again, deep as he could, spreading his ridiculous length as wide as he could. But now there seemed nothing but a silent grey vacuum filling all space, in which he was only a tiny point of consciousness. The swift, unbearable loneliness pressed him closer, threatening to swallow his own life. He stretched his eyes desperately. The greyness became a brown, ridged floor.

'Did you find him?' he blurted, raising himself up. 'What time is it?'

'Lie still, Guy,' Bob's voice said.

'He went down, Guy,' Anne said. 'We saw him.'

Guy closed his eyes and wept.

He was aware that, one by one, they all went out of the bunk-room and left him, even Anne.

46

Carefully, so as not to awaken Anne, Guy got out of bed and went downstairs to the living-room. He drew the drapes together and turned on the light, though he knew there was no shutting out the dawn that slithered now under the Venetian blinds, between the green drapes, like a silvery-mauve and amorphous fish. He had lain upstairs in the darkness awaiting it, knowing it would come for him finally over the foot of the bed, fearing more than ever the grip of the mechanism it set in motion, because he knew now that Bruno had borne half his guilt. If it had been almost unbearable before, how would he bear it now alone? He knew that he couldn't.

He envied Bruno for having died so suddenly, so quietly, so violently, and so young. And so easily, as Bruno had always done everything. A tremor passed through him. He sat rigidly in the armchair, his body under the thin pyjamas as hard and tense as in the first dawns. Then on the spasmic snap that always broke his tension, he got up and went upstairs to the studio before he actually knew what he intended to do. He looked at the big sleek-surfaced sheets of drawing paper on his work table, four or five lying as he had left them after sketching something for Bob. Then he sat down and began to write from the upper left-hand corner across, slowly at first, then more and more rapidly. He wrote of Miriam and of the train, the telephone calls, of Bruno in Metcalf, of the letters, the gun, and his dissolution, and of the Friday night. As if Bruno were still alive, he wrote every detail he knew that might contribute to an understanding of him. His writing blackened three of the big sheets. He folded the sheets, put them into an oversized envelope, and sealed it. For a long while he stared at the envelope, savouring its partial relief, wondering at its separateness now from himself. Many times before he had written passionate, scribbled admissions but, knowing no one would ever see them, they had never really left him. This was for Anne. Anne would touch this envelope. Her hands would hold the sheets of paper, and her eyes would read every word.

Guy put his palms up to his own hot, aching eyes. The hours of writing had tired him almost to a point of sleepiness. His thoughts drifted, resting on nothing, and the people he had been writing about – Bruno, Miriam, Owen Markman, Samuel Bruno, Arthur Gerard, Mrs McCausland, Anne – the people and the names danced around the edge of his mind. *Miriam.* Oddly, she was more a person to him now than ever before. He had tried to describe her to Anne, tried to evaluate her. It had forced him to evaluate her to himself. She was not worth a great deal as a person, he thought, by Anne's standards or by anyone's. But she had been a human being. Neither had Samuel Bruno been worth a great deal – a grim, greedy maker of money, hated by his son, unloved by his wife. Who had really loved him? Who had really been hurt by either Miriam's death or Samuel Bruno's? If there were someone who had been hurt – Miriam's family, perhaps? Guy remembered her brother on the witness stand at the inquest, the small eyes that had held nothing but malicious, brutal hatred, not grief. And her mother, vindictive, as vicious of spirit as ever, not caring where the blame fell as long as it fell on someone, unbroken, unsoftened by grief. Was there any purpose, even if he wanted to, in going to see them and giving them a target for their hatred? Would it make them feel any better? Or him? He couldn't see that it would. If anyone had really loved Miriam – Owen Markman.

Guy took his hands down from his eyes. The name had swum into his mind mechanically. He hadn't thought of Owen at all until he wrote the letter. Owen had been a dim figure in the background. Guy had held him of less value than Miriam. But Owen must have loved her. He had been going to marry her. She had been carrying his child. Suppose Owen had staked all his happiness on Miriam. Suppose he had known the grief in the months afterwards that Guy himself had known when Miriam died to him in Chicago. Guy tried to recall every detail of Owen Markman at the inquest. He remembered his hangdog manner, his calm, straightforward answers until his accusation of jealousy. Impossible to tell what really might have been going on in his head.

'Owen,' Guy said.

Slowly, he stood up. An idea was taking form in his mind even as he tried to weigh his memories of the long, dark face and tall, slouching figure that was Owen Markman. He would go and see Markman and talk with him, tell him everything. If he owed it to anyone, he owed it to Markman. Let Markman kill him if he would, call the police in, anything. But he would have told him, honestly, and face to face. Suddenly it was an urgent necessity. Of course. It was the only step and the next step. After that, after his personal debt, he would shoulder whatever the law put upon him. He would be ready then. He could catch a train today, after the questions they were supposed to answer about Bruno. The police had told him to be at the station with Anne this morning. He could even catch a plane this afternoon, if he was lucky. Where was it? Houston. If Owen was still there. He mustn't let Anne go with him to the airport. She must think he was going to Canada as he had planned. He didn't want Anne to know yet. The appointment with Owen was more urgent. It seemed to transform him. Or perhaps it was like the shedding of an old and worn-out coat. He felt naked now, but not afraid any longer.

47

Guy sat on a jumpseat in the aisle of a plane bound for Houston. He felt miserable and nervous, as out of place and wrong, somehow, as the little lump of the seat itself that clogged the aisle and spoilt the symmetry of the plane's interior. Wrong, unnecessary, and yet he was convinced that what he was doing was necessary. The difficulties he had hurdled in getting this far had put him in a mood of stubborn determination.

Gerard had been at the police station to hear the questioning on Bruno's death. He had flown over from Iowa, he said. It was too bad, Charles' end, but Charles had never been cautious about anything. It was too bad it had had to happen on Guy's boat. Guy had been able to answer the questions without any emotion whatever. It had seemed so insignificant, the details of the disappearance of his body. Guy had been more disturbed by Gerard's presence. He didn't want Gerard to follow him down to Texas. To be doubly safe, he had not even cancelled his ticket on the plane to Canada, which had left earlier in the afternoon. Then he had waited nearly four hours at the airport for this plane. But he was safe. Gerard had said he was going back to Iowa by train this afternoon.

Nevertheless, Guy took another look around him at the passengers, a slower and more careful look than he had dared take the first time. There was not one who seemed the least interested in him.

The thick letter in his inside pocket crackled as he bent over the papers in his lap. The papers were sectional reports of the Alberta work, which Bob had given him. Guy couldn't have read a magazine, he didn't want to look out the window, but he knew he could memorize, mechanically and efficiently, the items in the reports that had to be memorized. He found a page from an English architectural magazine torn out and stuck between the mimeographed sheets. Bob had circled a paragraph in red pencil:

Guy Daniel Haines is the most significant architect yet to emerge from the American South. With his first independent work at the age of twenty-seven, a simple, two-storey building which has become famous as 'The Pittsburgh Store', Haines set forth principles of grace and function to which he has steadfastly held, and through which his art has grown to its present stature. If we seek to define Haines' peculiar genius, we must depend chiefly upon that elusive and aery term, 'grace', which until Haines has never distinguished modern architecture. It is Haines' achievement to have made classic in our age his own concept of grace. His main building of the widely known Palmyra group in Palm Beach, Florida, has been called 'The American Parthenon' . . .

An asterisked paragraph at the bottom of the page said:

Since the writing of this article, Mr Haines has been appointed a member of the Advisory Committee of the Alberta Dam project in Canada. Bridges have always interested him, he says. He estimates that this work will occupy him happily for the next three years.

'Happily,' he said. How had they happened to use such a word?

A clock was striking nine as Guy's taxi crossed the main street of Houston. Guy had found Owen Markman's name in a telephone book at the airport, had checked his bags and got into a taxi. It won't be so simple, he thought. You can't just arrive at nine in the evening and find him at home, and alone, and willing to sit in a chair and listen to a stranger. He won't be home, or he won't be living there any more, or he won't even be in Houston any more. It might take days.

'Pull up at this hotel,' Guy said.

Guy got out and reserved a room. The trivial, provident gesture made him feel better.

Owen Markman was not living at the address in Cleburne Street. It was a small apartment building. The people in the hall downstairs, among them the superintendent, looked at him very suspiciously and gave him as little information as possible. No one knew where Owen Markman was.

'You're not the police, are you?' asked the superintendent finally.

Despite himself, he smiled. 'No.'

Guy was on his way out when a man stopped him on the steps and, with the same air of cautious reluctance, told him that he might be able to find Markman at a certain café in the centre of town.

Finally, Guy found him in a drugstore, sitting at the counter with two women whom he did not introduce. Owen Markman simply slid off his stool and stood up straight, his brown eyes a little wide. His long face looked heavier and less handsome than Guy remembered it. He slid his big hands warily into the slash pockets of his short leather jacket.

'You remember me,' Guy said.

'Reckon I do.'

'Would you mind if I had a talk with you? Just for a little while.' Guy looked around him. The best thing was to invite him to his hotel room, he supposed. 'I've got a room here at the Rice Hotel.'

Markman looked Guy slowly up and down once more, and after a long silence said, 'All right.'

Passing the cashier's desk, Guy saw the shelves of liquor bottles. It might be hospitable to offer Markman a drink. 'Do you like Scotch?'

Markman loosened up a bit as Guy bought it. 'Coke's fine, but it tastes better with a little something in it.'

Guy bought some bottles of Coca-Cola, too.

They rode to the hotel in silence, rode up in the elevator and entered the room in silence. How would he begin, Guy wondered. There were a dozen beginnings. Guy discarded them all.

Owen sat down in the armchair, and divided his time between eyeing Guy with insouciant suspicion, and savouring the long glass of Scotch and Coca-Cola.

Guy began stammeringly, 'What –'

'What?' asked Owen.

'What would you do if you knew who murdered Miriam?'

Markman's foot thudded down to the floor, and he sat up. His frowning brows made a black, intense line above his eyes. 'Did you?'

'No, but I know the man who did.'

'Who?'

What was he feeling as he sat there frowning, Guy wondered. Hatred? Resentment? Anger? 'I know, and so will the police very soon.' Guy hesitated. 'It was a man from New York whose name was Charles Bruno. He died yesterday. He was drowned.'

Owen sat back a little. He took a sip of his drink. 'How do you know? Confessed?'

'I know. I've known for some time. That's why I've felt it was my fault. For not betraying him.' He moistened his lips. It was difficult every syllable of the way. And why did he uncover himself so cautiously, inch by inch? Where were all his fantasies, the imagined pleasure and relief of blurting it all out? 'That's why I blame myself. I –' Owen's shrug stopped him. He watched Owen finish his glass, then automatically, Guy went and mixed another for him. 'That's why I blame myself,' he repeated. 'I have to tell you the circumstances. It was very complex. You see, I met Charles Bruno on a train, coming down to Metcalf. The train in June, just before she was killed. I was coming down to get my divorce.' He swallowed. There it was, the words he had never said to anyone before, said of his own will, and it felt so ordinary now, so ignominious even. He had a huskiness in his throat he could not get rid of. Guy studied Owen's long, dark attentive face. There was less of a frown now. Owen's leg was crossed again, and Guy remembered suddenly the grey buckskin work shoes Owen had worn at the inquest. These were plain brown shoes with elastic sidepieces. 'And –'

'Yeah,' Owen prompted.

'I told him Miriam's name. I told him I hated her. Bruno had an idea for a murder. A double murder.'

'Jesus!' Owen whispered.

The 'Jesus' reminded him of Bruno, and Guy had a horrible, an utterly horrible thought all at once, that he might ensnare Owen in the same trap that Bruno had used for him, that Owen in turn would capture another stranger who would capture another, and so on in infinite progression of the trapped and the hunted. Guy shuddered and clenched his hands. 'My mistake was in speaking to him. My mistake was in telling a stranger my private business.'

'He told you he was going to kill her?'

'No, of course not. It was an idea he had. He was insane. He was a psychopath. I told him to shut up and go to hell. I got rid of him!' He was back in the compartment. He was leaving it to go on to the platform. He heard the bang of the train's heavy door. Got rid of him, he had thought!

'You didn't tell him to do it.'

'No. He didn't say he was going to do it.'

'Why don't you have a straight shot? Why don't you sit down?' Owen's slow, rasping voice made the room steady again. His voice was like an ugly rock, solidly lodged in dry ground.

He didn't want to sit down, and he didn't want to drink. He had drunk Scotch like this in Bruno's compartment. This was the end and he didn't want it to be like the beginning. He touched the glass of Scotch and water that he had fixed for himself only for politeness' sake. When he turned around, Owen was pouring more liquor into his glass, continued to pour it, as if to show Guy that he hadn't been trying to do it behind his back.

'Well,' Owen drawled, 'if the fellow was a nut like you say – That was the court's opinion finally, too, wasn't it, that it must have been a madman?'

'Yes.'

'I mean, sure I can understand how you felt afterwards, but if it was just a conversation like you say, I don't see where you should blame yourself so awful much.'

Guy was staring at him incredulously. Didn't it matter to Owen more than this? Maybe he didn't entirely understand. 'But you see –'

'When did you find out about it?' Owen's brown eyes looked slurry.

'About three months after it happened. But you see, if not for me, Miriam would be alive now.' Guy watched Owen lower his lips to the glass again. He could taste the sickening mess of Coca-Cola and Scotch sliding into Owen's wide mouth. What was Owen going to do? Leap up suddenly and fling the glass down, throttle him as Bruno had throttled Miriam? He couldn't imagine that Owen would continue to sit there, but the seconds went by and Owen did not move. 'You see, I had to tell you,' Guy persisted. 'I considered you the one person I might have hurt, the one person who suffered. Her child had been yours. You were going to marry her. You loved her. It was you –'

'Hell, I didn't love her.' Owen looked at Guy with no change whatever in his face.

Guy stared back at him. Didn't love her, didn't love her, Guy thought. His mind staggered back, trying to realign all the past equations that no longer balanced. 'Didn't love her? he said.

'No. Well, not the way you seem to think. I certainly didn't want her to die – and understand, I'd have done anything to prevent it, but I was glad enough not to have to marry her. Getting married was her idea. That's why she had the child. That's not a man's fault, I wouldn't say. Would you?' Owen was looking at him with a tipsy earnestness, waiting, his wide mouth the same firm, irregular line it had been on the witness stand, waiting for Guy to say something, to pass judgement on his conduct with Miriam.

Guy turned away with a vaguely impatient gesture. He couldn't make the equations balance. He couldn't make any sense to it, except an ironic sense. There was no reason for his being here now, except for an ironic reason. There was no reason for his sweating, painful self-torture in a hotel room for the benefit of a stranger who didn't care, except for an ironic reason.

'Do you think so?' Owen kept on, reaching for the bottle on the table beside him.

Guy couldn't have made himself say a word. A hot, inarticulate anger was rising inside him. He slid his tie down and opened his shirt collar, and glanced at the open windows for an air-conditioning apparatus.

Owen shrugged. He looked quite comfortable in his open-collared shirt and unzipped leather jacket. Guy had an absolutely unreasonable desire to ram something down Owen's throat, to beat him and crush him, above all to blast him out of his complacent comfort in the chair.

'Listen,' Guy began quietly, 'I am a –'

But Owen had begun to speak at the same instant, and he went on, droningly, not looking at Guy who stood in the middle of the floor with his mouth still open. '. . . the second time. Got married two months after my divorce, and there was trouble right away. Whether Miriam would of been any different, I don't know, but I'd say she'd of been worse. Louisa up and left two months ago after damn near setting the house on fire, a big apartment house.' He droned on, and poured more Scotch into his glass from the bottle at his elbow, and Guy felt a disrespect, a definite affront, directed against himself, in the way Owen helped himself. Guy remembered his own behaviour at the inquest, undistinguished behaviour, to say the least, for the husband of the victim. Why should Owen have respect for him? 'The awful thing is, the man gets the worst of it, because the women do more talking. Take Louisa, she can go back to that apartment house and they'll give her a welcome, but let me so much –'

'Listen!' Guy said, unable to stand it any longer. 'I – I killed someone, too! I'm a murderer, too!'

Owen's feet came down to the floor again, he sat up again, he even looked from Guy to the window and back again, as if he contemplated having to escape or having to defend himself, but the befuddled surprise and alarm on his face was so feeble, so half-hearted, that it seemed a mockery itself, seemed to mock Guy's seriousness. Owen started to set his glass on the table and then didn't. 'How's that?' he asked.

'Listen!' Guy shouted again. 'Listen, I'm a dead man. I'm as good as dead right now, because I'm going to give myself up. Immediately! Because I killed a man, do you understand? Don't look so unconcerned, and don't lean back in that chair again!'

'Why shouldn't I lean back in this chair?' Owen had both hands on his glass now, which he had just refilled with Coca-Cola and Scotch.

'Doesn't it mean anything to you that I am a murderer, and took a man's life, something no human being has a right to do?'

Owen might have nodded, or he might not have. At any rate, he drank again, slowly.

Guy stared at him. The words, unutterable tangles of thousands and thousands of words, seemed to congest even his blood, to cause waves of heat to sweep up his arms from his clenched hands. The words were curses against Owen, sentences and paragraphs of the confession he had written that morning, that were growing jumbled now because the drunken idiot in the armchair didn't want to hear them. The drunken idiot was determined to look indifferent. He didn't look like a murderer, he supposed, in his clean white shirt-sleeves and his silk tie and his dark blue trousers, and maybe even his strained face didn't look like a murderer's to anybody else. 'That's the mistake,' Guy said aloud, 'that nobody knows what a murderer looks like. A murderer looks like anybody!' He laid the back of his fist against his forehead and took it down again, because he had known the last words were coming, and had been unable to stop them. It was exactly like Bruno.

Abruptly Guy went and got himself a drink, a straight three-finger shot, and drank it off.

'Glad to see I've got a drinking companion,' Owen mumbled. Guy sat down on the neat, green-covered bed opposite Owen. Quite suddenly, he had felt tired. 'It doesn't mean anything,' he began again, 'it doesn't mean anything to you, does it?'

'You're not the first man I seen that killed another man. Or woman.' He chuckled. 'Seems to me there's more women that go free.'

'I'm not going free. I'm not free. I did this in cold blood. I had no reason. Don't you see that might be worse? I did it for –' He wanted to say he did it because there had been that measure of perversity within him sufficient to do it, that he had done it because of the worm in the wood, but he knew it would make no sense to Owen, because Owen was a practical man. Owen was so practical, he would not bother to hit him, or flee from him, or call the police, because it was more comfortable to sit in the chair.

Owen waggled his head as if he really did consider Guy's

point. His lids were half dropped over his eyes. He twisted and reached for something in his hip pocket, a bag of tobacco. He got cigarette papers from the breast pocket of his shirt.

Guy watched his operations for what seemed like hours. 'Here,' Guy said, offering him his own cigarettes.

Owen looked at them dubiously. 'What kind are they?'

'Canadian. They're quite good. Try one.'

'Thanks, I —' Owen drew the bag closed with his teeth — 'prefer my own brand.' He spent at least three minutes rolling the cigarette.

'This was just as if I pulled a gun on someone in a public park and shot him,' Guy went on, determined to go on, though it was as if he talked to an inanimate thing like a dictaphone in the chair, with the difference that his words didn't seem to be penetrating in any way. Mightn't it dawn on Owen that he could pull a gun on him now in his hotel room? Guy said, 'I was driven to it. That's what I'll tell the police, but that won't make any difference, because the point is, I did it. You see, I have to tell you Bruno's idea.' At least Owen was looking at him now, but his face, far from being rapt, seemed actually to wear an expression of pleasant, polite drunken attention. Guy refused to let it stop him. 'Bruno's idea was that we should kill for each other, that he should kill Miriam and I should kill his father. Then he came to Texas and killed Miriam, behind my back. Without my knowledge or consent, do you see?' His choice of words was abominable, but at least Owen was listening. At least the words were coming out. 'I didn't know about it, and I didn't even suspect — not really. Until months later. And then he began to haunt me. He began to tell me he would pin the blame for Miriam's death on me, unless I went through with the rest of his damned plan, do you see? Which was to kill his father. The whole idea rested on the fact that there was no reason for the murders. No personal motives. So we couldn't be traced, individually. Provided we didn't see each other. But that's another point. The point is, I did kill him. I was broken down. Bruno broke me down with letters and blackmail and sleeplessness. He drove me insane, too. And listen, I believe any man can be broken down. I could break you down. Given the same circumstances, I could break you down and make you kill someone. It might take different methods from the ones Bruno used on me, but it could be done. What else do you think keeps the totalitarian states going? Or do you ever stop to wonder about things like that, Owen? Anyway, that's what I'll tell the police, but it won't matter, because they'll say I shouldn't have broken down. It won't matter, because they'll say I was weak. But I don't care now, do you see? I can face anyone now, do you see?' He bent to look into Owen's face, but Owen seemed scarcely to see him. Owen's head was sagged sideways, resting in his hand. Guy stood up straight. He couldn't make Owen see, he could feel that Owen wasn't understanding the main point at all, but that didn't matter either. 'I'll accept it, whatever they want to do to me. I'll say the same thing to the police tomorrow.'

'Can you prove it?' Owen asked.

'Prove what? What is there to prove about my killing a man?'

The bottle slipped out of Owen's fingers and fell on to the floor, but there was so little in it now that almost nothing spilled. 'You're an architect, aren't you?' Owen asked. 'I remember now.' He righted the bottle clumsily, leaving it on the floor.

'What does it matter?'

'I was wondering.'

'Wondering what?' Guy asked impatiently.

'Because you sound a little touched – if you want my honest opinion. Ain't saying you do.' And behind Owen's fogged expression now was a simple wariness lest Guy might walk over and hit him for his remark. When he saw that Guy didn't move, he sat back in his chair again, and slumped lower than before.

Guy groped for a concrete idea to present to Owen. He didn't want his audience to slip away, indifferent as it was. 'Listen, how do you feel about the men you know who've killed somebody? How do you treat them? How do you act with them? Do you pass the time of day with them the same as you'd do with anybody else?'

Under Guy's intense scrutiny, Owen did seem to try to think. Finally he said with a smile, blinking his eyes relaxedly, 'Live and let live.'

Anger seized him again. For an instant, it was like a hot vice, holding his body and brain. There were no words for what he felt. Or there were too many words to begin. The word formed itself and spat itself from between his teeth: '*Idiot!*'

Owen stirred slightly in his chair, but his unruffledness prevailed. He seemed undecided whether to smile or to frown. 'What business is it of mine?' he asked firmly.

'What business? Because you – you are a part of society!'

'Well, then it's society's business,' Owen replied with a lazy wave of his hand. He was looking at the Scotch bottle, in which only half an inch remained.

What business, Guy thought. Was that his real attitude, or was he drunk? It must be Owen's attitude. There was no reason for him to lie now. Then he remembered it had been his own attitude when he had suspected Bruno, before Bruno had begun to dog him. Was that most people's attitude? If so, who was society?

Guy turned his back on Owen. He knew well enough who society was. But the society he had been thinking about in regard to himself, he realized, was the law, was inexorable rules. Society was people like Owen, people like himself, people like – Brillhart, for instance, in Palm Beach. Would Brillhart have reported him? No. He couldn't imagine Brillhart reporting him. Everyone would leave it for someone else, who would leave it for someone else, and no one would do it. Did he care about rules? Wasn't it a rule that had kept him tied to Miriam? Wasn't it a person who was murdered, and therefore people who mattered? If people from Owen to Brillhart didn't care sufficiently to betray him, should he care any further? Why did he think this morning that he had wanted to give himself up to the police? What masochism was it? He wouldn't give himself up. What, concretely, did he have on his conscience now? What human being would inform on him?

'Except a stool-pigeon,' Guy said. 'I suppose a stool-pigeon would inform.'

'That's right,' Owen agreed. 'A dirty, stinking stool-pigeon.' He gave a loud, relieving laugh.

Guy was staring into space, frowning. He was trying to find solid ground that would carry him to something he had just seen as if by a flash, far ahead of him. The law was not society, it began. Society was people like himself and Owen and Brillhart, who hadn't the right to take the life of another member of society. And yet the law did. 'And yet the law is supposed to be the will of society at least. It isn't even that. Or maybe it is collectively,' he added, aware that as always he was doubling back before he came to a point, making things as complex as possible in trying to make them certain.

'Hmm-m?' Owen murmured. His head was back against the chair, his black hair tousled over his forehead, and his eyes almost closed.

'No, people collectively might lynch a murderer, but that's exactly what the law is supposed to guard against.'

'Never hold with lynchings,' Owen said. ' 'S not true! Gives the whole South a bad name – unnec'sarily.'

'My point is, that if society hasn't the right to take another person's life, then the law hasn't either. I mean, considering that the law is a mass of regulations that have been handed down and that nobody can interfere with, no human being can touch. But it's human beings the law deals with, after all. I'm talking about people like you and me. My case in particular. At the moment, I'm only talking about my case. But that's only logic. Do you know something, Owen? Logic doesn't always work out, so far as people go. It's all very well when you're building a building, because the material behaves then, but –' His argument went up in smoke. There was a wall that prevented him from saying another word, simply because he couldn't think any further. He had spoken loudly and distinctly, but he knew Owen hadn't been hearing, even if he was trying to listen. And yet Owen *had* been indifferent, five minutes ago, to the question of his guilt. 'What about a jury, I wonder,' Guy said.

'What jury?'

'Whether a jury is twelve human beings or a body of laws. It's an interesting point. I suppose it's always an interesting point.' He poured the rest of the bottle into his glass and drank it. 'But I don't suppose it's interesting to you, is it, Owen? What is interesting to you?'

Owen was silent and motionless.

'Nothing is interesting to you, is it?' Guy looked at Owen's big scuffed brown shoes extended limply on the carpet, the toes tipped inward towards each other, because they rested on their heels. Suddenly, their flaccid, shameless, massive stupidity seemed the essence of all human stupidity. It translated itself instantly into his old antagonism against the passive stupidity of those who stood in the way of the progress of his work, and before he knew how or why, he had kicked, viciously, the side of Owen's shoe. And still, Owen did not move. His work, Guy thought. Yes, there was his work to get back to. Think later, think it all out right later, but he had work to do.

He looked at his watch. Ten past twelve. He didn't want to sleep here. He wondered if there was a plane tonight. There must be something out. Or a train.

He shook Owen. 'Owen, wake up. Owen!'

Owen mumbled a question.

'I think you'll sleep better at home.'

Owen sat up and said clearly, 'That I doubt.'

Guy picked up his topcoat from the bed. He looked around, but he hadn't left anything because he hadn't brought anything. It might be better to telephone the airport now, he thought.

'Where's the john?' Owen stood up. 'I don't feel so good.'

Guy couldn't find the telephone. There was a wire by the bed table, though. He traced the wire under the bed. The telephone was off the hook, on the floor, and he knew immediately it hadn't fallen, because both parts were dragged up near the foot of the bed, the hand piece eerily focused on the armchair where Owen had been sitting. Guy pulled the telephone slowly towards him.

'Hey, ain't there a john anywheres?' Owen was opening a closet door.

'It must be down the hall.' His voice was like a shudder. He was holding the telephone in a position for speaking, and now he brought it closer to his ear. He heard the intelligent silence of a live wire. 'Hello?' he said.

'Hello, Mr Haines.' The voice was rich, courteous, and just the least brusque.

Guy's hand tried unavailingly to crush the telephone, and then he surrendered without a word. It was like a fortress falling, like a great building falling apart in his mind, but it crumbled like powder and fell silently.

'There wasn't time for a dictaphone. But I heard most of it from just outside your door. May I come in?'

Gerard must have had his scouts at the airport in New York, Guy thought, must have followed in a chartered plane. It was possible. And here it was. And he had been stupid enough to sign the register in his own name. 'Come in,' Guy echoed. He put the telephone on the hook and stood up, rigidly, watching the door. His heart was pounding as it never had before, so fast and hard, he thought surely it must be a prelude to his dropping dead. Run, he thought. Leap, attack as soon as he comes in. This is your very last chance. But he didn't move. He was vaguely aware of Owen being sick in the basin in the corner behind him. Then there was a rap at the door, and he went towards it, thinking, wouldn't it have to be like this after all, by surprise, with someone, a stranger who didn't understand anything, throwing up in a basin in a corner of the room, without his thoughts ordered, and worse, having already uttered half of them in a muddle. Guy opened the door.

'Hello,' Gerard said, and he came in with his hat on and his arms hanging, just as he had always looked.

'Who is it?' Owen asked.

'Friend of Mr Haines,' Gerard said easily, and glancing at Guy with his round face as serious as before, he gave him a wink. 'I suppose you want to go to New York tonight, don't you?'

Guy was staring at Gerard's familiar face, at the big mole on his cheek, at the bright, living eye that had winked at him, undoubtedly had winked at him. Gerard was the law, too. Gerard was on his side, so far as any man could be, because Gerard knew Bruno. Guy knew it now, as if he had known it the whole time, yet it had never even occurred to him before. He knew, too, that he had to face Gerard. That was part of it all, and always had been. It was inevitable and ordained, like the turning of the earth, and there was no sophistry by which he could free himself from it.

'Eh?' Gerard said.

Guy tried to speak, and said something entirely different from what he had intended. 'Take me.'

The Art of Enterprise Information Architecture
A Systems-Based Approach for Unlocking Business Insight

By Mario Godinez, Eberhard Hechler, Klaus Koenig, Steve Lockwood, Martin Oberhofer, and Michael Schroeck

ISBN: 0-13-703571-3

Architecture for the Intelligent Enterprise: Powerful New Ways to Maximize the Real-time Value of Information

In this book, a team of IBM's leading information management experts guide you on a journey that will take you from where you are today toward becoming an "Intelligent Enterprise."

Drawing on their extensive experience working with enterprise clients, the authors present a new, information-centric approach to architecture and powerful new models that will benefit any organization. Using these strategies and models, companies can systematically unlock the business value of information by delivering actionable, real-time information in context to enable better decision-making throughout the enterprise—from the "shop floor" to the "top floor."

Enterprise Master Data Management
An SOA Approach to Managing Core Information

By Allen Dreibelbis, Eberhard Hechler, Ivan Milman, Martin Oberhofer, Paul Van Run, and Dan Wolfson

ISBN: 0-13-236625-8

The Only Complete Technical Primer for MDM Planners, Architects, and Implementers

Enterprise Master Data Management provides an authoritative, vendor-independent MDM technical reference for practitioners: architects, technical analysts, consultants, solution designers, and senior IT decision makers. Written by the IBM® data management innovators who are pioneering MDM, this book systematically introduces MDM's key concepts and technical themes, explains its business case, and illuminates how it interrelates with and enables SOA.

Drawing on their experience with cutting-edge projects, the authors introduce MDM patterns, blueprints, solutions, and best practices published nowhere else—everything you need to establish a consistent, manageable set of master data, and use it for competitive advantage.

 Listen to the author's podcast at:
Podcasts ibmpressbooks.com/podcasts

Related Books of Interest

DB2 pureXML Cookbook
Master the Power of the IBM Hybrid Data Server

By Matthias Nicola and Pav Kumar-Chatterjee
ISBN: 0-13-815047-8

Hands-On Solutions and Best Practices for Developing and Managing XML Database Applications with DB2

Two leading experts from IBM offer the practical solutions and proven code samples that database professionals need to build better XML solutions faster. Organized by task, this book is packed with more than 700 easy-to-adapt "recipe-style" examples covering the entire application lifecycle—from planning and design through coding, optimization, and troubleshooting. This extraordinary library of recipes includes more than 250 XQuery and SQL/XML queries. With the authors' hands-on guidance, you'll learn how to combine pureXML "ingredients" to efficiently perform virtually any XML data management task, from the simplest to the most advanced.

Viral Data in SOA
An Enterprise Pandemic

By Neal A. Fishman
ISBN: 0-13-700180-0

"This book is a must read for any organization using data-integration or data-interchange technologies, or simply any organization that must trust data. Neal takes the reader through an entertaining and vital journey of SOA information management issues, risks, discovery, and solutions. He provides a fresh perspective that no corporation should overlook; in fact, corporations might head blindly into SOA implementations without this awareness."

–Kevin Downey, Senior Partner, Xteoma Inc., Canada

Leading IBM information forensics expert Neal Fishman helps you identify the unique challenges of data quality in your SOA environment—and implement solutions that deliver the best results for the long term at the lowest cost.

Podcasts

Listen to the author's podcast at:
ibmpressbooks.com/podcasts

IBM Press™

Visit ibmpressbooks.com
for all product information

Related Books of Interest

Mining the Talk
Unlocking the Business Value in Unstructured Information

By Scott Spangler and Jeffrey Kreulen
ISBN: 0-13-233953-6

Leverage Unstructured Data to Become More Competitive, Responsive, and Innovative

In *Mining the Talk*, two leading-edge IBM researchers introduce a revolutionary new approach to unlocking the business value hidden in virtually any form of unstructured data–from word processing documents to websites, emails to instant messages.

The authors review the business drivers that have made unstructured data so important–and explain why conventional methods for working with it are inadequate. Then, writing for business professionals–not just data mining specialists–they walk step-by-step through exploring your unstructured data, understanding it, and analyzing it effectively.

Understanding DB2 9 Security
Bond, See, Wong, Chan
ISBN: 0-13-134590-7

DB2 9 for Linux, UNIX, and Windows
DBA Guide, Reference, and Exam Prep, 6th Edition
Baklarz, Zikopoulos
ISBN: 0-13-185514-X

Lotus Notes Developer's Toolbox
Elliott
ISBN: 0-13-221448-2

IBM Lotus Connections 2.5
Planning and Implementing Social Software for Your Enterprise
Hardison, Byrd, Wood, Speed, Martin, Livingston, Moore, Kristiansen
ISBN: 0-13-700053-7

Mainframe Basics for Security Professionals
Getting Started with RACF
Pomerantz, Vander Weele, Nelson, Hahn
ISBN: 0-13-173856-9

The New Era of
Enterprise Business
Intelligence

The New Era of Enterprise Business Intelligence

Using Analytics to Achieve a Global Competitive Advantage

Mike Biere

IBM Press
Pearson plc

Upper Saddle River, NJ • Boston • Indianapolis • San Francisco
New York • Toronto • Montreal • London • Munich • Paris • Madrid
Cape Town • Sydney • Tokyo • Singapore • Mexico City

ibmpressbooks.com

IBM Press Program Managers: Steven M. Stansel, Ellice Uffer
Cover design: IBM Corporation
Associate Publisher: Greg Wiegand
Marketing Manager: Stephane Nakib
Acquisitions Editor: Katherine Bull
Publicist: Heather Fox
Development Editor: Susan Zahn
Managing Editor: Kristy Hart
Designer: Alan Clements
Project Editor: Andy Beaster
Copy Editor: Water Crest Publishing, Inc.
Indexer: Lisa Stumpf
Compositors: Nonie Ratcliff
Proofreader: Williams Woods Publishing Services
Manufacturing Buyer: Dan Uhrig

Published by Pearson plc
Publishing as IBM Press

Library of Congress Cataloging-in-Publication Data

Biere, Mike.
The new era of enterprise business intelligence : using analytics to achieve a global
competitive advantage / Mike Biere.
    p. cm.
ISBN-13: 978-0-13-707542-3 (pbk. : alk. paper)
ISBN-10: 0-13-707542-1 (pbk. : alk. paper) 1. Business intelligence. I. Title.
HD38.7.B534 2011
658.4'72--dc22

                              2010022974

Pearson Education, Inc
Rights and Contracts Department
501 Boylston Street, Suite 900
Boston, MA 02116
Fax (617) 671-3447

ISBN-13: 978-0-13-707542-3
ISBN-10: 0-13-707542-1

Text printed in the United States on recycled paper at Courier Stoughton in Stoughton,
Massachusetts.
First printing August 2010.

I wish to dedicate this work to my long-suffering wife, Shirley, as well as others in my family who endured my long absences and seemingly endless travels through the years. I also wish to mention my daughter, Tia, who has been my pride and joy, as well as giving me Julian, Noah, and Elijah to brighten my life every day and make the world a far better place.

Contents

Acknowledgments

I wish to thank the individuals who've helped on this work from the start and have been so supportive of this effort. There are three in particular I wish to call out: my technical editor, Monica Logan; my development editor, Susan Zahn; and acquisitions editor, Katherine Bull. There are so many individuals within IBM® and Cognos, and customers I have worked alongside, who have provided the materials and experience as the basis of this work. Bob Fox, I wish you well wherever you are! Finally, I want to thank Jim Reed and his team from IBM's Silicon Valley Lab for being the best group of individuals I have had the pleasure and privilege to work with.

About the Author

Mike Biere has 32 years of experience in the IT industry. He began working for IBM in 1978 as a large systems System Engineer but found his calling for Business Intelligence in 1981 when the Information Center initiative began. He has worked in the database and end user computing areas since then.

He has served in a variety of roles within IBM, from BI Technical Sales Specialist to world-wide Marketing Manager of Data Warehousing and Business Intelligence solutions. Mike served as Executive Vice President of Ferguson Information Systems in the mid-90s and was responsible for building a BI practice. He worked for Cognos from 2003–2007 as Director of Product Management, responsible for Cognos' initiatives with IBM.

Mike returned to IBM in 2007 and holds a position of Sr. Marketing Manager for Data Warehousing and Business Intelligence on System z as a world-wide support resource.

He has written a book on BI entitled *Business Intelligence for the Enterprise* (IBM Press (2003); ISBN: 978-0-13-141303-0), as well as being co-author of another IBM book entitled *New Intelligence for a Smarter Planet* (MC Press (2009); ISBN: 978-1-58347-086-2). Mike also has written numerous journal articles and white papers.

Mike is married with a grown son and daughter and resides in Cincinnati, Ohio. He is the proud grandfather of Julian, Noah, Elijah, Chris, Nick, and Leilani. His real passion beyond BI is playing guitar in a retro rock band called Those Guys.

I

Introduction to Business Intelligence Today

Business intelligence is defined as "mission critical" by many senior executives today. The emphasis and interest in BI, as we will often refer to it, has placed it in the forefront of the list of major corporate objectives. This adjective is quite valid because the value of unlocking critical information held in corporate and external data sources can be a significant game changer. At the enterprise level, BI is often just a stated goal with little actual practice other than perhaps setting a standard for a suite of tools. Having an enterprise goal and set of standards does not end with creating an approved vendor list—it is just the beginning. BI at the enterprise level suggests that there is a common vision and set of goals in the deployment and use of BI on a broad scale within the entire organization.

In my opinion, business intelligence is the application of end-user query, reporting, dashboards, and other non-programming technologies to provide information that is not available to the business using traditional programming methods and services. BI requires a clear direction at the enterprise level with the realistic expectation of the skills required to deliver BI output that is mission critical. It also requires a support infrastructure to ensure accuray of results produced and that the proper skills are in place.

Let's think about how you would proceed with a corporate-wide ERP or CRM system and the resources, dedication, and critical scrutiny you would apply in selecting, implementing, and supporting one of these major application solutions. Would you have the system installed, show a few people how to use it, tell everyone it's now the corporate standard, and then trust its acceptance to mere synergy? I certainly hope not! Yet, this is often the case when a BI solution has been chosen.

In this book, I have taken the approach of opening a frank, personal dialogue with you. It is an open discussion about enabling BI at the enterprise level. It rarely mentions any product, but rather addresses the requirements and thought processes necessary to succeed at the macro level of BI. It is intended to assist in forming, articulating, and defending a global BI strategy and vision. For the most part, the days of acquiring a set of independent BI tools and turning them loose in the enterprise are over. However, the majority of clients I talk to have an already-established set of BI tools in-house. They may have from three to a dozen different BI tools with overlapping functions. One of the first steps in establishing enterprise BI sanity is a bit of winnowing out of the less productive or dated ones. I will have much more to say about this later.

One of the first rules of thumb today regarding BI enablement is to totally avoid the "Fire! Ready! Aim!" approach. Uncoordinated, anarchistic BI has never been effective, and it can be costly. Your end users can easily populate a spreadsheet in a myriad of ways and run amok without much assistance. When you do not have a plan for BI, this is the most common form of analysis within any enterprise. End users will always find their own way if they are not led in a positive, orderly manner.

If you believe that a BI solution can change your corporate world, there must be an internal paradigm you adhere to. Typically, BI is thought to have the following characteristics, at a minimum:

- An effective set of tools for accessing data and delivering business information
- A means to gain insight into areas of the business not accessible with existing systems
- Advanced analytics that, if applied, can actually "discover" new information

- The capability to make people more productive and less reliant upon IT
- The capability to provide a different interpretation of critical information than we have today

The corporate BI quagmire becomes deep when a mismatch between desire and commitment becomes apparent. I often get engaged in BI conversations where a client will talk about his avid interest in BI and how he feels it can make a significant difference in his success. Then, as I probe a bit about the overall plan, it becomes apparent far too often that much of the "plan" is based upon assumptions about what BI solutions really do, along with the ease of use factors the client believes will be in play but that have not been proven.

In this chapter, we discuss overall BI scenarios today, the view of the CIO, the IT perspective, the end user perspective, and establishing a vision. Lewis Carroll wrote in *Alice in Wonderland*, "If you don't know where you are going, any road will take you there." I would also add: "How do you know when you've arrived?"

Setting Expectations

"I am not sure what BI really is these days, but our execs tell me we need it." This was quoted in a seminar on business intelligence by an experienced IT individual who had been forced to attend the event in mid-2009. You may be tempted to snicker at this naïveté in this day and age but, as the old saying goes, sometimes ignorance is bliss. When probed a little further regarding his inquiry, what he was really asking was: "Why is BI suddenly such a hot topic with our senior management team? We are already using several end-user tools and yet they want more!"

Having worked in this arena since 1981, I can think of countless customer engagements where this question arose in some manner or another. My answer in 2003 (Mike Biere, *Business Intelligence for the Enterprise*, Upper Saddle River, NJ: Prentice Hall PTR) was, "Business intelligence is a *word problem!*" What I meant was that BI transcends simple query and reporting. It eclipses dashboards and charts and portals. It is often applied to solve complex business problems and provide an answer heretofore unknown. It often requires complex logic to be applied. I also constantly ranted about the lack of BI skills that fell short of the desire to deliver BI analyses. There is a certain level of skill required for the various degrees of BI complexity being addressed that many end users ignore until they get in over their heads. There is a continuing gap between user groups where "power users" still produce the bulk of the output for consumers, regardless of how much easier to use many BI tools are touted to be.

BI skills are not easily mastered; nor are they acquired by those who do not have the proper technical skills to work with a tool that may require extensive manipulation of data. This text is not a rehash of the first edition but a guide on BI today. The world of BI today is dramatically different than a few years ago and must be examined in a new light.

The emerging tidal wave of BI interest was beginning to dramatically build in 2003 and, at that time, the emphasis was on making people aware that BI efforts needed to be properly supported, that skills had to be assessed realistically, and that we must not assume that just anyone in the enterprise would be able to use a tool effectively. The ongoing myth of ease-of-use and universal applicability of a BI tool being a trivial exercise had to be addressed. The transition toward self-service, on-demand BI was beginning to take place, and it deeply affected the marketplace and how many viewed BI in a new light.

BI should be considered a "potentially" powerful weapon in the hands of all employees within an enterprise. In today's world, it is best to think of BI as an integrated solution suite, where its power and functionality may be utilized by anyone who touches data within a particular context. It is all about equipping individuals with the proper functions based upon their needs and skills. It is far less about equipping everyone to be a BI hands-on tools "mechanic." The push today is to drive BI deployments as broadly and deeply into the organization as possible. It is also about providing BI functions that add tremendous value without the end user having any skills in the tools being used. This is referred to as "embedded BI." The age of the BI consumer is here.

The business intelligence market is heating up but with an entirely new suite of players, such as options available on the open source market. Well-established vendors are piling on to this enormous market by acquiring others to fill in portfolio gaps, and thus we see a series of mergers absorbing some of the longer-standing independents. This is wonderful news to a BI vendor but, for anyone involved in the acquisition process, it can be a nightmare. There are decision points and options not available in the past, but the options have also become far more complex in many ways.

The Face of Business Intelligence Now

Business Intelligence today is vastly different than in years past in so many ways, as follows:

- Mergers and acquisitions have dramatically altered the marketplace.
- Economic influences have driven initiatives such as server consolidations and BI tool consolidations.
- BI solutions have emerged as integrated platforms, not loose collections of tools.
- Service providers have offered alternatives (Software as a Service—SaaS) to in-house infrastructure and support.
- Initiatives such as cloud computing have changed the deployment strategies for many.
- Appliances have emerged with "black box" BI solutions.
- Real-time or near real-time BI projects have appeared.
- Increased emphasis has been placed upon the merger of BI and collaboration.
- ...and many more.

At the enterprise level, we see a keen interest in providing a corporate infrastructure for BI solutions that is extensible, cost-effective, secure, highly available, and scalable. BI for the Enterprise is all about having vision and goals to attain that vision. Recent surveys have shown BI to be the top priority of most CIOs—CIO surveys for the past four years have placed BI at the top of the list. I suggest that you use your favorite search engine to query CIO surveys rather than have me cite specific ones. With these surveys suffice it to say, there have been many, and the responses have consistently placed BI and analytics at the top of the list (see Figure 1-1).

Why do we find BI to be such a critical initiative after all these years of applying end user-oriented technology to solve business problems? Don't most enterprises have it under control today? The answer is, no.

BI is on the agendas of the majority of CIOs because they have become extremely aware of its importance in providing a competitive differentiator at all levels of the business. They read about some competitor who is using a BI infrastructure to cut costs, improve customer

A Typical CIO Survey

Topics you may see listed on a CIO survey today might encompass the following when asked "What do you believe will add the greatest impact upon your business today?"

Risk management and compliance
Customer and partner collaboration
SaaS (Software as a Service)
Cloud Computing
Mobility solutions
Self-service portals
Application harmonization
Business process management
Virtualization
Business Intelligence and analytics
Service-oriented architecture/Web services
Unified communications

Business Intelligence and Analytics has emerged as #1 every time!

Figure 1-1 A typical CIO survey

satisfaction, shorten sales cycles, and more. They may have had some success internally with a new BI project and now want more.

Regardless of the vision held, there is an ongoing dilemma with most BI initiatives—effective deployment. As shown in Figure 1-2, there is a definite "gap" in the intended usage of BI technologies and the actual application of them. The casual users are often locked out of participation due to a number of factors, as follows:

- The data provided is too difficult to work with.
- The end user has no time to develop skills other than rudimentary usage.
- The tool provided is too difficult for the user based upon his level of technology skills.
- The business problem faced is too complex for the casual user.
- The software provider has overstated their case for ease of use and deployment.
- The training is inadequate, and there is no support organization, such as a BI competency center.
- All of the above.

The BI utilization and uptake 'gap'

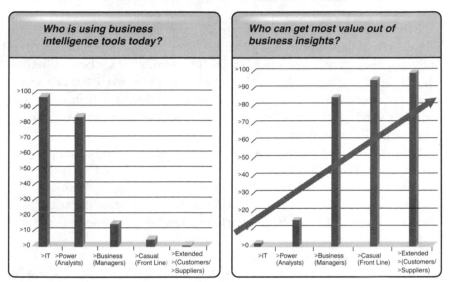

Figure 1-2   The BI utilization and uptake gap

As shown in Figure 1-2, there is a wide gap between deployment and usage, with a preponderance of BI usage on the IT and power user end of the chart. The desire by most is to drive the bar to the right. For a vendor, this often translates to trying to make their wares easier. For the organization, it most often translates to thinking, "There has to be something out there that our end users can use more effectively."

Shifts in closing the gap and moving to the right will not occur by maintaining the present course and speed, hoping that momentum will naturally build. Any BI tool has its unique strengths as well as a set of end users who find it to their liking. To assume that others should be able to use a BI tool because a few have taken to it easily is a severe error. "We don't understand why those other folks in sales aren't using our new BI gadget! Why, Ray and Frieda worked with it for a week, and look what they can do now!" There is a natural tendency to cover your struggles on the job when you see others having great success with a new gadget. Allowing users to flounder because they don't quite "get" the tool is inexcusable. I'll cover this more when we discuss the impact of BI on roles within the enterprise.

The Characteristics of a BI Vision and Strategy

BI visionaries today see an enterprise approach from vastly different perspectives depending upon where they reside in the corporate infrastructure. If you are a part of the IT organization, the emphasis is clearly upon the technology. How does any proposed BI tool comply with our standards? What is its behavior within our infrastructure? Does it use our data sources effectively? How does the vendor support it? The usual IT concerns apply.

From the perspective of end users, the issues are more functionally oriented and business related. They want to know how to use the tool. How easy is it to learn? How do they access their data and how do they perform a specific task? What do they need on their workstation? Can they access their BI "stuff" from their PDA? It's all about usage and results.

So, now we face a real conundrum with our BI plans. The CIO and other "C Level" individuals have made BI a priority for our enterprise. We already have a smattering of tools, each with their own population of loyal users, as well as processes and possibly applications in place. Do we just make changes in how we operate and support BI within the organization, or do we take a step back and map our vision to a set of clear goals and objectives? Why not start with a clear, concise vision statement? I'm not talking about one where someone has it printed in pretty lettering and hangs it on the walls in corporate meeting rooms (well...maybe I am), but where everyone involved and responsible could articulate it when asked: "What is your strategy—your enterprise vision of BI?"

It may sound a bit trite, but I have seen some very senior people go blank when I ask them this question. It is imperative that a person be able to articulate his BI plan, or we will watch him continue down the same path with little or no hope of change.

A sample vision statement might look something like this:

Our corporate vision for BI is to create and support an infrastructure with secure and authorized access to data held anywhere in the enterprise. Our corporate standard for a BI tool is _____. We staff and measure our BI competency center based upon end-user satisfaction surveys and successful deployments. An important segment of our end-user community requires near real-time data access. Therefore, we have provided such an infrastructure to accommodate them. We currently support ____ users representing ____ % of our *user population. Our goal is to increase the usage by ___ % by (date). We weigh the potential costs of increased BI usage against the business value and ROI we receive. Thus, we have a clear view of our success that is measured, accountable, and defensible.*

If your view of BI is the provisioning of a suite of tools and gadgets that are low cost and designed to get the end users out of your hair so you can do the real work, this book is not for you. If, however, your goal is to establish something akin to the vision statement articulated previously, please read on.

Setting the Stage for BI Success

No successful BI endeavor occurs within the full synergistic cooperation of IT and the business users. This is particularly true at the enterprise level, although you will find occasional pockets of success where the end users prevailed despite their poor relationship with IT. You need to keep in mind that everyone involved should be acknowledged as having taken part in a challenging journey that has reaped significant rewards and is far from over.

I reference the enterprise throughout this book. The enterprise encompasses all facets, all functional areas, and all business processes that interact to drive the entire organization. I mean that an enterprise cannot provide an effective infrastructure for BI by allowing multiple tools to be disseminated throughout the organization. I mean that an enterprise cannot have BI success without a plan and a proper support organization in place. I do not mean that you need to drop all BI tools except for one thought that would make life far easier. I do mean that it is not wise to maintain 5 tools that perform query and reporting just because they have all been adopted over time. It is an organizational nightmare to continue to maintain a poorly planned BI infrastructure that is not cohesive and clearly understood by all throughout the enterprise.

Within the IT Organization

IT must be equipped to handle BI from an infrastructure perspective as well as a business standpoint. The primary factor driving most IT decisions today is cost. Perceived platform costs (for example, a distributed environment versus a mainframe) often drive a BI decision without any thought being given to the incremental work and loss of productivity associated with data capture, replication, increased server growth, staff to support a large distributed environment, lag time in replicated data, and more. Looking at BI through cost-covered glasses will often result in a disconnection within the organization.

Such a disconnection is usually due to the lack of emphasis upon aligning the BI infrastructure with clearly understood business goals. One CIO told me: "All anyone seems to pay attention to is my overall cost; they don't understand the value my organization brings to the business." Was this the CIO's fault, or was the organization myopic in their view of IT? I don't know, but I suspect it may be a little bit of both.

Here is an example of aligning BI efforts in IT with key business areas. There is the emerging trend of operational intelligence where there is an increased emphasis on near real-time BI to provide a better experience for customers. Customer service reps are being equipped with up-to-date information about a customer's buying records so they can have a closer, more personal conversation with the prospect.

In order to deliver operational intelligence solutions, IT often has to make significant changes in their infrastructure. For an enterprise whose directions in data warehousing and BI have been to offload data from a mainframe, reversing course to take advantage of the information without offloading is not a trivial pursuit. If such realignment is required, then the effort and additional cost for IT must be understood and approved. IT must be made to understand the significance of such a change, and the end users need to support this fully.

In an operational intelligence scenario, it is imperative to place the BI functionality as close to the data as possible at point of capture. These applications traditionally utilize more highly detailed data than what may be fed to a data warehouse. In many scenarios, an operational data store (ODS) is provided as an intermediary source for capturing the data in a real-time mode and then being a source to an operational scenario as well as trickle-feeding a data warehouse. I will cover this more in-depth in Chapter 4, "The Scope of BI Solutions Today and How They May Relate to You," when we discuss the scope of BI solutions today.

If we map the business requirement (an operational scenario) to the current infrastructure, and we have a clear understanding of the business value and ROI associated with it, the challenge now facing IT is to construct the most effective delivery system for the end users, where business value is the primary driver and cost is second.

Within the End User Community

The first and foremost issue end users have to grapple with is being able to articulate their requirements and associated business value to complete the IT mission in crafting an enterprise BI framework. "We just need to get to the data and get some reports out and maybe create a few dashboards for our management team." There is nothing in that statement that suggests one iota of business value, yet it is often the best that many end users can articulate.

If you are an end user, spend some time assessing how much time and effort you are willing to invest in any BI project; make sure you have the time. Once you have a clear evaluation and realistic view, it is time to spend some quality time with your IT folks to understand the data they will provide and how you will access it. It will be critically important to map your analysis requirements to the proposed data structure. Later, I will discuss BI efforts based upon roles and skills within the organization.

Figure 1-3 shows a theoretical graph of BI skills in contrast to the complexity of the business problem and analysis required. This is not an uncommon mismatch seen in many organizations. When we look at the right-hand side of the chart, we see a horrendous mismatch between the user skills and the problem at hand. If we have a realistic view of our own situation, we may evolve a better approach to our proposed BI infrastructure. In particular, we may drastically alter our data structure we provide.

You will not make up for the skills gap in such situations by acquiring a tool that is considerably easier to use than what you have in-house (unless you are writing in the assembler language or Sanskrit). Such a tool does not exist. At this point, it is more important to have a proper business case handy for the potential ROI for the required BI process and to make sure it is understood and agreed upon. If the return is high enough, additional resources are easily justified.

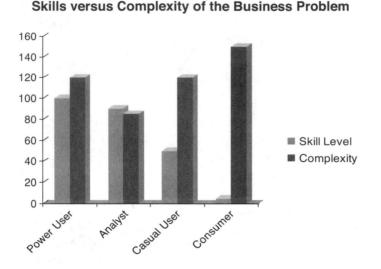

Figure 1-3   Skills versus complexity of the business problem

Summary

As we continue our story about how best to enable and utilize BI at the enterprise level, it is beneficial to keep our vision statement in mind. If you really don't have one, it may help to take a moment and see if you can write one down. BI at the enterprise level is drastically different than departmental, localized efforts. It requires a holistic view of the organization, as well as a more altruistic approach to creating a BI infrastructure that benefits all associates.

The primary goal of BI at the enterprise level is to deliver critical business information and analysis from all data sources in context and in a timely manner. It requires a rock-solid infrastructure, a set of common goals by all, and a crystal-clear vision statement in which everyone truly believes. Terms such as "best effort" and "attempt" have no place here. It is not a game of horseshoes, where coming close to the stake may earn you a point; it is about speed and accuracy. Coming in #2 in a race may bring you more money than the others, but you are still behind #1. Being #1 is what it's all about.

We now begin looking at business intelligence in today's world and define it in today's terms.

2

Defining Business Intelligence Today

In this chapter, we begin to delve deeper into BI today and how many in the industry envision it in the context of the many changes in technologies and shifts. This chapter is devoted to developing a BI definition within your organization that encompasses more than just connectivity to a data warehouse and internal analytics. Although there are many definitions we might borrow from, the only one that counts is how *you* define it. I'd like you to take a moment and jot down your definition of BI at the enterprise level—at least form some words in your mind as to what you would reply should someone ask you: "So, what do you think enterprise BI really is?"

Defining Business Intelligence within Your Organization

One way to look at a BI definition specific to your requirements is to put the piece parts together. A definition of Enterprise BI (EBI) may look something like this:

Business Intelligence within our enterprise is the application and usage of the following BI functions {list} applied to all data within the enterprise including {list} as well as the intention to support {list} in the future. We see BI as a separate but integral part of our data warehouse initiatives. Our deployment model is a single, integrated solution architecture provided by {name} that we host on the following platform(s) {list}. We discourage the proliferation of multiple tools and have targeted {list} for removal. We carefully segment our end users into the following categories {list} and provide support and training according to their needs.

This definition, or one that fits you, accomplishes several things at once. First, it provides a basis for discussion internally—"this is what we believe BI to be." Second, it provides a list of sanctioned technologies, as well as acknowledgment that some existing products are targeted to be removed. Third, it demonstrates some glimpse into the future of things that will be considered. Finally, it establishes the fact that different users, user types, and skills exist. If there is some offering perceived to have strong business value and is *not* on the list, an argument may be made to bring it in.

CHECKPOINT

What is your philosophy on BI tools? Do you sanction multiple offerings in-house, or are you of a mind to reduce the ones you have and standardize upon a single provider/architecture? The ramifications of either option will have a profound effect upon your ability to deliver BI effectively at the enterprise level.

Establishing a definition of Enterprise BI is *not the same* as having a vision statement. A definition should set the standards for what BI entails within the enterprise, and a vision statement concerns how these standards will be applied. A BI definition should clearly articulate the technology factors under consideration but in the context of business applications. Report classification is a good example to begin with.

In the typical request for information/request for proposal (RFI/RFP), you will see reporting as a key requirement. I have seldom seen an RFP where the request for reporting gets granular enough. Reports targeted for BI creation and deployment should always be accompanied by an illustration and specific functions associated with them.

A BI definition at the enterprise level should be documented. It should list the major elements and delve into sub-elements, such as the functionality expected within a specific report type. These requirements should be taken directly from the corporate BI requirements put forth by IT and your end users. If this is properly done, your vendor selection process and choice of deployment model(s) will be considerably easier and defensible. Given a comprehensive definition of BI, if a vendor falls short in its ability to address the requirements put forth, then they are a poor choice. However, these requirements need to address things that you firmly believe are critical and will be used—not a wish list. Too many RFPs list things that are never put into play, yet were considered "important" somehow.

At the enterprise level, the definitions and functional requirements list can be daunting. It is often far easier to opt for an approved vendor list than to properly screen and examine those knocking on your door. What about a single provider with a rich portfolio?

If you have an issue with too many BI tools, how do you defend this today? I can understand why you would be leery of relying upon a single vendor solution, but given the changed BI market, it may prove to be your most effective option. I think of having multiple tools performing roughly the same function as similar to the days when each rifle was unique and there was no common caliber or bore for sharing ammunition. You may have a mixed arsenal with little chance to pull it all together.

Platform Implications

I will address platform choices more in Chapter 11, "Platform Selection, Technology Biases, and Other 'Traps'," but this is a good time to inject a brief discussion about platform selection. The BI tools opted for are usually hosted on servers that are separate from other applications and functions. The one significant anomaly in this case is a mainframe or, as IBM® terms it, System z®. BI processes may be co-hosted with batch, OLTP (on-line transaction processing e.g. CICS®), data warehouse, and web server applications, and more.

I see installations that are considering hosting new services back on the mainframe due to its emerging new architecture and solutions. In data warehouse scenarios, there is an emerging trend to move the BI processes as close to the data source as possible. I often hear, "It takes too long to get my data updated on my distributed DW platform." So, I suggest that they examine their System z infrastructure with new eyes, and then hear, "Oh no! Our strategic direction is distributed, and we aren't going to change!" OK...so you have problems with your stated course but aren't willing to entertain alternate solutions—I cannot help you.

In cases where internal strife and 'strategies' are at odds, the user must take a step back and approach their dilemma from a business perspective and not a technology one. I have seen numerous macro-changes occur where the users have developed a clear and strong business case based upon the value to the organization should the change be approved.

One very strong argument today is the difference in effectiveness provided by more real-time access to the data. In many cases there is documented value published by competitors where they are taking a new approach to their own BI infrastructure. The measurement of BI success (or lack thereof) is a key element to forcing a change in strategy. The proof of enhanced business value or improved operations will trump pure cost analysis every time. This is particularly true when facing a showdown with IT as they are always being hammered upon about cost, cost, cost.

Here is an example of a BI tools usage "wagging the dog," if you will. One customer recently reexamining their data warehouse and BI platform selection was spending in excess of €6,000,000 per year on file extractions from a mainframe to a distributed environment. This data was already stored in a relational database on the mainframe but was now being cloned to get it to a different environment. The data was fed into a relational database from operational systems (verified and cleaned along the way); then they turned around and extracted data *out* of the database to feed to this BI tool. Why? Because the tool worked better with its own proprietary format.

They had set a course of BI on distributed but had selected a tool that operated poorly on their primary data source. This tool was not unique in its functions, but they had been going down this path and spending a considerable amount of money to do so.

There is a significant difference between an internal definition of BI and an internal *agenda* surrounding BI. Agenda-based BI initiatives often leave new solutions or rethinking existing infrastructures aside. Nobody wants to be branded as an internal *heretic* for suggesting an alternative solution. If the agenda is business solutions-oriented, there is a chance of success. If the agenda is one based upon technology and platform alone...I wish you luck.

What Is "Mission Critical"?

As stated earlier, many top executives state that BI is "mission critical" to their corporation. Mission critical implies that there are dire consequences should something fail. Is this what they are suggesting? Do they have this in their BI definition statement? Typically this means that significant investments have been made to integrate BI within business processes to the extent that they cannot be removed and, in some cases, return significant value.

Does this indicate that this particular enterprise has managed to make more of its employees proficient in BI than the average enterprise; thus, it permeates their culture? This is hardly the case in any instance I have seen. The deployment rate for BI still remains low compared to the expressed desire of most enterprise accounts. Mission-critical applications involving BI may only involve one critical group but have been elevated to the highest levels within the organization—thus, the term "mission critical."

You will also hear mission critical applied to BI from those who have invested in a BI strategy with clearly articulated goals. These are typically people who have tasted success and have become believers. They are also those who will probe more on how increased utilization of BI will change their internal processes. These are the organizations that will ensure BI permeates the enterprise because they understand the value and power it contains.

Along with mission critical, I see other terms often used today regarding BI that were not so common in the past, as follows:

- Competitive differentiator
- Productivity improvement
- Collaboration enhancement, both internal and external
- Customer satisfaction increase
- Enhanced corporate performance tracking
- Improved planning and forecasting
- Critical weapon for the data warehouse
- An extension of our ERP (Enterprise Resource Planning) and CRM (Customer Relationship Management) solutions

Today's definition of BI embraces all these positive attributes and more. It seems we are over the hump of establishing BI as a key element within any organization.

BI Solution Elements

There is also a solid, generic understanding of the basic functions of BI solutions. The following are the general categories you see on an RFI being handed out to prospective providers:

- Query
- Reporting
- Charting
- Dashboards
- Scorecards
- KPIs (Key Performance Indicators)
- Metrics
- Analytics
- Advanced analytics
- Predictive analytics
- Collaborative portals
- Personal collaboration (PDAs and so on)
- Event-driven BI (triggers and so on)

I still see organizations set up BI "beauty contests" in the form of a proof of concept (POC), where several vendors are pitted against each other to provide proof that their wares are best of breed. But, for the most part, there appears to be a level of understanding that any BI vendor worth consideration has incorporated these functions within their offerings, or they will not be around very long.

Vendors should not be pressed to prove that their checklist is worthy; they should be pressed to prove that their solution set fits your BI business model. Keep in mind that the functions I have listed are common to most vendors. The differentiator in selecting one over another often comes down to someone's opinion of ease of use. One of the "killer" criteria is the ability to mimic what is being considered for replacement.

"It has to do what we already do before we even think about replacing what we have!"

BI today is more about how well a vendor's solution can be fully integrated within the corporate infrastructure. Does its technology embrace modern standards, and is it extensible? Obviously, the BI functionality has to be there. You can argue how much better Product X is than Product Y when it comes to creating an object (report, chart, and so on). However, if Product X has been developed with limitations in platform selection and data access, you must take a step to the rear and give this some thought. It is not about short-term benefits anymore; it's about meeting today's needs as well as those of the future.

In Figure 2-1, we see a simplistic view of the BI continuum from its early stage to some of the issues and functionality of today. This is not a complete picture, but it does illustrate the emergence and evolution of functions and technologies that affect BI solutions today. The number of bubbles will continue to grow with technologies and functions heretofore not envisioned.

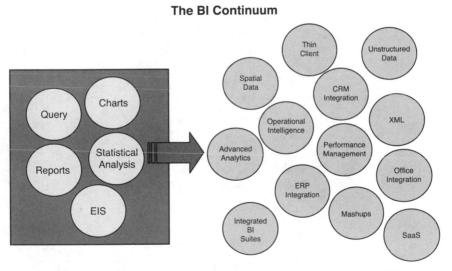

The BI Continuum

Decision Support Systems   **Business Intelligence Suites**

Figure 2-1   The BI continuum

The term suite refers to those vendors that have created all-inclusive offerings where the individual components (query, reporting, dashboards, and more) have seen a metamorphosis from piece-parts to an integrated set and can exchange functions easily such as using a common metadata layer to move output back and forth from function to function.

In your environment, it would be good to draw a similar diagram and try to identify all the bubbles in relation to your BI user population—with the larger the bubble, the greater the user population and/or the importance of the particular function. In your instance, I would suggest mapping out a set of functions by data source or sources. I have done this in "white board" sessions that generate a rigorous debate as to the "weight" of each bubble.

Figure 2-2 depicts a view of a data source and the BI functions we are using or expect to use against it. This example weighs the size of bubbles by end user population. Any bubble that falls outside the large bubble suggests that it is not covered wholly by the data source or it is used with other data sources.

BI Mapping by Data Source

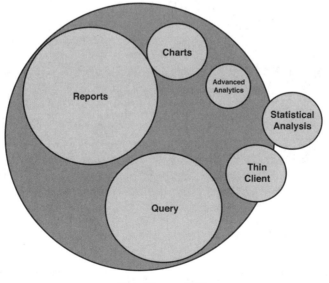

Data Source ABC

Figure 2-2 BI mapping by data source

Some of the bubbles fall entirely within the data outline and some are peripheral players. For example, we see that a portion of the *thin client* function falls outside data source outline. This suggests that there is a population in the end-user community that may be using rich client or thick client access, but the majority of the users will be accessing the data using a browser.

We note that the reporting bubble is larger than the query bubble. This would typically mean that multiple reports are to be run from the same query. Reporting is the dominant function for this database. A visual map of your BI "intent" helps in discussing what elements are more important and the scope of support you believe must be put in play to service the user population.

If you engage in developing diagrams like this in interactive sessions, what emerges is that the elements that may not be so critical are often regarded in a new light. This is particularly helpful when you are in the RFI/RFP phase and are working from a wish list. It is a powerful consensus-building exercise.

Business Intelligence and Data Warehouse: Are They Synonymous?

In order to answer this question, let's examine a couple of points right up front:

- **Synonym defined:** Two words that can be interchanged in a context are said to be synonymous relative to that context.

- **Fact:** Business intelligence and data warehousing are *not* the same thing. They are not synonymous. This is a consistent misconception applied by many in the industry that adds an element of confusion and needs to be addressed. BI tools are not dependent upon a data warehouse, but you seldom see a data warehouse that is not driven by BI initiatives. BI existed long before data warehousing was "de rigueur" and, in the context of all the information in today's world, it is now just one more source available to an end user. You can access and analyze your data in any form without a data warehouse but having one sure makes life easier.

The definition of a data warehouse today has been greatly expanded. Consider the fact that roughly 80%+ of the information in the world is held in unstructured or semi-structured formats. There is a lack of attention paid to efficient and meaningful ways to access and expose critical BI data that may be held in these formats. It comes up as an ancillary topic in many BI discussions, but the primary conversation still centers upon structured data. This is especially true with the close affinity of BI and data warehousing. One oft-quoted factoid as of this writing is the latest metric on known data in the world—988 exabytes estimated for the year 2010. An exabyte is equal to 1000 petabytes or 10^{18} bytes.

Folks, we have a lot of data out there! Because the number changes exponentially, every time you visit one of those "clever" web facts sites, the number will change. To put that into perspective, you'd need over eight billion of Apple's most capacious iPods to store it all. Much of this data resides in video streams and other such formats, but the fact is, we have an ever-burgeoning world of data that may be of relevance to our BI processes. The world's data is potentially within your *virtual* data warehouse and should be incorporated into your strategy. It should be made part of your definition statement for data warehousing, as well as BI.

The world is your data warehouse, and BI is your primary means to access it and make sense of it all.

Business Intelligence as a Key Differentiator from Competition

Many perceive BI to be effective only when applied to large-scale, enterprise accounts. I view an enterprise as any business entity regardless of scope and scale. When you consider the power in the proper application of BI, you realize that it is mostly about the impact upon the business and far less about size. BI with a purpose (having a vision and a definition) and mission is what I mean, as noted in the following:

> Research firm AMI Partners (AMI) has released a report that details how cost-conscious businesses are turning to business intelligence software for a competitive advantage. AMI discovered that small and medium businesses are deploying business intelligence software as a stand-alone tool. The study found that these businesses are transforming from a modular use of business intelligence software to a stand-alone deployment model. These organizations are using

business intelligence as part of a collaborative system that integrates databases and generates intelligent reports around revenue generation, research, and new business development.

According to AMI, nearly half of all U.S. small to medium businesses will be or are planning to use business intelligence software in the next three to six months. AMI's research matches up well with data earlier this year from research giant Gartner. Both AMI and Gartner are predicting that the need to derive detailed data insights via business intelligence software will be driven and executed by business users, not IT professionals. This move to the business user desktop for business intelligence tools will be seen at the business unit level for large organizations and for most small- to medium-sized businesses according to Gartner. (TIBCO Spotfire: Bill Peterson, 11/03/2009.)

Such stories and testimonials about the competitive effectiveness of BI usually lead to one or more visionaries within the organization. Regardless of the deployment model, the key word we often see is "collaboration." Collaboration today transcends the notion of tying some BI output to your email system. The trend today is toward real-time, immediate, and actionable feedback systems. I would challenge the deployment of BI as standalone systems, but you can't argue with success.

Take a moment and perform a quick search on the Internet using "business intelligence competitive edge" as search criteria. You will find a myriad of other references, all of which are public domain. In fact, if you are near an Internet-accessible machine, pause and do this right now. It doesn't hurt to have a little homework from time to time. OK, so now you are back (assuming you did this little task)—what did you find? I just did the same thing, and my results were: Results 1–10 of about 457,000 for business intelligence competitive edge.

By the time you perform this search, the count will certainly not go down. We see nearly half a million references to BI from a competitive-edge perspective alone. Many of these will be vendor-prompted (shall we say solicited?), but that does not negate the importance of these solutions in any way.

Every BI vendor will provide stories of how their wares were used to provide Company ABC with a competitive edge. Because they all can provide examples, it becomes quickly apparent that any BI tool can provide significant potential to outdistance your competitors. Lest we wander into the weeds of vendor comparisons, these results should suggest to you that there is a high probability that BI applied with goals and purpose can make a huge difference.

One customer example I can think of is where a client tied their customer database together with current sales information and then "mashed" this together with information on their closest competitors being fed from the Web. By incorporating external data into this application, they were able to ascertain market reactions to competitive sales campaigns and more. They were able to detect key moves and pricing actions by their competition using web "crawling" technology.

In days past, you would have to acquire competitive information or spend a great deal of time scanning printed sources. Today, much of this information is available online and is up to date. This experience led to a broader view of the applicability of BI in their organization. It also taught them that creative approaches to BI can go both ways...who was tracking them?

The story continues. The next step they were about to undertake was linking their customer service applications to new promotions while ensuring that their competitor's data was also available, lest the CSRs were unaware of opposing offers. Sometimes such solutions are well thought-out and crafted in a holistic manner. Sometimes they fall together in an ongoing, patchwork-quilt manner as more and more features, functions, and value are added. With the emergence of service-oriented architectures (SOA) and cloud computing, it will become easier to strap on and extend a BI solution than before. Your definition of BI must incorporate innovative applications, such as the one just described.

The AMI article talks about the movement toward BI as standalone systems. I believe this is because there is a shift toward BI usage as a "system" in these cases. The insular approach has immediate value but can be risky at the enterprise level. We often hear lamentation about insular silos of information. The next woeful cry could be about insular silos of BI usage. In the majority of enterprises, we see this already in their usage of multiple tools. Later in this book, we discuss the scope of various BI deployment models. One thing not mentioned in the article was any aspect of increased productivity—do BI solutions make people more productive?

Productivity Factors—Working Smarter

Increased productivity suggests that an individual either does more with less or he crams more productive work into less time. In the context of BI, this might mean that he is able to take action on some critical task faster and with better information. Or, it could mean that the individual doesn't have to look for things for as long as he used to. At the risk of repeating myself endlessly, I encourage you to perform an Internet search on various topics raised here.

Lost productivity due to the need to stop what you are doing and search for information is a significant factor. In a Butler Group study cited in 2006 (*NetworkWorld*, Denise Dubie, October 20, 2006), the following points were made:

> Employees performing ineffective searches and wasting time looking for information can cost companies up to 10% in salary expenses, research shows. Butler Group, a London-based IT research and analysis organization, this week released a report titled "Enterprise Search and Retrieval," which concludes that "ineffective search and discovery strategies are hampering business competitiveness, impairing service delivery, and putting companies at risk." Specifically, the research firm contends that as much as 10% of a company's salary cost is "frittered away" as employees scramble to find adequate and accurate information to perform their overall jobs and complete assigned tasks.
>
> "Over 50% of staff costs are now allocated to employees performing so-called information work," said Richard Edwards, senior research analyst and co-author of the 240-page report, in a press release. "Employees are suffering from both information overload and information 'underload.' As a result, the typical information worker now spends up to one-quarter of his or her day searching for the right information to complete a given task."
>
> The lost productivity and wasted salary cost findings support Butler Group's stance that search and retrieval tools should be part of enterprise companies' IT arsenal, as the technologies "enable organizations to exploit the information assets they already have. They also enable companies to identify opportunities, reduce risk, and garner insight," according to the press release.

Many regard information today as a vast, unending river that is continuously spilling over its banks as there is too much for the human mind (or technology) to absorb. Stream computing is an emerging technology that attempts to continuously monitor, filter, and collect data that is relevant to the user and the business problem at hand. Think of 15 petabytes of data being created every day. That is more than 8 times the volume of information contained in all the libraries in the United States.

You should also consider all the emerging sources of information where opinions and facts are posted continuously such as the myriad of blogs in place or the massive amounts of chatter being generated within Twitter and more.

If we acknowledge that this is a known concern, we need to extend this to the time that we personally spend looking for things. Implementing a search engine to cut our non-productive time is far more than scanning documentation. It should also take into account the need to search internal BI "objects," such as reports, emails, publications, and more. Have you ever been a user of a BI tool and said aloud: "Now what was the name of that report I ran last week?" At the enterprise level, there are often many shared objects that could be of importance...*if* you can find them. Setting up BI information on a shared basis is an art form in itself.

Productivity from a BI perspective ought to be part of your vision statement. It should incorporate the concept that rapid access to information when we need it helps us make better decisions faster and be more productive. It should also include the concept of "think time." People just cannot work endless hours and be productive. If you can make a decision in 30% less time than before, you may have some time on your hands just to relax for a few minutes. It would be nice to have that extra cup of coffee and do some thinking.

How many times have you had to perform a "take over" for some project because you had a lull in your daily pressure and immediately realized something was missing or you instantly deduced a better way? Think time is essential, and we do not get enough of it. Many times, the only break you get is in transit to and from work. If you have an epiphany on the way home, will you extend your work day before the thought gets away? If it occurs on the way in, will you remember it once you walk in the door and get hit with today's crises?

Productivity is also greatly enhanced when collaborative BI implementations incorporate the ability to provide triggers and events to auto-notify the user regarding certain things that have happened. Significant productivity gains can be made if you are auto-notified rather than having to constantly search and query just in case something has taken place. Rather than look for some critical information that may or may not be held in a report, why not set a notification process in play? BI automation and notification should be part of your definition. It may be the most significant element of all for many of your end users.

Summary

I have recommended that you spend time defining BI within your organization and then spend time refining it. Does it incorporate the elements of functional evaluation, segmentation of function by users, and critical factors of productivity? I have separated BI from data warehousing while expanding the scope of data warehousing to encompass all the accessible data in the world, not just what we host in-house.

I firmly believe that BI can make you more productive but that you need to have a distinct business purpose to be maximally effective. Your BI definition should strongly recommend competitive differentiators and collaborative features. Because we have seen BI solutions in the market since approximately 1975, why are we grappling with the same factors 35 years later? Why not dive into your current BI infrastructure and gain a personal, historical insight into where you have come from and where you want to be?

3

The History of Business Intelligence within Your Organization

I discussed the evolution of BI quite thoroughly in *Business Intelligence for the Enterprise*, so I will not repeat my "in the beginning" stories described there. It may be better to begin with "Once upon a time...."

There has been a natural evolution of BI within the past three decades, and your journey into the future will depend upon where you entered the market and what your current inventory of BI tools may be. It is time to delve into your specific environment and see what an Enterprise BI play may look like for you. By now, you should have at least a rudimentary vision statement and BI definition that you believe in. From these two foundations, you can make a realistic and open assessment of your BI situation as it stands today and where you would like it to be.

Mapping Your Environment to the BI Evolutionary Tree

Initially, BI tools emerged out of desperation from the need to access data faster and without having to wait for IT, thus opening a floodgate of opportunity for vendors. The earliest tools were either used to access highly technical data such as VSAM or IMS™ or they provided their own internal data format that had to be loaded. In some cases, end users entered their own data. We see this today with many spreadsheet users. Data is the foundation upon which BI begins. It has to be there to do anything meaningful, and the typical end user will get to the data any way they can.

BI has adjusted and morphed from the following milestone technologies or events:

- **Early stage of BI: End user computing era and information center.** Many tools emerged in this era, including offerings from vendors such as SAS, Information Builders, IBM, and others. Due to the lack of data cleansing and validation functions and tools, each BI tool was "beefed up" by the vendor to provide these functions. Data inaccuracies, as well as restructuring, were handled by the individual tools. Many production applications (online transaction processing, or OLTP) were written in these 4GLs and may run within your enterprise today.

- **The implications of charge-back systems on corporate BI productivity.** With the emergence of early BI tools and their impact upon host processors, most customers implemented charge-back systems to discourage growth and increase usage of BI tools. To this day, the implications of internal charge-back systems have an effect upon platform choice and attitudes about where to host BI applications. Do you have an internal charge-back system?

- **The impact of the PC and client/server technologies on the industry.** The impact of non-mainframe solutions was enormous. All you had to do was get the data off the expensive host platform and onto a smaller, self-contained environment, and then bash away at the data as much as you liked. However, there was that little problem of getting current data into these offloaded environments. This holds true today and has become increasingly less attractive as more and more enterprise accounts look at providing near real-time BI and analysis.

- **OLAP solutions and advanced analytics, such as data mining.** OLAP products opened the door to providing extremely fast analysis. Data could be loaded at a lower (also known as "leaf") level, and massive calculations were applied to build a "cube" of information that could be sliced, diced, and drilled. The keystone of OLAP solutions was that they were (and still are) very, very fast. Despite the fact that the information tended to be frozen in time, OLAP sources provided analyses previously unheard of and supplanted performing masses of queries. Data mining and advanced analytics offered insight into data not available before. Most of these solutions still had a common fault; they required data extractions and views into information that were frozen in time.

- **Data warehousing.** The emergence of data warehousing solutions was aimed at two specific BI aspects. The first was to organize the information into a shape that was optimized for BI queries, especially multidimensional ones. The second was to ensure data accuracy and consistency. The typical data warehouse has its data aggregated to some level appropriate for analysis within the enterprise. Most commonly, the level of aggregation is aimed at managerial levels and above. We still have the issue of data latency from the instant of capture and that of inserting or updating data into the warehouse.

- **The Internet and web browsers.** Not only did the Internet open the world's data to anyone who could find the correct site, one of its most significant innovations was the ability to provide a common end user interface: the browser. No matter how elegant or hideous the underlying system, the information contained could be presented in any manner one could think of. With the exposure of so much critical information on the Web, we see the world's data explode to unimaginable volumes and sources. The world is now your data warehouse; what you host internally is a minute fraction of it.

- **Operational Intelligence.** This is an emerging discipline whereby highly detailed information is accessed in a real-time or near real-time manner. This BI approach is targeted at service support individuals or anyone else who directly interfaces with a customer. The users aren't analyzing anything other than the customer's mindset and issues being conveyed over the phone or in a live chat. It requires access to data that is up to date, highly detailed, and not being aggregated for analysis. Operational data is often held in an operational data store (ODS) for later updating as a warehouse.

- **Server-based BI and analytics.** We are back at ground zero in many ways as the availability of a common, thin-client user interface has turned everyone's attention back to provisioning a server environment that is secure, that scales, is available 24x7, and will not go down. Modern BI tools are being delivered that require only a browser to create BI output and consume it. Today, the proper server to support a BI environment is a hot debate. I will go into this more in Chapter 4, "The Scope of BI Solutions Today and How They May Relate to You."

- **BI appliances.** BI appliances are self-contained systems that are the subject of endless debate in the market today. They are perceived to be less expensive and modular in nature by combining both hardware and software in a "black box" approach to BI. We still have the problem of getting data into an appliance, much as in the other BI solutions available. BI appliances are considered optimal for some because they are dedicated to delivering some specific analyses and that is all.

- **Offsite hosting environments.** Some have just opted to give up the BI fight and defer the implementation and support to others. Outsourcing your BI to an external provider relieves some of the pressure in keeping service level agreements, maintenance, and support up to date.

Figure 3-1 depicts the most common BI implementations and deployments. Several of these offerings were in their infancy or simply not available just a few years ago. You may argue with some of the attributes in the boxes, but more importantly, which of the deployments do you have in-house? In many cases, I have found clients with most of these deployment options in play. If this is the case, you have an enormous task ahead of you if you are attempting to rein in some of this anarchy. I suggest going back to a basic definition of what you are trying to accomplish from a business perspective. For example, if you can live with and prosper with data that is somewhat dated and frozen in time, your options are quite different from those with near real-time requirements. If you merely assume that the end users will not need timely information, you may be in for a surprise.

In numerous conversations with clients, the discussion around the need for more timely data has arisen with alarming frequency. One of the oft-repeated comments is: "We didn't know our end users were in need of data that is so new; we thought this was all about doing some analysis and reporting as we've always done!" Time happens. Requirements change. A BI infrastructure that is not based upon flexible access to data but more on the BI tools will always be at risk and will be perceived as having less value.

Where are you in the spectrum of BI chronology? Do you have tools that date back to the earliest era and earliest offerings? I have found that

The BI Technology Spectrum

Early 4GL Tools	Early Standalone Systems	Client-Server Tools	Rich Client Tools	Thin Client Tools	Open Source Tools	Software as a Service	Cloud Computing	Appliances
Data extractions	Support of specific departments or job functions	Complex networking	Cooperative processing	Server centric	Accessible to anyone	Hands-off environment	Public or private	Self-contained
Complex logic	Data extractions	Access to back-end data	Offload of heavy BI processes	Browser based	Low cost	Managed by others	Rapid deployment option	Dedicated to the BI application
Access to non-relational data	EIS-like	Emerging data warehouse	Intelligent decision on where a process was to occur	Heavy reliance upon app. servers	Range of function simple to complex	Sign up for a service and pay	Self-service BI subscription basis	Perceived as inexpensive
Online applications	Calculations and data that only reside here	Workstation based	Workstation and browser based	No hardware upgrades required	Less structured environment	No interaction with internal IT	End users totally insulated from the environment	Scale by adding appliances or processors
Batch systems and processing	Complex logic performed off-host	Processing on back end and within the tool	Challenging to administer	Scale by adding servers	ETL may be required	Rapid deployment option	IT managed with private Cloud	Data extractions or CDC
ETL functions	Data frozen in time	Heavy network traffic	Occasional hardware upgrades	No standalone capability	Data extractions perhaps	Self-service BI subscription basis	Outsourced to a provider	Limited in scope
Calculations and data that only reside here	Dedicated systems	Challenging to debug and tune	Data extractions perhaps	SOA-based	Little control or influence on the provider	End users totally insulated from the environment	Public Cloud option available to extend outside the organization	Speed is the primary driver
Mainframe based	Proprietary	Target use was to offload the mainframe	Role-based	Role-based	Closet industry	SOA-based	Role-based SOA driven	Both hardware and software offerings

Figure 3-1   The most common BI implementations and deployments

realistic inventories of an enterprise's BI investment can be quite sobering. Many organizations are unaware of just how deep and how wide the penetration of BI tools has become. We see a similarity to server consolidation evaluations in many companies.

In a recent meeting with a client, they told me they had just taken an inventory of distributed servers within the organization. They had been carrying a total of 900 "on the books" that IT would own up to. The actual count was in excess of 2,700! How these things can multiply! The same is true of BI tools. People just get busy, problems need to be solved, projects get underway that are not necessarily strategic, and IT is often held at arm's length.

In the case of the more "dated" BI tools, the most significant impact is the continued use of them to provide applications that are considered production status. It tends to be the most common reason why the XYZ tool cannot be dislodged. The cost and implications of such applications can be significant. For example, I recently met with one client who is spending in excess of €600,000 annually on an older end user tool. The user base is quite small and is spread across three systems. This is the same client I mentioned earlier who was spending in excess of €6,000,000 annually on file extractions.

They have allowed expensive, highly reduced usage to continue to run without encouraging any growth or reexamination of their BI strategy. Until now, they had not considered a replacement. Given new cost reduction mandates and modernization directions, they are currently assessing the feasibility of replacing this offering.

Does this hold true in your organization as well? It often seems easier and far less complicated to just continue to pay for the tool(s) and slowly move in a different direction. Given the average enterprise account's investment in BI tools, any change will be costly—but continuing to pay for a less-than-optimal solution borders on laziness.

Creating an Internal Record of BI Usage

One of the first orders of business is to take a thorough inventory of your existing BI portfolio. In Chapter 2, "Defining Business Intelligence Today," I recommended creating a bubble diagram of BI tool usage in-house. You have to identify the depth and breadth of your BI investment.

An inventory of BI tools is just the beginning. What is really called for is an inventory of applications, end users, and perceived business value. Given the fact that a small number of power users typically support a larger population, I suspect that each BI tool within the organization delivers less value than originally planned.

Now, if possible, can you create an inventory of usage by product, by number of users, and by the associated costs? Taking our customer with the underutilized query tool and the massive expense in data extractions, we see a table that looks something like that shown in Table 3-1.

Table 3-1 Ten Years of BI Product Usage

Years	Tool Name	No. of Users	Annual Cost	Cost per User
	BI Query Tool			
Year 1		100	€600,000	€6,000.00
Year 2		90	€600,000	€6,666.67
Year 3		85	€600,000	€7,058.82

Table 3-1 Ten Years of BI Product Usage

Years	Tool Name	No. of Users	Annual Cost	Cost per User
Year 4		70	€600,000	€8,571.43
Year 5		50	€600,000	€12,000.00
Year 5		40	€600,000	€15,000.00
Year 6		35	€600,000	€17,142.86
Year 7		35	€600,000	€17,142.86
Year 8		35	€600,000	€17,142.86
Year 9		35	€600,000	€17,142.86
Year 10		35	€600,000	€17,142.86
Total cost 10 years			€6,600,000	
	Data Extract Tool			
Year 1		70	€6,000,000	€85,714.29
Year 2		60	€6,000,000	€100,000.00
Year 3		60	€6,000,000	€100,000.00
Year 4		50	€6,000,000	€120,000.00
Year 5		50	€6,000,000	€120,000.00
Year 5		50	€6,000,000	€120,000.00
Year 6		50	€6,000,000	€120,000.00
Year 7		50	€6,000,000	€120,000.00
Year 8		50	€6,000,000	€120,000.00
Year 9		50	€6,000,000	€120,000.00
Year 10		50	€6,000,000	€120,000.00
Total cost 10 years			€66,000,000	
Total cost both tools 10 years	€72,600,000			

In this case, I have not accurately portrayed the number of users of the extraction tool. This was not divulged; thus, I have taken some liberties here. We see an expense of €72,600,000 that we know for a fact. Setting aside ancillary expenses such as support, storage, processing, and more, this is a large sum of money. Does this make either tool a liability? Without having an accurate assessment of the business value provided, all we see is an expense.

What if we had 10,000 users of the data extraction tool shown previously? The cost per user would drop dramatically, but the business value doesn't change one iota. In this particular case, as I mentioned earlier, the extractions could have been avoided altogether given the proper BI infrastructure. That was identified right up front. Does this imply that the €6,000,000 per year was a total waste of money? Potentially, yes. Whenever you note declining usage and popularity of a BI tool, a warning flag should go up immediately. When you cannot quantify our ROI for our BI investment, we are vulnerable to extreme measures and harmful impact upon our end users.

Because the majority of BI tools today are purchased by user type, user role, or CPU-based pricing, it is imperative that you factor in the original acquisition and contrast this with the actual deployment. Table 3-2 shows customer examples that you may relate to.

In our example, we see a couple of milestones. First, the initial outlay and cost per user deployed is high, which is to be expected. We then see an increase in the number of users deployed on a total user basis. The usage peaks at Year 5 and then begins to taper off at Year 7, but the maintenance continues. If you substitute this pattern for your own experience, you gain an accurate picture of some of your BI investment. Do not be discouraged if you see a pattern similar to the one presented; you are not alone.

Perhaps even with reduced usage, the value returned is far greater than the outlay. Perhaps there are mission-critical aspects of the tools. In either case shown, we simply do not know. When the only scrutiny is based upon cost savings and not business value, you are operating blindly. It is one of the things I see over and over—those who do not acknowledge the past are doomed to repeat it. If all you know about your BI environment is the cost, what prevents you from just dropping the majority of your current inventory and mandating a change? Some have been known to remove a tool from a system and see who complains about it...if anyone.

Table 3-2   BI Product X Cost versus Deployment

	Original Purchase	$1,500,000			
	Users Purchased	Users Deployed	Maintenance*	Annual Cost	Cost per User
Year 1	4000	100	$0	$1,500,000	$15,000
Year 2		130	$270,000	$270,000	$2,077
Year 3		150	$270,000	$270,000	$1,800
Year 4		200	$270,000	$270,000	$1,350
Year 5		250	$270,000	$270,000	$1,080
Year 5		250	$270,000	$270,000	$1,080
Year 6		250	$270,000	$270,000	$1,080
Year 7		200	$270,000	$270,000	$1,350
Year 8		120	$270,000	$270,000	$2,250
Year 9		70	$270,000	$270,000	$3,857
Year 10		50	$270,000	$270,000	$5,400
Total cost 10 years			$2,700,000	$4,200,000	

*Assuming that 18% applied to full purchase.

In the days of the information center and in today's world of a BI competency center (BICC), a total assessment strategy was and is in order. I will discuss the BICC a bit more in Chapter 4, "The Scope of BI Solutions Today and How They May Relate to You," but let me mention one of its primary roles while I have your attention. It is imperative that any BI investment be reviewed and measured both from a cost perspective and that of its ROI. As shown in the preceding two tables, the view paints a bleak picture of the value of any of the tools in play. In Table 3-2, what if the 50 remaining users represent a core group that provides invaluable sales and marketing analysis? Other users have migrated away as a new reporting tool had been implemented in Year 6 and there was a natural movement away from the one depicted.

NOTE

In your environment, do your contractual agreements with your BI vendors provide flexibility of maintenance based upon actual usage? One thing observed in most BI deployments is that the power users are the ones who get off the ground quickest. They also tend to be the longer-running users of any tool, and they tend to cost more per seat in role-based deployments. This would have significant implications for our previous calculations.

An internal historical perspective should contain a table/matrix/assessment that is considerably more detailed than the preceding one. Is it possible to provide a column with ROI numbers? There must be pluses as well as minuses involved in BI efforts or the entire exercise is futile. It is difficult to defend costs, but this is the typical lens through which BI is measured and assessed.

Analysis of Displacement

For argument's sake, let's assume you have an inventory of four BI tools in-house, each with its population of users. We can look at it from a variety of angles, such as total annual cost of each tool, number of users, degree of displacement difficulty, and perceived business value.

Figure 3-2 shows a rudimentary analysis of displacement for the four BI tools. Note that Product D is the most widely used tool and the lowest in cost, but also the lowest in perceived business value. It is also assessed as being relatively easy to displace on a scale of 1–10, with 10 being the most difficult. If you view this as an outsider, you may take one of several views regarding Product D, as follows:

1. Product D seems to serve many people at a lower cost despite the business value.
2. Due to its low perceived business value, Product D might be eliminated or absorbed by one of the other BI tools in-house.
3. Contrast Product D with Product B, which appears to have the lowest number of users, is rather expensive, and offers moderate business value, yet it appears to be difficult to displace.

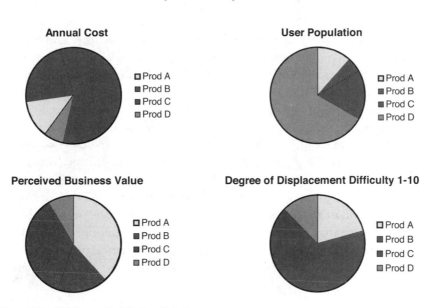

Figure 3-2   Displacement of the four BI tools

We can look at each one in order and formulate some opinions and generic statements about them. Product C appears to be costly. It is moderately used at best, has fairly high business value, and is challenging to displace. If you had to pick one to start with having just been handed a mandate to reduce the number of tools, which would you choose? The correct answer is...we don't know enough here. But, once you begin an honest assessment of your BI inventory, your plan to deliver an enterprise BI vision begins to take form.

It may be extremely difficult to dislodge some BI tools due to internal politics, valid mission-critical designations, and other factors. If any of the tools has extremely unique functionality offered only by that tool, a displacement strategy is impractical. If, however, the reason displacement is viewed as difficult is because of the ubiquity of skills, and it just seems like a long, uphill climb...well, that's the struggle many are facing as they attempt to change their BI landscape.

Summary

Now that we have had a look at your current BI inventory and history, I hope it has given you some food for thought. It is apparent that cost-based assessments alone simply demonstrate the amount of money you have poured into BI.

An assessment should incorporate the number of users, deployment patterns, associated costs, and business value and ROI if you can provide them. Degree of displacement difficulty is very hard to assess without a fully cooperative effort. Displacements will contain things like actual costs, which are easy to obtain. They will also contain qualitative aspects, such as human skills invested and perception. These are often the most difficult to determine but must be a part of the overall effort.

Let's assume that you are on a course to change your approach to BI on an enterprise level. What are the deployment strategies available to you today, and what are their advantages or disadvantages? Which are pragmatic at the enterprise level?

4

The Scope of BI
Solutions Today and How
They May Relate to You

There are a myriad of deployment options available today, along with drivers of BI solutions. Let's define at least a basic framework or infrastructure for the majority of BI solutions available. They may reside on one or many platforms and possibly offsite. Assuming you have your vision statement in place and a clear definition of BI, the infrastructure should be something you can draw.

The BI Infrastructure

As mentioned earlier, there are many new deployment options available today in comparison with years and technologies past. The scope of solutions is broader than ever, while the underlying technologies have become increasingly more complex. I will not recommend one deployment over another; recommending one would be wrong, as there is no single "optimal" configuration. Rather, let's delve into current trends, newer options, and ancillary products and functions that may affect your decision.

I tend to look at a BI environment as a "layer cake" with definite tiers. Each tier has a profound influence upon a BI infrastructure. You may not diagram the infrastructure as I have shown, but we have to begin somewhere.

Figure 4-1 depicts a view of a BI infrastructure. At the bottom tier, we have our structured data sources layer. In your enterprise, this would be a view of all the data you provide in-house. It is the information you maintain within your span of control for all applications and use. Note that we have shown extract, transform, load (ETL) processes, as well as change data capture (CDC) as options from operational sources. Many installations are using data directly from operational sources today, as well as using it to feed to the normal warehouse build and update functions.

Business Intelligence Infrastructure Tiers

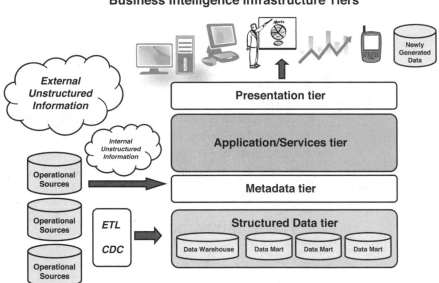

Figure 4-1   A BI infrastructure

In a tiered infrastructure, any additions to a particular layer should be easily implemented and not create havoc, such as major maintenance or having to reinstall. Adding a new data source should be relatively straightforward with established practices and procedures in the definition and metadata layers.

The metadata layer is absolutely critical to the entire structure. It is not only where you define the sources, but where you may opt to add definitions, calculations, and more. This is the often-discussed "single version of the truth."

NOTE

The greater the investment in the metadata layer, the less reliance upon BI tools to provide calculations and new data formats. It is one area where OLAP solutions shine, as they contain all the "math" required as well as the aggregations. The IF-THEN-ELSE aspects of many BI problems are resolved within OLAP cubes.

The application/services tier is where we offer our many BI functions such as query, reporting, analysis, and more. As in our data layer, the addition of a new or modified service should be easily incorporated into the existing functional layer. With the proper administration functions, it is also where we provide control over which users have access to specific functions.

I have omitted the administration functions from the diagram because they would apply to all layers and may be maintained on different platforms. For example, data definition and similar functions are often installed on a rich client workstation that communicates with the database tier, as well as other tiers. The definitions created are, in turn, sent to the BI server platform for use by the end users who only require a browser interface. Given the options of administration available, part of your mission should be to decide and control who has access to what.

For example, access to data is often controlled at the metadata access layer. End users are fed the values they are allowed to use for queries, reports, and so on. What if there is no control at the data layer? An end user with some savvy executes a statement such as SELECT * FROM TABLE, which would return all rows—and there goes security.

The presentation tier should offer a wide variety of output devices and styles that do not require a proprietary output driver to be defined. For example, if I create a report from a relational data source, I should be able to push it to any number of devices (PDA, spreadsheet, HTML, and so on) without having to create a specific report for each device.

NOTE

One output style that I find fascinating is the ongoing requirement to support output of data to spreadsheets such as Excel®. The exposure from the taking away of critical information that has been so carefully managed is very high. Nonetheless, it is most often an integral part of many BI infrastructures, and people live with the risks.

I have added two unstructured "clouds" of data: one for external information and one for internal information. Note I have not drawn any connections or processes in the mix because this is the state where we find most installations today. The view of information available to you may be more expansive and granular, but we at least have a picture to start with.

If we agree that this is an accurate pictorial of a standard BI infrastructure and that we want it to be extensible, open, and interoperable, where do we go for such a solution? What market factors have created this particular tiered approach? Is this the optimal view of a BI platform?

What deployment strategies exist, and is there an optimal solution for the enterprise? To pursue an enterprise BI agenda today, some hard and fast choices must be made. The very first and most important one of all is: Will you set a course for standardization and reduction of the number of BI tools in-house? (Yes, I keep hammering away at this.) Or will you pursue a multiple BI tool strategy and support an "approved list"? Let's look at various BI drivers, sources, and deployment options.

BI Drivers, Trends, Sources, and Deployment Options

There are numerous new factors driving BI decisions and deployments today. In the following sections, I describe some of them. Although the number of mainstream BI providers has been reduced by acquisitions, there are new ones emerging who offer different deployment models and architectures. For anyone wanting to develop and maintain an enterprise BI model, the challenges of making the best decision for the organization are significant.

Consider the range of solutions, from creating a full internal solution suite to farming out your BI to an outside provider and letting them worry about it. What is the best option for you? Would it be best to embrace several options depending upon your requirements? Let's dive in a bit deeper.

Mergers and Acquisitions—The Emergence of BI "Mega-Vendors"

When I wrote *BI for the Enterprise* in 2003, there were a number of independent BI vendors in the market. Several of them were perceived to be powerhouses, and all of them had a significant installed base. As the BI market evolved over the past decades, each BI vendor found itself extending its functions to include ETL processes, metadata mapping, data access connectors, and more. It was unavoidable, as one would make a technology move, forcing the others to follow. I predicted it would be somewhat like a house of cards once one large vendor absorbed another.

Lo and behold, we have seen several significant acquisitions since then. Beginning with Oracle taking Hyperion and Brio, we then saw SAP take Business Objects/Crystal Reports and finally, in late 2007, IBM acquired Cognos®. Then, in 2009, IBM acquired SPSS®. The implications were that each would continue to be "open" to solutions involving the competition but would also begin massive efforts to create tightly integrated solutions with the newly acquired technologies. Both IBM and Oracle provide enterprise-scale databases that enable them to provide the entire spectrum of the infrastructure depicted previously with the exception of the unstructured sources.

Some refer to these new powerhouse combinations as BI "mega-vendors." In the case of IBM and Oracle, the vendors provide a rich, deep set of database offerings and tools to support them. Ownership of a database should be considered an extremely critical aspect of a BI decision-making process. The mega-vendors offer connectivity to other databases besides their own, but the ones developed in-house will receive the lion's share of attention, development, and support.

We see the evolution of integrated BI platforms from these industry giants. Selecting one of these vendors today has implications for your future in many ways, as it makes sense that each would put forth its greatest effort in making its own unique combination of products to interoperate in a superior manner and distance itself from its competition. This is a work in progress today.

The option to embrace a single solution provider requires enormous trust upon your part that the path your favored provider is taking will be optimal for you at the technology and business levels. Looking at our preceding tiered diagram, we are suggesting that all functions will come from a single source, or at least the overwhelming majority of them will.

The mutual leverage between provider and customer has significant implications depending upon the size of the investment from both sides. The customer sees not only advantages in pricing, but they have influence upon the direction the vendor is going and may be able to influence certain decisions on feature and function in coming releases. I favor this option above all others provided both sides learn how to play fairly and an appropriate support infrastructure in put in place. Later on, when we discuss role-based BI and support, this will become clearer.

BI Suites/Platforms versus Independents

We also have a number of independent BI vendors each with their own strengths and unique capabilities. Some of these vendors are SAS, Information Builders, and MicroStrategy. Whereas large, complex BI suites are offered by vendors who also provide enterprise databases, the independents provide connections to a number of databases and do not favor a particular one over the other. They have to be able to connect to anything as they do not provide operational data stores of their own, although each does have its own file or database formats. The independents typically have a suite of their own ETL, CDC, and metadata layers designed to isolate the end users from the underpinning data.

Architecturally, we see entire BI platforms (acquisitions) and functional BI suites (independents) as the primary options at the enterprise level. Given the fact that most enterprises will have a smattering of several of these tools in-house, we face a set of difficult choices. Is it feasible to consider setting a course for BI standardization, or are we too far down the road with them and have to somehow evolve a coexistence strategy? We discuss BI standardization later, but this is a good time to plant the thought for discussion.

It helps to return to our definition of BI and the diagram shown previously and try to form a consensus in the enterprise that we all agree upon. It is extremely inefficient in many ways to support multiple BI platforms and suites. Given the need to provide several of the tiers as part of any BI solution, can't we just use one suite's tiers and utilize several BI front-end tools to work with the data? Once you have your data house in order, the need to utilize all elements of multiple suites diminishes.

Now we enter the precarious area of supporting multiple front-end tools, each with their unique set of functions, interfaces, peculiarities, and more. If we replace the presentation layer elements in our diagram with multiple tools, we have at least the majority of our infrastructure in a shape where we can move forward.

The reality most face is that there are many intermediate processes and steps in place from years of evolution within the installed BI tools inventory. As discussed earlier, once you have BI applications in place, it is challenging to eradicate or condense them. One approach is to look to the outside for managed services or even tools on the open source market that are extremely low cost.

Open Source BI Tools

There are several BI tools in play today on the "open" market. They range in function from simple web reporting to integrated, open suites. The overall perception in evaluating such tools is that they are less expensive than the traditional BI offerings. One's comfort zone is sorely tested when considering such solutions. This is especially true at the enterprise level. Even if a solution appears to be less costly and not as encumbering as others, be very wary of embracing such an option.

The greater the dependence upon tiers below the front-end tool layer, the greater the risk should one of these solutions ultimately fail. The open source BI providers have fallen into the same set of circumstances as all the other iterations of BI vendors over the years: the need to offer extensions beyond the basics of analytics. They also have to access every possible data source, and thus there will not be advantages in one database over another.

Open access to all sources of data is a good thing until you are looking for a tool to take advantage of a particular function, such as those found in many RDBMSs on the market. Generic access typically comes with less effective utilization of a source or the need to create and maintain specific drivers for a DBMS.

One aspect of an open source provider that comes up as a constant concern is the long-term viability and support they will provide. If your data is absolutely clean and orderly, and the supportive metadata is ideal for all your end users, you can afford to be a bit more "open" in your selection of tools. Remember that every BI tool comes with a price, even if it is perceived to be free. It will require system resources, support, training, tuning, debugging, and more. Nothing is free in the world of BI.

In Information Management online, Sunil Mistri (June 9, 2009) proposes that open source BI tools are gaining traction as part of an enterprise's BI infrastructure. The basis of the argument is centered upon TCO (total cost of ownership) which I disagree with but it may appeal to you. BI is about the business value not how inexpensive the tools and components are. However, the emerging open source BI tools market cannot be overlooked.

The other elements cited are:

- BI product selection and user requirements
- Complexity of development
- BI project timelines
- Product support and third party support
- Performance and scalability

I see nothing here that highlights business value. If you are going to accept an open source solution as part of the enterprise BI strategy then pay very close attention to the elements that are far beyond your span of control such as product support, enhancements, and training.

Software as a Service (SaaS)

One "modern" approach is to utilize an outside provider to host and provision a BI infrastructure. You can also create your own service-oriented architecture (SOA) for certain BI functions within reason. Some organizations will use a vendor's API to customize BI functions and isolate the base product from the end users.

A significant advantage to using outside providers is the ability to rely upon others who bring a wealth of expertise and integrated systems into play. Rather than having to unbuckle and rebuild from the inside, it may seem easier to leave it to the experts. However, what gets lost at times is the in-depth application and business process information necessary in a majority of BI applications.

You will pay for each and every service and function provided with this option, but that may not be a bad thing. If you are planning a renewed BI effort and really require a makeover, it could be the best option for you. This approach will quickly fall down if you do not have a true vision in place because you will pay out a lot of money for an ever-changing experiment.

There are a number of discussions and debates about SaaS. In the context of BI, it is an option that largely depends upon the underpinning data and the complexity of the BI services required. The range of resources taken by BI queries can wildly vary. The unpredictable nature of the resources taken by BI processes makes it difficult to assess how effective this option might be. We need to return to our definition of BI for our enterprise. Is it feasible to delegate your BI infrastructure to another?

One example of a very successful SaaS provider is Salesforce.com. Here we have a web-based provider with an entire application and data infrastructure in place to support a highly focused solution. However, the large BI vendors such as SAP (with Business Objects) and IBM (with Cognos) have entered this arena as well. You will find some interesting blogs on the subject as companies search for the perfect BI solution. Applications like Salesforce.com are easy to implement because there are known, customer sales-related functions and features everyone uses. There isn't a need to perform advanced analytics in such applications; they are very well structured and have inherent restrictions and discipline.

The provisioning of a well-defined and clearly understood BI mission to an outside provider becomes far more realistic as you simplify and restructure your global approach to BI. Adding a new SaaS BI solution to an already complex and anarchistic suite does little other than having at least one BI application maintained in a more orderly fashion.

On the other hand, if you have struggled with achieving success in-house and have a project with high ROI and minimum risk, going outside while you get your house in order may not be a bad idea, if done properly.

Cloud Computing

Cloud computing today provides a series of unique implementations and offerings. You can sign up for an external cloud (another form of Software as a Service), you can create a private cloud for internal processes, and you can develop an external cloud to offer to your customers and others.

There are many blogs and opinion sites that discuss BI clouds in-depth. One of the interesting aspects of cloud computing is the ability to lower your cost of doing business and for software vendors to make their software products and services available to more people 24×7.

Cloud computing is gaining a ton of interest for a number of reasons, but the most prevalent is the low cost of entry and the sheer convenience factor of having such services available.

Another aspect of cloud computing is the ability to provide massive deployments rapidly. IBM has implemented a BI cloud for System z based upon its internal success with deploying its investment in Cognos. The project used to develop the methodology provided the knowledge and lessons learned aspects to be able to make this offering public. This is currently a private cloud offering, but nothing precludes it from being expanded to external consumers.

Colin White of BeyeNETWORK stated the following in an article dated July 30, 2008:

> *Over the past few months, both mainstream and startup software vendors have been announcing a steady stream of hosted business intelligence (BI) solutions. The various terms used to describe these offerings are often confusing. Examples of terms here include* on-demand BI, BI software-as-a-service (SaaS), *and* BI in the cloud. *The objective of this article is to help reduce this confusion by explaining the technologies behind these terms and providing an overview of the capabilities they provide.*

You can find this article and many more published since then that go into great detail on the subject. Can a BI cloud service enterprise-level requirements? Given the many references, including IBM's, the answer is obviously, yes. Do not confuse a BI cloud with external hosting; that is just one version of a cloud.

If I look at cloud computing for BI at the enterprise level, I see an infrastructure where the data layers, the metadata provided, and the underpinning processes are all in superior order. The cloud then offers a series of services to sign up for such things as data to access, BI functions required, and more. In such cloud environments, a significant advantage is that scale and growth are the responsibility of the provider. Stringent service-level agreements accompany any cloud effort.

You can find numerous definitions of cloud computing on the Internet, including the following:

- en.wikipedia.org/wiki/Cloud_computing
- www.webopedia.com/DidYouKnow/Internet/2008/
  terms_to_know_2009.asp
- wekti.com/glossary/

- www.financenewmexico.org/glossary.html
- www.servepath.com/support/definitions.php

And there are many, many more. The point is, cloud computing is becoming more pervasive and is a growing area of interest in the BI space.

The best example I can think of regarding a BI cloud is IBM's own use of Cognos internally. IBM has announced a private cloud offering called the Smart Analytics Cloud based upon its own implementation of massive numbers of internal users enabled on a powerful set of mainframe servers. This project allowed IBM to consolidate a large number of distributed servers and the associated complexity and costs onto a small number of mainframes.

A critical success factor in doing so was the development of best practices and methodologies to allow potential users to subscribe to services with minimal IT involvement (see Information Week online November 16, 2009). The IBM solutions are delivered to over 100,000 users and growing. It is an ideal model of dynamic infrastructure and deployment for large-scale BI.

BI Appliances

BI appliances tout a consistent set of advantages in their value propositions. They are economical, fast, and scalable. The overwhelming advantage here is they are dedicated to BI processes and nothing else. They do not come with their own internal data; thus, each has a methodology and architecture for adding and updating data. Live feeds are built into the typical appliance.

As data volumes have grown, and the complexities of queries and analysis have increased, traditional approaches to accessing, processing, and delivering required results into data have often fallen short. In many cases, the performance and scale of legacy data warehouses and relational databases has not kept pace with the growth of data volumes and complexity.

Appliances come in many shapes and sizes. Some come in the form of bundled hardware and software, and some may be software only. If there is a business area that can benefit greatly from an appliance for BI, it should be considered very seriously. The appeal here is much like that of a cloud computing environment: The infrastructure is self-contained. Where they break down is in being able to link the appliance with other areas of the business. For targeted BI solutions, they can be the best choice.

Offerings available on the market today vary widely in scope. For example, IBM and SAP have a combined BI appliance offering solution for very large, very complex enterprise BI requirements. IBM's Cognos arm had acquired Celequest prior to their acquisition by IBM and produced the Cognos*Now!* BI appliance that is positioned for SMB BI environments or larger. It is deployed either on-site or via a hosted/on-demand approach. There are other, "open source" appliances that consist of software-only appliances designed to run as virtual machines. Such offerings may be loaded onto a variety of hardware platforms.

This is a good compromise and a reasonable approach as an open source play because it does not require a particular hardware platform or vendor. The hardware choice is left up to you, the customer.

Dynamic Warehousing—Extending Beyond Structured Information

The concept of dynamic warehousing is an approach that acknowledges the fact that a single, mega-warehouse is not realistic for enterprise accounts. The proliferation of data across databases, platforms, forms, and formats within the typical enterprise drives this initiative. The concept is to implement the tiered approach to warehousing and BI, whereby any and all "layers" are extensible and interoperable.

Going back to the massive amounts of unstructured information in the world, dynamic warehousing would accommodate new formats and sources. In the unstructured data areas, we see several advantages with dynamic warehousing. First, we have added it to our definition of BI, as well as targeted it for use with our end users. Including unstructured information to our data sources and exposing it within BI applications adds a new dimension to our ability to monitor events that occur outside our structured data warehouse. It also sets a framework for creating structured BI data out of unstructured sources.

Joseph Rozenfeld wrote an interesting article in *Information Management Magazine* (February 2007). Mr. Rozenfeld states:

> *Today's information environment has evolved in ways that would have been hard to envision for the early pioneers of business intelligence (BI). The data landscape now encompasses a dizzying array of new information channels, new sources of data, and new analysis and reporting imperatives. According to*

analyst groups, nearly 80 percent of today's data is unstructured, and new information channels such as web, email, voice over IP, instant messaging (IM), and text messaging are rapidly creating huge stores of nontraditional data. Never has there been a better opportunity to gain real insight from data—or a bigger challenge for BI practitioners and technologists. While most businesses are eager to turn this new data into useful information, many find that their current BI technology, designed for a simpler data landscape, cannot deliver robust and thorough analysis of mission-critical unstructured data.

There are many articles written since then, but he captures the essence of the dilemma most businesses face: They have not tackled this sticky problem, and few have a plan in place to use unstructured data for BI purposes. Thus, we define dynamic warehousing in the context of data as having global reach and extending far beyond our internal walls.

From the BI perspective, this means that our front-end tool(s) must be able to consume or co-reside with unstructured information. The "dynamic" part suggests the infrastructure must be malleable and extensible without a massive architectural change. It also provides motivation for our move toward a standardization agenda (I am making a major assumption here!).

Another aspect of dynamic warehousing is the ability to place multiple information packages on the screen and possibly tie them together via a "mashup." Events that are permitted and desired "on the glass," such as wiring different output results together, should be an inherent part of your BI infrastructure. The advantage of coordinating events from different systems and sources is far easier to implement and more dynamic in nature than trying to build and load the ultimate mega-warehouse.

Continuous updating of the information in our structured data warehouse(s) is another aspect of dynamic warehousing. The dynamic warehouse concept has been refined and expanded since its inception in 2006. One might call a BI appliance an example of dynamic warehousing brought together in a practical and definable solution.

So, we envision dynamic data, unstructured information, and a modern BI suite capable of utilizing these elements in a scalable and well-managed environment. This expansion of the traditional data warehouse has caused many an enterprise to rethink their goals and objectives.

Operational and Real-Time BI

Today, people want and need information right now. We have morphed into a global society where news and events and more are known instantly, thanks to the Internet. BI has taken on the same characteristics. Information that affects a business plan or a critical decision may be available now but wasn't a moment ago. Individuals who provide customer service types of interactions need data that is absolutely current. Access to detailed operational data falls into the category of operational BI that is called operational intelligence.

Claudia Imhoff, well-known industry pundit, stated in October 2008 (well-blogged, by the way):

> Operational BI is becoming quite the buzz today. There are countless articles, tips, vendors with operational BI offerings, case studies, etc., available today. Yet, I still get asked the very basic question of how do you get started. What are the first steps? Well, here are my thoughts on how to get started....
>
> I plan to focus a lot of my attention on operational BI this year and next. It is a fascinating and critical form of business intelligence but it is also quite foreign to traditional BI implementers for one very big reason—it requires climbing back into the world of operations and truly understanding the processes, procedures, and workflows of operations. We in the BI space were happy to turn our backs on operational procedures and processes, choosing to create a completely separate world where we could store our data and then analyze it until the cows come home. We gave little thought or care about what was happening in operations. That was the operational IT folks' problem....

One major objective of an operational BI system is to react faster to business needs and to anticipate business problems in advance. Operational BI processing requires tighter connections between the BI system and collaborative users. It absolutely requires timely and detailed data not typically stored in a warehouse. The timeliness of operational data varies by industry and application. Data mining algorithms are often associated with operational BI applications, as customer profiling or fraud detection are often extremely valuable to customer-facing applications.

Real-time BI and operational BI are not synonymous, although their attributes tend to be. Real-time is more of a generic attribute or adjective we apply to the majority of BI solutions today. However, let's go back to our corporate definition of BI. Have we added a clause concerning operational or real-time BI as a part of the mandate? If it is not part of the plan, when do you introduce it?

In one customer visit (insurance industry), the organization was maintaining a data warehouse on a mainframe as well as spinning off some application-oriented data marts. The cycle they had established was to fully refresh the data once a month using internal programs and processes they had developed to address very specific analyses.

The calculations and aggregations they were using were quite sophisticated, so don't let the latency of the data fool you. However, they had been listening to their users, as well as paying a lot of attention to what their competition was up to. They were looking at ways to provide near real-time data to their end users, as well as more operational processes via the Internet.

In order to do so, they would have to perform a drastic revamping of their entire infrastructure on the data warehousing side, as well as look at a new set of BI tools in order to support this venture. The lag time of the data in relation to their competitor's services was the primary motivator. The end users had been complaining for a long time about latency, but that was not deemed critical enough until they started to lose market share.

This situation had nothing to do with platform choice or even the BI provider. The corporate attitude toward BI was one of having BI provide a periodic look into how they were doing and showing trends in relation to historical information. The world has changed, and so must they.

ETL and Change Data Capture—Their Impact and Importance on BI

ETL stands for extract, transform, and load. You will also see the term ELT, which is extract, load, and transform. The interposing of the transform and load functions is the determinant. It has a great deal to do with where the data is initially captured and where it is to be loaded. If the data is to be moved from one platform to another, it may be more efficient and less costly to do it on the target platform.

In the BI world, this is by far one of the most critical areas to pay attention to because it determines the success or failure of your BI initiatives. Why is this? Your data determines every step and every process your BI environment will address. If the data is of poor quality, there will be no trust. If the data is too dated, decision making will always be a step behind. If the data is not available at the proper level (for example, too high level and aggregated for general use), the user population will be restricted.

There is another area of ETL-ELT that deserves special attention—dimensionality. In developing a data warehouse or data mart, the typical approach is to create a new database in a format that is optimized for BI queries. BI queries tend to be multi-dimensional in that users tend to probe the data along lines of aggregation, such as total sales by area and so on.

Figure 4-2 depicts a star-schema structure where the values being queried (numeric) are contained in the central fact table. The dimensions by which we look at aggregations are stored in fact tables. There are other designs similar to this, such as a snowflake structure, but the star schema is a good place to start.

A Typical Star Schema Database

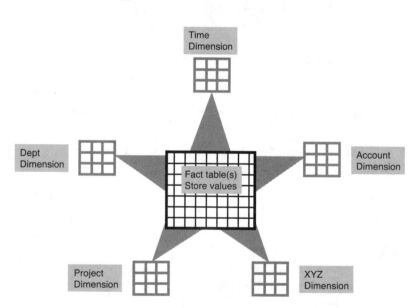

Figure 4-2 Star schema

Modern BI-oriented ETL-ELT offerings are designed to take data from source systems and put it through the proper processes as rapidly as possible in order to keep the data warehouse or mart up to date and accurate. The implications of these processes mostly lie in the quality of the data and the application type. For example, let's assume it is customer data that we capture on a system that has been in place for a long, long time.

We have issues with proper identification and accuracy of customers' information at the point of capture, so we perform our cleanup after the point of capture. Our intention is to load and use the accurate customer information both in a data warehouse as well as within an operational BI portal. We have a need to provide an alerting mechanism for our customer service representatives, as some customers have been shown to be less than reliable to the point where we will not allow new purchases. There is also the threat of fraud in some cases.

We have several logic and processing points to address in the scenario, as follows:

- Our data at point of capture is not verified and cleansed accurately—do we rewrite the front end or add routines to that capture process?
- If we do not perform the verification and cleansing at point of capture, we must do this post capture. Do we correct the data in the source database or move it along to an operational data store and perform these steps at that stage?
- If we intend to use the data for operational purposes as well as a data warehouse, it must be clean and accurate prior to loading to either source, and it makes sense to only clean it once.
- We believe the best methodology is to clean it prior to loading/updating our ODS and then use the single version to load/update the data warehouse.
- The ODS will provide our source for our customer service application.
- Our BI tool must efficiently handle both ODS and DW data, as well as be able to call a data mining routine we have been working on.

We have a very specific set of functions that involve the ETL layer. Where we capture our initial source data and where we host our data warehouse will strongly influence the infrastructure. In many cases, I have seen the situation where the existing ETL-ELT infrastructure is too restrictive to address the scope we've just described. Most BI vendors offer integrated suites for ETL processes supporting their tools, but do they service a larger picture such as our scenario?

Master Data Management (MDM) and Its Role within a BI Infrastructure

There are endless articles and blogs on MDM in conjunction with business intelligence. The goal has always been to provide a unified and accurate version of the truth regarding data definitions. Who is the customer, and where does the ultimate definition reside? Where is the definitive sales data, and how do I know it is accurate? What on earth is this term I see in corporate reports? Where did these things come from, and how do I know they are accurate?

Without a solid MDM infrastructure for BI that is approved and supported across the enterprise, you will never develop the user confidence that is required at the enterprise level. The age-old story of different people walking into a meeting with different results from the same data (or so they thought) has been repeated endlessly. Unfortunately, this is only too true.

MDM is primarily an IT project and a massive one, but it needs to incorporate the business side as well. For example, let's say we have a calculated (formula) value we would like to provide in our metadata layer and make sure all users are operating off the same definition. We choose to do this so the business users do not have to figure out how to create this calculation in every report, chart, and other BI object.

If formulae and calculated values change periodically, how do I know if I am using the latest one? If I am doing a historical comparison, it may well be that I need to use the older formula for older data and the newer one past a specific date. As BI processing, formulae, and underpinning data change constantly, it is a huge challenge to keep it all aligned.

MDM solutions are considered part of data governance, which is the greater discipline that includes data security, definition, reliability, and more.

Figure 4-3 shows a few of the issues prevalent with data in the typical enterprise. The schematic of data and its many connections can look like the circuitry on a computer chip. In efforts to ensure proper data governance, the issues are: Who owns the master record, and where does the validation and cleansing take place?

Data Quality and Governance a Persistent Problem

- Most enterprises are running distinct sales, services, marketing, manufacturing and financial applications, each with its own "master" reference data.

- No one system is the universally agreed-to system of record.

- Enterprise Application Vendors do not guarantee a complete & accurate integrated view – they point to their dependence on the quality of the raw input data.

- Data quality continues to erode at the point entry, though it is not a data entry problem.

Figure 4.3   Issues of data quality and governance

Somewhere, somehow, someone needs to develop an MDM strategy and enforce it with the proper technologies that adhere to your enterprise standards. Note that even enterprise application vendors do not provide guarantees because the data entry point is always open to human error.

MDM and associated data quality, validation, and verification functions are designed to ensure a single version of the truth. MDM is the underpinning 'super-glue" that binds an effective enterprise strategy together. So many surveys and presentations concerning BI today present 'facts' about some percentage of users or executives don't trust their data Regardless of the percentages touted by many in the industry, this should be something you evaluate as it relates to your own infrastructure. If you are uncomfortable with the accuracy and validity of your data, then an MDM strategy should be the first part of your plan.

The Impact of XML Data

If we consider the growth of XML data, we see that it began in 1998 and has evolved into a World Wide Web Consortium (W3C) standard. It was first proposed as a format for defining data markup languages that describe a document's content and logical structure. XML documents consist of data values and "tags" (markup) that describe the data—for example, <phone>123-456-7890</phone>.

More and more we see the need to support XML data as a BI source. The beauty of XML is that it can contain such a rich mixture of information, both structured and unstructured. Assuming that you can access and render XML data with a BI tool, there are far greater options for data storage and discovery.

Using XML, businesses can specify a wide variety of data using a format that applications running on any platform can easily import and process. XML is increasingly being used by companies and government agencies as an internal data format for capturing data from electronic forms, such as W3C standard XForms. It is also used for modeling their business.

Many XML-based industry standards have been developed to provide a common format to simplify the exchange and processing of data across and within companies. Some examples of these standards, in a variety of industries, are Association of Cooperative Operations Research (ACORD) in insurance, Financial Information eXchange Markup Language (FIXML) in finance, Health Level 7 (HL7) in healthcare, National Information Exchange Model (NIEM) for government agencies, Association for Retail Technology Standards (ARTS) for retail, Universal Business Language (UBL) for business documents such as invoices, and Modernized e-File (MeF) for tax filing. And there are more.

In the past, anyone wanting to process and store XML had limited options. They either placed the full XML content into a giant string and stored it in a file system or a database large object (CLOB or BLOB) column, or parsed (i.e., shredded) the XML to extract specific elements and discarded the rest, storing the extracted items in columns in relational tables.

The first option did meet regulatory requirements, but it was highly inefficient, since each access of the data required a transfer of the whole document for re-parsing in order to access the desired content. The second option caused a loss of the context in the original XML document, as well as loss of the discarded content. The inefficiencies and overhead made XML an awkward format to deal with despite its attractiveness.

XML data can be queried with standard SQL, but this is far less efficient than XQUERY. There are also hybrid forms for XML access. I will just assume you have an XML plan in place and applaud you for it. I have already mentioned the enormous volumes of data in the world and its rampant growth. As more and more information is accessed and delivered through web interfaces, the more uptake we will see in XML as a data source.

The industry standard databases all support XML in varying degrees. Your selection of any BI tool should involve a very serious discussion of XML support and directions by the vendor. Discussions around XML data sources will require an in-depth study of both the database and the BI tool.

BI Provisioning Models—What Is Best for You?

Here is where I delve into pure conjecture and extreme bias. I am always a proponent of maximum control over your own destiny. If I had to rank BI provisioning models from high to lower value, I would place them in the following order in terms of value:

- Single solution provider—an Enterprise BI Suite.
- Single-tiered backbone infrastructure with a limited set of BI tools that do not overlap in function.
- Private cloud for enterprise deployment, where users subscribe to a set of services and are isolated from specific BI tools.
- BI appliance for specific application usage.
- Software as a service from an outside provider.

What I have seen in 99% of the organizations that I have worked with is that their BI requirements continuously change. The business does not stand still and new pressures and innovations force a constant reevaluation of how best to support these changes.

When you turn to the outside for BI support, you often lose the ability to react quickly enough to change. You find yourself constantly discussing and negotiating your infrastructure and requirements as the world moves on. The only exception I have seen is where a targeted application area with very specific requirements that have not changed much (especially in the shape of the data) is in play.

From an enterprise perspective, it is essential that provisioning is firmly agreed to and the implications of each form are clearly understood. When you opt for an outside source, for example, your end users will pay for everything they use. If they are not very BI literate or data savvy, they will crank out usage costs that may be hard to justify. If the business changes dramatically, every change is going to cost you. The question is: "Which option is less expensive or more easily modified...internal or external?"

Establishing a BI Competency Center (BICC)

I am also a shameless proponent of setting up a BICC regardless of how you have chosen to deploy your BI infrastructure. Someone must own the mission to ensure that the proper expectations are set, skills are developed and grown, and the proper solutions are set in place and monitored.

Forget about deployments for a moment and think about what the normal scenario looks like when you have multiple BI tools in house and no BICC. You have pockets of expertise, no structured "hub" to ensure that the correct tool is selected, no users trained properly, no measurement of ROI or business value, and no mechanism for growth. These roles and functions are assumed with a BICC.

In *Business Intelligence for the Enterprise* (Mike Biere, Upper Saddle River, NJ: IBM Press, 2003), I devoted a section to promoting and defending the need for a BICC. In the years since then, I have seen a huge number of articles emerge about the value and need for a BICC, but the uptake in enterprise accounts has been low.

This lack of a BICC clashes with the emerging trend among CIOs that BI is mission critical—yes, I am beating that drum again. In many cases, there is a perceived BICC where skills are spread out within different user populations. In such cases, there are known pockets of expertise in specific tools. Where do these local experts go when they have a problem?

I return to the vision statement I put forth in the first chapter of this book. This sample statement clearly calls out a BICC as part of the enterprise infrastructure for BI. Without one, you will continue to see disjointed BI efforts and far less coordination across the corporation. One area that will suffer greatly is that of a shared, common set of skills in the BI tool(s) installed. Everyone either discovers the same BI tidbit independently or they glean skills from others who may not be doing a particular function well at all...it's all they know how to do!

Creating an Information Agenda

This concept is primarily an IBM-initiated one, but I think it applies to all technologies and all enterprise accounts. An information agenda is really the basis for all we've discussed so far. The creation of an information agenda ensures that all the piece parts are being considered and the plan is approved by all.

Figure 4-4 shows the four pillars of such an agenda. We tie our business priorities to our data both currently in existence as well as data we are considering. Our strategy is enforced with road maps that clearly map our current data assets and utilize open, flexible technologies to ensure we can accommodate the future.

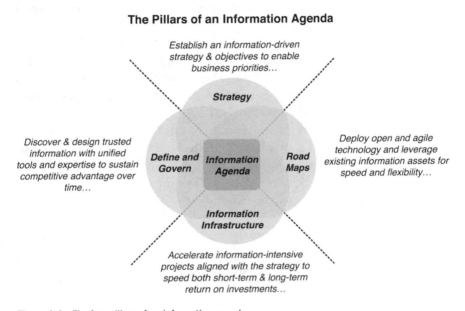

The Pillars of an Information Agenda

Establish an information-driven strategy & objectives to enable business priorities...

Strategy

Discover & design trusted information with unified tools and expertise to sustain competitive advantage over time...

Define and Govern   **Information Agenda**   **Road Maps**

Deploy open and agile technology and leverage existing information assets for speed and flexibility...

Information Infrastructure

Accelerate information-intensive projects aligned with the strategy to speed both short-term & long-term return on investments...

Figure 4-4   The four pillars of an information agenda

We define and govern our data assets with the creation of trusted information in mind. All this may sound a bit "noble" and fluffy, but these are the terms and goals used by those who aspire to deliver lasting, expansive BI infrastructures.

In your world, I assume that you are looking at this from the perspective of how these wonderful terms relate to BI. If you take the elements of your vision statement and your definition of BI, you can drop them on the four different pillars and see if there is a high degree of affinity. I also assume that you are a BI strategist at some level in the organization;

thus, you have influence within your enterprise that relates to BI. You could take the chart shown here, replace information agenda with BI, and hardly change a word.

Summary

Given the vast array of deployment options and the increased complexity of most BI infrastructures, an enterprise must set a BI course very carefully. Regardless of deployment models, a BI competency center is crucial to your success.

An overreaching BI consensus is imperative for success and growth, as well as keeping all technology decisions within the framework of the vision you have established. The changing world of data and formats such as XML has had a huge impact upon BI solutions today, as has the push toward real-time or operational BI.

As powerhouse vendors acquire and consolidate their offerings, new resources such as open source providers have arisen. Self-contained BI appliances are attractive offerings if their focus is upon a specific business area. It all goes back to the data at hand for BI. It is either accurate or it is not. It is either timely or it is not. It is both available and secure, or it is not.

The enterprise deployment model and infrastructure selected are not as easily ripped out and replaced as in years past; thus, the selection of vendor(s) and model(s) requires more careful thought than ever.

5

Elements of BI Solutions: The End User Experience

I listed components of most BI solutions earlier, but here I want to delve a bit deeper into each of them in the context of personal experience and how an end user is affected or influenced by each. This chapter is aimed primarily at the new or novice end user. If you have had extensive hands-on BI experience, this is probably a bit rudimentary for you.

If you support end users or are responsible for training them, it may help to have them read this chapter. Setting the proper expectations and goals to attain realistic skills are paramount to success. Allowing naïve assumptions to run wild with the end user community is a formula for disaster. So, what does an end user need to know?

End User Assumptions

To begin with, drop any and all assumptions about usage of any BI tool if you have not had any experience with it before. Even if you have had some experience with another tool, you will drive yourself crazy comparing Product A to Product B. The chance that two tools do the same thing the same way is very, very slim.

The very first thing I recommend is to get an outline of the data you will be working with. I assume you will be accessing at least one database that will have column names you will use in creating your BI output (reports, charts, and so on). You probably have no control over this data unless you have been involved in the early stages to define it.

You are obviously intending to use the information handed to you to produce something of business value. In such a case, you have some idea of the analyses and output you anticipate producing. Now once you have the data definitions in hand, the next step is to write down descriptions of the output and analyses you hope to complete.

For example, let's say you intend to create quarterly sales revenue reports that will require totals at the end of some logical grouping (department or sector), as well as detailed information for each quarter. Your management has requested that the report also contain a column with running totals for each week of the quarter. Just when you are about to get started, the problem changes a bit to where the report must now include annual comparisons where the years are to be ranked in terms of total sales from highest to lowest. And later, some other new criteria get thrown in.

Any credible BI tool can produce a report like this, but the question is: "What level of skill is required to produce it?" Depending upon how your organization is structured and how training is delivered, this could be a straightforward task or an onerous one.

Whenever I have been asked to create a report in any BI tool, I always take the time to draw a crude representation on paper and, if there is anyone with some expertise nearby, I try to sit with them and see if the output I am proposing is feasible. I never assume anything other than whatever I have been asked to do will probably take longer than I imagined.

Another assumption you need to discard is promising any specific output format without knowing how easy the result is to produce. Many of us are accustomed to using a tool like Excel, where the placement of the data on the sheet and the capability to calculate any grouping of cells can be done in a BI tool. This is erroneous as Excel provides a totally free-form approach to data and its placement. You can, for example, define an entity that is comprised of a collection of cells that are scattered throughout an Excel sheet. Typical BI tools have to be dealt with in a rows and columns structure and tend to be more rigid in their ability to define ranges of values. Specific placement capabilities of BI output must never be assumed; this is a dangerous area for the uninitiated.

The important thing to accomplish is to create the output with clean, accurate data and present it in some manner that is clear and logical for interpretation. Try not to fall into the trap where someone absolutely must have it a particular way without knowing if the output can be created in that manner. I have seen reports that were 95% completed in a very short time, and then someone took hours and hours to complete the remaining 5% because, "It has to be that way!" Assume nothing, and question everything.

Setting Up Data for BI

The most effective BI endeavors are those where careful mapping of the business problems to be tackled are matched by supporting data in the right "shape." The emergence of data warehousing structures, such as star-schema databases, was a result of the many years of end user queries being thrown at databases where aggregations and groupings were always a part of the queries. It proved to be far more efficient to build new structures optimized for queries across different dimensions and groupings.

Sometimes you will find that the data provided seems to work for most individuals, but it is awkward for your purposes. Perhaps you have to utilize extensive calculations and functions to finish your task, and this must be done for every new report. It would be far better to go back to your data creation and support personnel and see if there is a way to solve this complexity with a different view of the data. In many cases, new information doesn't have to be created (such as a new database), but a fresh new shape can be provided using the same data.

The types of queries and the behavior of your usage will be very influential on the optimal shape of the data you need to access. For example, it is common for some end users to want to access multiple views of data by slicing, drilling, and manipulating the data from a variety of views. Such behavior favors an OLAP source where the typical paradigm is to slice, dice, and drill. However, OLAP viewers often have a reduced set of reporting capabilities. This cuts into the heart of many end user usage dilemmas: Are you trying to solve a problem, or make something look pretty? There are times when you can do both, and times when you cannot.

NOTE

I always recommend a "white board" session with the end users and IT. The drawing out of the data and usage scenarios face to face can cut through a myriad of misunderstandings and misconceptions.

From your perspective, it is imperative to understand the depth of skill and the functions you will require to accomplish your goals. If it looks too hard and you do not understand how to do it, stop! Don't get into the mind set of, "I don't want to appear a dummy, so I'll work on it later."

Figure 5-1 depicts a rudimentary planning (white board) session with some of the outcome items from the meeting. This may seem a bit simplistic, but I have done these many times, and every session has yielded some unpleasant surprises.

Aligning the Data with Usage – A Working Session

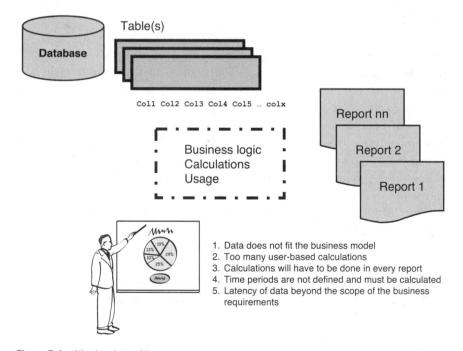

Figure 5-1   Aligning data with usage

NOTE

It is imperative to understand the seriousness of misaligned data in the context of BI applications. Once you have agreed to a design, shape, and format, it will be locked in for quite some time. If the situation is serious enough, it will be compensated for later, and you are back on the road of constant sorrow. Questions about the alignment of data with BI processes must be addressed and not avoided. This is particularly true at the enterprise level.

The Functional Area of BI Tools

There is a fundamental set of functions every BI tool is expected to be able to perform such as query, reporting, charting, and more. In the BI market, vendors strive to outdo their competitors by adding many gadgets and features that they hope are appealing as well as providing a competitive edge over others. In this section I will cover the more essential aspects of BI tools and shy away from the more esoteric options. The options and functions that are really needed to provide a solid BI foundation are confined to a core set. It is imperative that you do not let the end users get stars in their eyes over some "'cool" functions that provide little or no business value to the enterprise.

Query Tools and Reporting

About 99% of the time, you will be working with a relational database, which implies that you will be issuing SQL statements to query the data. The tool selected will have an interface often referred to as a GUI (a "gooey" or graphical user interface). The most common query and reporting interface is one where the data is presented in a part of the window, and there is an open palette where you drag and drop the columns onto it and watch magic happen.

The first things to understand are the various options available (icons, drop-down lists, and so on) and their behavior. If you are still in the evaluation phase, you are in a marvelous place to shake down the intended BI tool. Question #2 after taking any action should be: "Where is the undo function?" Some tools offer full forgiveness, and some only offer partial forgiveness. This is especially true when you have played around with the interface itself by repositioning panes and other features. How do you get back to the original view? If you cannot, you should be very wary of this solution.

One of the primary attractions of most BI tools is to mask the SQL statements created beneath the GUI so that complex syntax does not have to be dealt with. It is also important that the tool be able to expose the underpinning SQL statements if a tech wants to look at them to see what is happening, in case there is a performance issue or the answers generated seem a bit off.

Some report writers generate the results immediately upon dropping the data values on the palette and some will defer showing the results until you press a RUN button. I prefer an immediate feedback style, but this is more about personal preference.

Be aware that most tools either have a governor in place or the capability to implement one that limits the number of rows returned to a report while you are in creation mode. Tools that impose a governing function then have the capability to execute the report against all rows. The execution style of your report writer needs to be clearly understood. This is especially important when you are running a POC, so you clearly understand any differences between running a report with limited data and a report with the full answer set behind it.

With the emergence of thin client tools (browser-based), the entire query and report creation function is handled by a back-end process. Some BI tools provide a subset of the function in thin client mode and then require a "rich client" workstation to perform the more sophisticated work. Such tools rely upon workstation size and speed for functions. If you are going to utilize such technology, be aware of which functions are offered in the different modes.

Some tools provide a separate query and report style of interface or at least offer this as an option. By separating the two, it enables you to use a query for multiple reports, charts, and other purposes. The downside of this is you have to remember to link the query to the report if the tool doesn't remember what query it ran with a particular report.

I stated earlier that BI functional definitions do not go deeply enough in most RFP/RFI situations I have seen. Query and reporting execution styles rarely make it to the checklist. Quite often, I have heard a new user, and even some experienced ones, say: "Gee, I didn't know it did that!" It's a bit late in the cycle to bring up such opinions.

If you are a spreadsheet user, think about when you first started play-ing around with the worksheets and cells and all the odd things that have become second nature. Or, think about the last car you bought that had dramatically different options, gadgets, and ways of doing things.

NOTE

You need to establish a comfort zone with a query and reporting tool at the interface level. The worst possible thing you can do is to just dive in and play around without a purpose. Do not begin creating a report that is targeted for production use before you know how to drive the engine.

OLAP and Advanced Analytics

Next, we look at OLAP and more advanced analytics. I am going to assume you are not an OLAP cube developer but an end user. In the advanced analytics area, I will assume the same. Those who build OLAP cubes or develop output in the more advanced areas of BI understand the underlying technology, or you wouldn't be able to do it.

As an OLAP user, you will be working with an interface (possibly even Excel) to slice, dice, and drill up, down, and around your data. OLAP cubes are filled with numbers, not text fields, and are for special-ized usage. Certain OLAP cubes are also good for "What If?" scenarios because you can change values, write back the data, and then perform a series of views into the business.

Depending upon the technology, OLAP cubes have a standard para-digm in their creation. Data is accessed (source data), it is passed through a builder process, and a proprietary cube is created that you now work with. They take time to build and will contain historical information.

Some solutions providers offer a "drill-through" capability, where the OLAP cube can reference back to a database and call for more data "on demand." Much of this is driven by the fact that OLAP cubes tend to be built for use "just in case" the data is needed. By that I mean the cubes are built for all the *intended* use. In scenarios where the maximum time to build a cube (typically batch) is reached, people start looking for drill-through options to be able to deliver a larger "virtual cube" environment.

Would it not be better to have a clearer view of what the end users are really looking at and build OLAP sources accordingly? Setting up drill-through functions has become a lot easier technically, but the reasons for doing so are often driven by poor planning. The concept of OLAP has one basic premise, as well as one major BI benefit: The basic idea is speed. You can grab on to a cube and slice, dice, and drill to your heart's content. OLAP is made for investigatory work so the user doesn't have to issue query after query against a database that is time and resource consuming. Because the data is loaded and calculated, there is an element of freeze-frame analysis to OLAP. There are solutions that provide dynamic cubes, thus offering a more near real-time scenario. But OLAP is primarily about speed.

A second benefit—and, to me, the more significant one—is that OLAP processes take all the "math" and apply it appropriately for all values across all dimensions (assuming that the math is not erroneous). All the IF-THEN-ELSE logic in contained within the cube(s) and isolates the end user from making mathematical errors.

I believe that OLAP processing is extremely valuable for certain applications and should be considered with the enterprise's BI planning. However, I also believe that many OLAP offerings get away from their core strengths by trying to be all things to all people. The situations where I find OLAP to be less valuable are those where the end user population tends to be OLAP dominant and wants to drive all queries and all analyses through the OLAP front end.

NOTE

Clearly understand the building process in relation to your data. It is imperative that you firmly grasp what is required to build the OLAP cubes, the timeliness, and the limitations, such as having a cap on the size of an OLAP cube based upon internal file limitations or the batch window available to build them. It is also key to understand that effective use of OLAP technologies can significantly reduce the overhead on a traditional relational database by offering an alternative to the masses of queries that would have to be executed to mimic the OLAP data.

For advanced analytics, we typically think of predictive models and data mining. Such analyses are usually the domain of a small set of end users in the enterprise. Data mining in particular is a useful tool for performing deep analysis to discover trends or patterns that enable you to deliver high-value information.

Where you fall into a trap with the advanced analytics offerings is when the vendor has extended the functional possibilities to traditional BI actions, such as reporting. In these scenarios, the vendor has gotten off their game plan. Keep focused upon the business goals and how the particular tools are to be used.

If you are looking at a provider for advanced analytics, my recommendations are as follows:

- Keep the usage to the advanced analytics processes and try to avoid using functions that exceed the vendor's core strengths.
- Look for a provider who can directly access your database(s) and avoid extracts.
- Make sure the results (output) are understandable for the average business user—stay away from rocket science interpretations.
- Buy only what you need (seats and so on), and try not to be tempted to stretch the vendor's capabilities.
- Understand the business value and applicability by the end users...validate the capability of such a solution to deliver what is expected.
- Always demand a proof of concept (POC) by the vendor.

OLAP and advanced analytics are extremely useful tools but they are not targeted toward the general population. They need to be thoroughly tested and kept within the scope of their basic design points and not be proliferated, where they offer little or no value.

ROLAP Solutions Versus OLAP

I mentioned relational OLAP (ROLAP) earlier. This approach is where the database engine serves up OLAP-like data using the engine itself to mimic a cube. The language typically used to query multi-dimensional sources is called multi-dimensional expressions (MDX).

More and more vendors are piling on to the support and use of MDX within their portfolio. Much like the SQL language when it emerged, MDX offers a standard means of querying data in a multi-dimensional language.

By having a database that can handle MDX queries, you are opening the door to being able to build dynamic cubes and smaller cubes—the query only builds what is requested instead of all possible combinations, just in case they are needed.

One issue of ROLAP versus OLAP is that it may not perform with the blinding speed of a true OLAP engine. However, depending upon the vendor, the resulting cubes may be stored in memory and made available to others. This can have a very attractive use for a wider audience where they are looking at freedom from heavy OLAP cube building and may need to view data that is a bit more current.

ROLAP, like OLAP, has significant advantages in processing compared to traditional queries if it provides a caching mechanism. For example, if numerous people share the same data and tend to execute similar queries, a ROLAP solution could cache the results (after the first person executes it) and make it available for subsequent users. Once built, a virtual cube is pretty fast, and now additional queries do not need to go back to the database.

NOTE

The options for embracing OLAP versus ROLAP should be clearly understood by the end user community. The data-mapping session I recommended earlier should have a healthy discussion about such options. Do you need absolute speed? Do you need sophisticated "math" applied accurately at all levels? Does the ROLAP solution provide the same calculation capabilities as the OLAP solutions we have looked at?

Understanding the Critical Role of Time Dimensionality

I seem to be hitting 100% on this topic when I ask data modelers, OLAP developers, and BI analysts/technicians which dimension is the most critical in the data modeling piece. For those who have worked on and designed a data warehouse, a data mart, or an OLAP solution, you will, no doubt, understand why I am raising this issue.

Every BI query has an aspect of time to it. People want to know how much of ____ was produced or sold or lost in the last ____ compared to the previous _____. It is how we think in business terms and is critical to the delivery of BI output of value.

The problem I most often see is that the users see a value for DATE in the data being modeled or provided and they make that critical error once again...they assume they can treat the DATE or TIME dimensions any way they want. We look at dates and times in aggregations or blocks of time; thus, aggregations by year, quarter, and so on are to be expected. Now do you think it is trivial to calculate groupings of this year's data in terms of percentage increase over the previous year?

It's time to go back to the white board session or when you are preparing for a training session. Have your BI analyses in mind, jot them down, and ask specific questions about how you will accomplish this. I have mentioned several times that it is better to build calculations into the data model than within each BI entity (report and so on), so if things change, you have far less work to do.

I tend to be a fanatic for driving a POC within any enterprise solution. It offers a chance to really test the proposed tool, as well as a chance to match your processing requirements to the data you will be expected to work with. Do not let anyone dance around the time aspects of your BI efforts. Make them show you exactly how the periodicity of information will be handled. If it appears to be too complex, it probably is.

Let's say you have some odd number of weeks that constitute a period in your line of work. If this is not built into the data model, are you being provided how will you group the information for analysis? All the grouping and selection of the odd time periods will have to be handled by...you! This is also a situation where such time anomalies must be handled in every query, every report, and so on. This is very inefficient and often prone to error.

I would urge you to identify every time period and its associated usage when you sit down to discuss your requirements for analysis, and make sure someone takes you through the steps required to perform what you need.

NOTE

I have seen so many BI systems where the end users were unfortunately surprised by their inability to handle periodicity per their needs. If your requirements are for standard blocks of time such as month, quarter, and so on, this is less of an issue. If you have varying time periods that fall outside the traditional views, *please* make sure you have someone address these as early in the process as possible. If you already have several BI tools in-house, do not let others convince you that "we have ways to handle that." "Ways" typically implies a Simple Matter of Programming (SMOP). SMOP and BI should not be considered synonyms.

Data Mining

I covered this a bit in a previous section, but it is worthwhile delving a bit deeper into now. One definition of data mining might be: "*Data mining is the process of extracting hidden patterns from data.*" Another interpretation might be: "*Data mining refers to the process of analyzing data in order to determine patterns and their relationships.*"

You will frequently hear the terms "hidden" or "discovery" in discussions around data mining. Both are true. Some might say, "*Data mining is sorting through data to identify patterns and establish relationships,*" which is also true. Generally speaking, you will see most people think in terms of data mining as being able to plod through large volumes of data to uncover something you didn't know or a pattern that was unclear using normal query and logic.

Today we see a heavy use of data mining to provide exposure of things such as fraud. Data-mining algorithms are often embedded into BI processes so that the typical business user can take advantage of the mining analysis in making a decision. For example, is a customer a good prospect for a loan? Do they have any history of fraud or some less-than-ideal attribute?

I provided a checklist earlier for data-mining evaluations; please use it. As you explore the use of data-mining capabilities at the enterprise level, make sure the results are actionable—make sure the discovery and exposed new information is easily conveyed, whether by internal processes or workflow applications or embedding in a BI application. Make sure you dispel the myth that data mining is only for the super-geeks in the organization. From the perspective of understanding how to build the appropriate model for analysis, this is true. From the perspective of potential users, this is not.

A quick web search for "data-mining success stories" will yield a number of hits. There are numerous vendors and solution providers in the market today. All of them can cite specific successes at customer sites. The important thing to note is that those with significant citations of ROI have a specific application usage in mind. Data mining is not about throwing some sophisticated algorithm at a large data source and seeing what happens; it is about setting up a scenario where you are looking for a pattern or cluster that is not readily apparent.

Data-mining examples are easy to find, and some of the examples are quite unique, such as one from IBM with the Texas Education Agency. IBM's work at the Texas Education Agency (TEA) served as a catalyst to help TEA develop powerful data-mining capacities to help measure student success, a major component of Texas' nationally-recognized public education accountability and assessment system.

Texas Education Agency's "Just for the Kids" program evolved from IBM technology.

A nonprofit organization based in Austin is utilizing the TEA information in a most creative way. "Just for the Kids" has a website, www.just4kids.org, where anyone can examine performance measures of any public Texas school. The statistics offer five years of longitudinal data, a breakdown of statistics by grade and ethnicity, and a comparison of school performance to schools with similar socioeconomic characteristics.

This use of performance information underscores the role data mining can play in "slicing and dicing" statistics. More important, "Just for the Kids" demonstrates how powerful information can be made accessible within security boundaries to any parent, teacher, or student, and used as a tool to improve classroom learning.

This solution has been in place for over a decade and still delivers value. In your planning, an entire segment of the discussion ought to be based upon what data mining is most effective for the enterprise and how you can utilize it within your business processes.

Text Analytics

This is an area that I predict will become very critical to you in the near future, if it is not already. The majority of the data in the world is held within unstructured data sources, and much of it is exposed today through the power and scope of the Internet. In addition, there are masses of unstructured information sources held in your organization. You have documents, memos, emails, and any number of sources not held in a structured database format.

The key here is to look at this information as a potential source for BI analyses.

Figure 5-2 depicts a simplistic example of the use of text analytics. I have been involved with projects where there have been "discoveries" of critical information to be included in BI objects (reports, charts, and so on) from unstructured sources, such as metrics on a competitor or some internal data that had been published but not included in BI data sources.

Text Analytics – The New Frontier

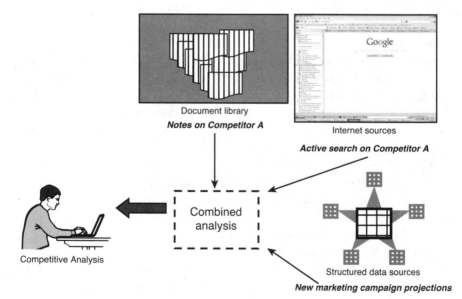

Figure 5-2 Text analytics

The key to unlocking this data is that it changes every instant. Monitoring unstructured sources and weighing the value contained therein can be automated today. Text analytics is a bit different than using search technology. For example, you could issue a search on a competitor based upon some criteria. You typically get back a list of "hits." Scanning each one for value pretty much defeats the purpose of doing a search because now you realize that there are a slew of things that you don't know.

But, if there were some software to intercede on your behalf and deliver the information not only in context but the associated values, you have gained new insight as well as critical business information.

I have found few clients with a firm grasp on what they have in mind for text analytics. Most have a plan and many have a text store and retrieval system in place. This is a pure technology play, where someone in the organization needs to be charged with finding the best solution in relation to what the enterprise has installed and where it is going.

In recent events (such as trade shows and user conferences), I have heard many references to text analytics being an untapped resource, but I have seen little action as a result. One good source of the latest information is the following website: http://social.textanalyticsnews.com/.

There are several major events and symposia on text analytics. The annual Text Analytics Summit conference is an excellent venue where you can talk to industry experts, as well as create a vision for your enterprise. This is not a role for the same people who support your structured data environment, but they should be involved in the evaluation and decision-making process.

Spreadsheets—Effective Use and the Implications on Security/Compliance

Spreadsheets are pretty much the universal interface for the majority of end users. Even the most powerful BI vendors in the market will all provide an interface from their query and reporting technologies to a spreadsheet. The most ubiquitous one is obviously Microsoft Excel.

I covered this extensively in my previous book, cited several times prior to this, so I'll not repeat that information. Spreadsheets as a BI tool are a given fact in every enterprise. They provide a tremendous amount of flexibility and autonomy for the end user. They are popular because users can sit with their data and play until their fingers fall off. They can create complex formulae and macros and all sorts of calculation objects that address their specific processing requirements.

We all know what we can do with spreadsheets. The most pressing issue today is the proper management of the information contained in a spreadsheet regarding security and compliance. Nothing can stop you from walking out with a copy of a spreadsheet or sending it as an attachment outside the firm. There are some very tightly controlled environments in the world, but by and large this data is open to abuse.

You may already have a corporate policy regarding spreadsheets that provides a framework for appropriate use. If you do not, it's best to get one. Those I have seen that have a bit of clout to them include the following:

■ Clearly stated appropriate usage
■ Guidance on how to populate data from internal sources
■ Business guidelines on the use of decision making
■ Guidelines on the validation and cross-verification of results
■ Clear policy on abuse and fraud
■ Clear policy on proper use and/or inappropriate use

There is probably more data held in spreadsheets than in all other structured data sources in the world. They are probably the most productive, yet most often abused, BI tools ever created and must be managed effectively at the enterprise level.

In *Information Systems Journal* (March 25, 2008), there is an article on spreadsheets that is informative. The article primarily emphasizes that the uptake of IT solutions is heavily predicated upon the amount of training (or lack thereof) has a significant impact on the usage of BI tools such as spreadsheets. Spreadsheets are perceived as easier to use than many other BI technologies hence the significant usage of them contrasted with other potential solutions. Management indicated a high degree of interest in BI but, rightfully so, only where it is relevant to their own work.

The title of the article is "Managers, Spreadsheets, and Computing Growth: Contagion or Control?" It continues to describe the rampant but casual use of spreadsheets and how "dangerous" a user can become with very little knowledge or skill. When this is applied to all users in an enterprise, where there are loose standards or none at all, it is a formula for disaster.

Executive Information Systems (EIS)

Today, we see few, if any, true EIS offerings that are targeted at the top tier in the enterprise. Years ago, we saw an endless stream of offerings that provided dashboards, metrics, gauges, and so on to the "C" level. Now dashboards and KPIs and more are included in every BI tool on the market. The term is even included in the Encyclopedia Britannica, so it is certainly a mainstay in the industry.

One term being used now is that of an "actionable" EIS capability. This means that the management and executive levels in an enterprise are no longer isolated on the internal Mt. Olympus, but rather have a means to communicate their discoveries and decisions down to others to act upon.

The concept of collaboration is firmly entrenched in most quality BI tools today. What does this mean? It means that decision making is a cooperative process. Let's say a sales executive has been using some BI functions in a corporate portal, where she can slice/dice/drill and play with numbers being fed by part of a data warehouse. She has a break-through in thinking and wants to get buy in. Having collaborative functions in the internal portal have made it very easy for her to convey her results, add in her projections and new thought, and establish a two-way conversation or n-way conversation with her peers and others.

An EIS today is merely a means of using technology—not a "thing" or offering. I would not even begin to entertain a standalone EIS given the wealth of solution providers with this capability embedded. An EIS is really more about how you implement your BI infrastructure.

In the case of an enterprise customer today—you—I would ask: "What is the proposed information exchange between levels within the organization?" Let's say you have a data warehouse with some of the data aggregated at a level that pertains to the upper echelons in the organization. Such an aggregation is meaningful to them but useless to many below them. However, there are a variety of aggregate levels in the data warehouse; thus, when some inquiry or mandate gets pushed down, the next level can query information at their level and perform their own analysis and response. How will you do this?

If you consider a corporate EIS to be a methodology and not a product, the greatest challenge is in building an infrastructure where lines of discussion and shared analysis are well defined and understood. Have you taken this approach in your BI strategy, or do you have isolated executives breathing rarified air and held apart by a wall of information that only they can view and communicate?

Today's global economy and typically distributed workforce demand a methodology that allows open communication and rapid decision making and sharing.

Craig Schiff (CEO of BPM Partners) wrote an article that was posted by BeyeNetwork. The original was published on November 10, 2009. He stated the following:

So where is EIS today? Essentially it has been reborn as the performance dashboard, a key component of business performance management (BPM). Learning from the mistakes of the past, leading systems are dynamic, interactive, and real-time when they need to be. In the best implementations, there are a series of interconnected cascading dashboards so everyone in the company can see the information that is relevant to them. As mentioned, there is still the risk of populating these dashboards with the wrong information; but if companies follow established best practices, they will start at the top with executive input on current strategy and establish a cross-functional team to flesh out the details.

In most companies, it is also understood that while the dashboard sits at the top of the information pyramid, it cannot sit there alone. Without master data management (MDM), planning and budgeting, consolidation, governance, risk, compliance, and several other systems and initiatives, the dashboard's potential value is greatly diminished. The good news for business performance management is that, unlike EIS, most vendors and many companies (usually with the help of experts deploying best practices) are getting it right. Thanks to them, BPM is bucking the normal trend of three-letter acronym initiatives and actually living up to its hype.

There are many more salient points in Mr. Schiff's article, including a bit of historical perspective on EIS in the past. His point reinforces my statement that an approach to an EIS today is about collaboration and an architecture that permits it in a business sense.

NOTE

One point that needs to be strongly stated and reinforced about an EIS is that there are new, well-defined best practices models on how to build an effective infrastructure. The scope and planning at the enterprise level is very, very different than that of a departmental or single functional level.

So how do you develop and maintain the data to address the multiple levels within an enterprise? One problem with many data warehouse solutions is that they store and aggregate data at a level that only services certain individuals in the enterprise. What about making BI available in a pervasive sense? How do individuals such as customer service reps benefit from BI technologies? One answer is the creation of an operational BI layer within the enterprise's infrastructure.

Operational BI

Operational BI (also known as operational intelligence) is a methodology and infrastructure where you capture and store data at highly detailed levels for use by individuals, such as customer service representatives when they are talking to a customer and need access to the latest customer data right away.

One of my heroines in the arena is Claudia Imhoff. Some information on her is as follows: Claudia Imhoff, Ph.D., is the President and Founder of Intelligent Solutions, a leading consultancy on data warehousing and business intelligence technologies and strategies. She is a popular speaker and internationally recognized expert, and serves as an advisor to many corporations, universities, and leading technology companies on these topics. She has co-authored five books and more than 100 articles on these topics and has a popular blog at www.b-eye-network.com/blogs/imhoff/. She can be reached at CImhoff@IntelSols.com.

I have worked with her (seminars, events, and webinars) and have gleaned a wealth of information and knowledge from her work with customers. Our passion about the operational BI concept is shared. We believe that it is one of the waves of the future, and those who have implemented it today have a significant leg up on their competition.

Figure 5-3 depicts the BI pyramid from the perspective of numbers of users and the volume of queries they typically execute, the higher up you go, the less "busy" work against data occurs. If you turn the pyramid upside down, you would get a view of the amount of data each layer consumes. By this I mean that the folks at the top typically look at data that has been aggregated from a huge base of information and condensed down to a dense number. If you are a lower-level individual, you will probably look at far less data but at a more detailed level. A sales executive would look at the total of all sales by some aggregation. A sales representative would look at sales only pertaining to them.

The characteristics of an operational BI structure would be as follows:

- Large volumes of data contain highly detailed information.
- The system works in real-time or near real-time in its capture and availability.

- End users are typically BI illiterate and use the functions to query data through a portal.

- BI processes are called as a service, including data-mining algorithms in some cases.

- The data is stored at a far more granular level than what is typically found in a data warehouse.

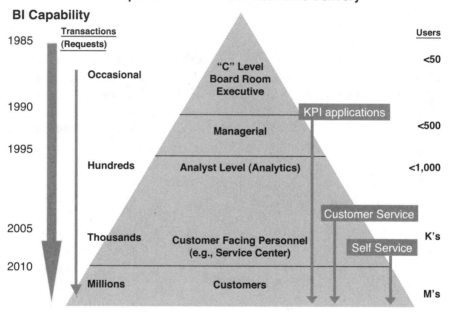

Figure 5-3   Operational BI

In an operational BI system, there is a strong requirement to capture data as rapidly as possible and make the new information available in near real-time. What most critically affects the success of an implementation is the ability to quickly make the data available. Depending upon the source data where the information is initially captured, the operational process may be a challenge to enable. Let's take an example that is typical in today's market. An enterprise captures transaction data on a mainframe and stores it in a database that is ideal for transaction processing but not for BI.

A copy of the data is subsequently transferred to a distributed environment where it is validated, altered, and used to update a data warehouse. In so doing, some levels of detail are stripped away, and the lag time for loading to the warehouse can range from minutes to days. This information is useless in an operational BI scenario. The dilemma they face is that many of the transactions have anomalies and inaccuracies that are cleaned up in an ETL process after the point of capture and while en route to the data warehouse.

I have discussed similar scenarios with a number of customers. Their typical tactic is to reengineer some parts of their infrastructure in order to make the data available faster and at the proper level of detail for new operational use. In such cases, a significant payback (ROI) for operational use must be identified and agreed to.

The clients will look at several options in such cases once they deem operational BI to be essential and of value, as follows:

- Validate and cleanse the data at point of capture, which still isolates its use from BI processes.
- Immediately copy the data to an operational data store (ODS) and validate and cleanse it there.
- Use the ODS for both operational BI processes and to trickle-feed the data warehouse.
- Re-platform the data warehouse and BI processes on the mainframe to provide a single, interoperable infrastructure.
- Provide some compromise where the operational data is more current but not as up to date as may be desirable...

Regardless of how you decide to provide this capability, do you have an operational BI requirement in your organization? It is always a challenge to deliver an operational change once you have a well-established infrastructure. The key drivers for such systems are typically a need to provide improved customer service, competitive pressures, or both. Regardless, when you step into the realm of operational BI, you will be forced to make specific product choices. The typical operational BI situation provides these functions in an embedded manner, where the end users are oblivious to the underlying technology. What is embedded BI?

Embedded BI and Event-Driven Processes

There are articles dating back to 2004 regarding the concept of embedded BI. Colin White of BeyeNetwork stated the following in an article dated May 23, 2007:

> By its nature, event-driven operational BI is able to react much faster to changing business circumstances than demand-driven BI. When close to real-time operations are required, the best way to implement event-driven BI is to embed it in operational business transaction processing. In an SOA environment, this can be achieved by placing BI service calls in the business transaction workflow. BI services called in this manner can do data validation and cleanup, update a data store or cache, send a message to a message queue, perform inline BI analyses, or update an operational BI dashboard.
>
> We can see then that embedded BI is not really a different type of BI processing, but rather an approach for implementing event-driven operational BI. This style of implementation tightly integrates BI with operation processing, while at the same time proving a flexible development environment. It also enables organizations to use BI to make rapid decisions and, in some cases, to fully automate the decision-making process.

From this article and many others emerges the clear message that embedding is about tying a BI process to a specific business requirement. This not only holds true for operational BI but also for the many events that occur with possible impact upon your organization and your position.

First of all, embedded BI processes defined to an SOA are reusable resources. They are defined once and used over and over. The advantage is that if the definition changes, it is altered once and used accurately on a global basis. Another advantage is that multiple processes can be tied together and, in most cases, without any programming required. If done properly, the typical end user can create a personalized, dynamic BI interface.

One example of an embedded BI application might look like this. The user is responsible for monitoring a competitor. They have a BI service that queries and monitors information held in external systems and sites that relate to the competitor. They also have a service that provides a near real-time feed of their organization's current sales metrics.

Pricing and promotions are determined by market position and actions taken by the competition. A data-mining process is used to assess how effectively any new offering or action is in their current market position. You can extend the story at your whim, but here we have three distinct services that are placed upon the user's personal portal.

Could we extend this even further to think in terms of event-driven BI? Yes, we can. Event-driven BI is an area where I find that many clients do not take significant advantage of the capabilities. I don't know about you, but I get very tired of having people tell me some new tidbit has been stored somewhere and I need to look at it. Why not just notify me that there is something of importance when I have a need to know?

Most quality BI offerings contain a mechanism to detect an event and take an action. If there is some milestone occurrence (such as a number that exceeds or falls below an acceptable level), unless I am one who just constantly queries, reports, charts, and spends significant time doing BI chores, what do I normally do? The best practice would be to establish event detection and action as a key requirement of your BI infrastructure and carefully assess how potential offerings satisfy the automation of such events and potential actions that can be taken. Typical end users will have some time table they employ, such as running a report once a week, or whatever they need to do. In many cases, the information they receive merely validates what they already know. However, sometimes they can be very unpleasantly surprised by finding out that a key metric is out of scope, and then they wish they had known earlier.

Some end users don't want to be bothered at all unless there is an action they need to take. They can also make significant use of embedded BI processes. Those of us who wallow in this space sometimes forget that the majority of the people we service have "real" jobs. These are people who only need BI processes as a tool and not an avocation. Regardless of your position in the enterprise, it is imperative that you develop a delivery mechanism that is optimized for the target users. Take advantage of hands-free BI processes by enabling events, and make sure your vendor(s) can do this to your satisfaction.

ETL/ELT and Real-Time Change Data Capture (CDC) Options

The underpinning data you use for BI will emanate from some source system that may not be conducive to BI applications. I have already discussed some of the ramifications of ETL versus CDC in terms of timeliness of data. For the enterprise, this decision has a greater impact than at particular departmental levels. It is an area where the ability to utilize the full range and scope of your BI arsenal in the most effective manner will be realized or limited.

The majority of enterprise accounts state that they have issues with data quality as well as being able to collect it and create a common view from a multitude of sources. One approach that can be taken is to use data federation technology that enables you to keep the data in place and join it to treat it as one unified database. The problems with federating are performance and accuracy of the data. If there are no common keys to link multiple sources together, federation is not viable. If there are anomalies or incorrect values in any of the sources, it's a moot point to begin with.

Where last-minute, real-time data is not an issue, an ETL (or ELT) approach is a good one. This enables you to capture data and perform the operations to transform it to being BI friendly on an orderly basis. Obviously, the timeliness of the information is what you need to look at. In some cases, however, I have seen changes in data transfer, and validation applications take a huge step backward.

Let me cite a personal example of how *not* to do things. I have a significant number of air miles logged with a certain carrier. They merged with another not too long ago and merged their IT infrastructures. I used to be able to check my mileage credit online nearly the instant I stepped off a plane because they posted the data in near real-time fashion. It was a marvelous customer service application. Since the merger, I now find my mileage credits to be lagging significantly. I have had to contact the new organization (including writing letters and enclosing lots of documentation) several times of late, as I have been given reason to doubt their accuracy. I have gone from being a really happy customer to one of extreme mistrust. I am limited to a few airline choices where I live, so I feel trapped. Their CDC or ETL processes are broken, and they do not seem to be inclined to change. Due to my advanced status on this airline, I will keep using them for selfish purposes but will never sing their praises again.

CDC is a part of the normal ETL process, as well as a mechanism to provide near real-time processing for BI, assuming the data is clean and accurate. In situations where steps have been taken to ensure cleanliness and accuracy at point of capture, you have the greatest flexibility because you start with good information.

Figure 5-4 shows the implantation options for ETL/ELT/CD as they relate to a BI infrastructure. Each has its advantages as well as stress points. For example, the most elegant way of addressing the data quality issues is to validate and clean at the point of capture. In many cases, this is impractical due to lack of automation technology for the database being used. It can also be affected by the type of application, such as extremely high volumes being captured by service representatives who cannot verify certain information and do not have the time to perform the validation necessary.

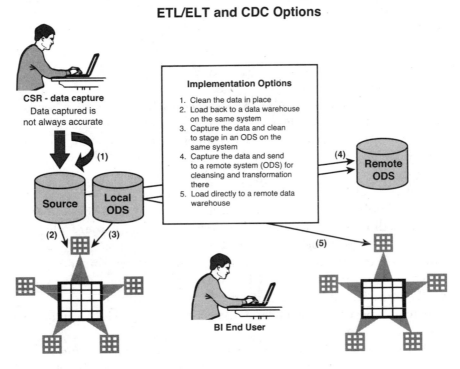

Figure 5-4 ETL/ELT and CDC options

Your decisions and discussions will also depend upon your interest and need for operational BI where the timeliness of the data is critical and affects how well a particular process is enabled. Massive changes in infrastructure with no net new business benefit are impractical, but if you see a need now or down the road for a significant change in the data warehouse and BI cycle, it's time to at least try and gain agreement on a plan.

If you have existing processes in place that preclude you from maximizing your BI potential due to data issues, it is time to formulate a better plan. I have said endlessly in my discussions with clients: "It's all about the data." The shape of the data, the timeliness, the accuracy, and the detail being matched to the BI process are all areas where people often fall short. ETL and CDC processes are an IT decision not to be taken lightly. Unless you make known your specific requirements, you may inherit an infrastructure that is too far down the road to call back, and you will have to make up for this in ways that are inefficient and not cost-effective.

Summary

I have bounced around a bit from BI-specific functions to infrastructure topics that impact the end user. The majority of difficulties in BI implementations I have seen are based upon lack of communication and coordination. The end users don't know what to ask IT, and they don't want to appear ignorant, so they don't challenge issues they should.

You will have to learn some level of usage for the BI tool(s) you have opted to implement. If you make assumptions about what they can do or how something will work and are surprised later, that is your fault.

Not only does the accuracy of data have a bearing upon your success, but it affects the "shape" of the data as well. If system impact and resource utilization are issues with your query technology, maybe OLAP is a better solution. However, if you are using OLAP, and you are trying to extend it beyond the boundaries of what it is designed for, you may be asking for trouble.

At the enterprise level, BI solutions will receive enormous scrutiny. One group may totally fall in love with a specific offering, whereas another may not agree. In many cases, the choice is to bring in both tools—no one will arbitrate, and you wind up with two tools that do very similar things. In such cases, this often is where there is poor leadership.

Each topic in this chapter should be a part of the enterprise BI definition and some elements within the vision statement. The worst thing to do is to assume or not question things that need a response in your mind. Make sure you have been shown exactly how things work within a particular BI tool if you are one who will build things. If you are a casual user (recipient) of BI, understand that there are methods and functions that may be easy to extend to make your life easier, such as embedded BI processes.

All BI users are not created equally. What should individuals expect based upon their role within the organization?

6

The Impact of Business Intelligence on Roles within the Enterprise

Regardless of what your plan, vision, or current BI situation happens to be, it is a given that there will be a variety of users with different skills and requirements. However, I have found few clients who attempt to segment their end users into specific categories and manage this accordingly.

Many modern BI tools offer a variety of roles and charge by type of user as well as other variations, such as a processor-based method. If we set aside cost factors and assume that you can have an "all you can eat" environment, would you just hand out user seats with maximum functional capability? Or, would you still dole out user seats that are appropriate to the actual skill levels and user types?

End User Categories

Depending upon the particular tool and vendor, we will see different end user roles given names such as consumer, advanced author, administrator, and so forth. There is a dual purpose behind such segmentation. First, it enables vendors to adjust their billing by offering pricing flexibility and a point of negotiation based upon what the customer's needs may be. Second, it provides a means for the customer to dole out an appropriate level of functionality and not overwhelm their end users with more features and functions than is necessary.

For the sake of discussion, let's begin with a set of user types that we define and then look at how best to deal with segments of end users. Please keep in mind that segmentation does little good beyond getting a price break if you have no intention of evolving a plan for how to define, measure, educate, and then support them. Here are the types of users:

- **Administrator:** This individual is permitted carte blanche to perform any task, from data modeling to advanced authoring and more. In any given enterprise, this would be a small set of end users who have a major stake in the definition, deployment, and success of a particular BI tool. Such user seats are usually more costly due to the depth and breadth of functions they are permitted to employ.

- **Advanced Author:** This user would be capable of performing most tasks in the creation of BI objects (queries, reports, OLAP, and more). He would not have access to functions such as data modeling or the ability to add/modify/delete end users as part of the BI environment.

- **Basic Author:** This individual would have access to a limited, albeit still rich, set of capabilities. He would be able to create BI objects but would have some restrictions in contrast with an advanced author.

- **Consumer:** This individual cannot create anything. He may be permitted the capability to fill in some parameters at runtime, but he is pretty much a "consumer" of what others provide for him. A common consumer would be a role taken by many who are recipients of embedded BI.

These are product-functional categories. There also are categories that are more business and skills oriented. Among these are the following:

- IT systems support
- IT database support
- IT BI tools support
- Business analysts

- Departmental specialists
- Non-technical (casual) users, such as customer support reps and others
- Executive and management levels
- External users (B2B and so on)

Figure 6-1 depicts a typical distribution of users by volume: the BI "pyramid scheme." Each role has an impact and influence on the business based upon their level of involvement with the BI infrastructure. If this was mapped out based upon skills required, the pyramid would be inverted and the roles would remain in place. This is not to say there is an implied importance by role. From an immediate revenue perspective, a population of CSRs armed with a high-powered BI application may have a more positive influence on the bottom line than an executive armed with a dashboard yet making unwise decisions. There is a place for BI usage for everyone in the organization.

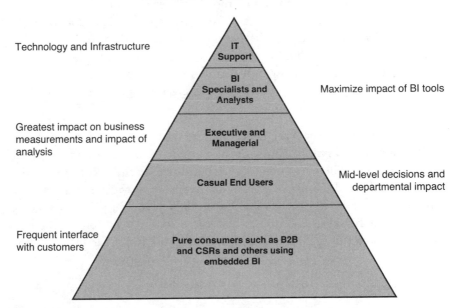

Figure 6-1   End user populations by role

You may have a few different categories of your own. If you try to match the product categories with the user types, it is plainly evident in some cases which ones fit. Obviously, it is a rare executive who will be a "tech-heavy" user. However, the push down through the enterprise to deliver the required metrics and analyses will be more heavily influenced by these casual users than all the technicians in the organization.

The external users, such as those you may sell to on the Internet or in business-to-business endeavors, will also be casual users but will require an extraordinary amount of support as well as the heaviest scrutiny for security issues and availability.

At the heart of all the BI actions are those who create and support the many who benefit from their skills, hard work, and ability to analyze and deliver. In order to sustain and grow success in BI, this is the group that will require the greatest amount of attention and focus.

NOTE

Many enterprises have not awakened to the new age of BI. Everyone today is working harder and doing more with fewer resources. The old model of bringing in a set of BI tools and turning them loose for all to perform self-service BI, regardless of how sophisticated the business problems are, is gone. The myth of ease-of-use for anyone has been proven to be just that...a myth. It is time to face the reality of what certain people can or cannot do with BI tools given their skills and time.

If you agree with the basic concept here, let's look at what an orderly, well-tuned organization would do to support a BI environment with such a mixture. The very first thing we see is that the successful enterprise will take and maintain a constant inventory of their end users. In a number of consulting situations where a client is looking for a change in their current BI infrastructure, I have asked for an inventory of the end users by product usage. More often than not, this is not easily produced.

End User Management

The dilemma is that BI simply "happens" in most organizations, and the overall impact, growth, and activities simply get lost in the everyday shuffle of doing business and getting the job done. Chapter 13, "End-User

Support and Productivity," covers the end-user support issues, but this is a good time to set up the discussion. I simply do not understand how you deploy, measure, and expand the success of any BI endeavor without the establishment of a BI competency center.

Looking back at the past two decades of BI and its evolution, the amount of support and assistance has waned despite the fact that BI has emerged as a major entity within the majority of corporations. There always seems to be someone in charge of a segment or a product, but quite often this role is vague or ill-defined.

Regarding BI roles, Maureen Clarry wrote the following (BeyeNetwork; December 4, 2007):

> *The Data Warehousing Institute (TDWI) initiated annual research in this area starting in 2000 and continuing through 2007. Based on the TDWI Salary, Roles, and Teams Report research in 2000, 91% of the BI professionals surveyed indicated that they fulfilled multiple roles on their team. On average, each BI professional filled 4.8 roles. Only 9% performed a single functional role. Although there appears to be somewhat of a trend toward more specialization, 89% of the BI professionals surveyed in 2006 still indicated that they fulfilled multiple roles. However, their average number of roles decreased to 3.27. Those performing a single functional role remained constant at 9%. Here's the question: With the range of 4.8 to 3.27 roles, how might BI professionals describe their .8 or .27 role? If roles are shared, how do we divide the partial role to create clarity? The answer lies in defining specific responsibilities that are a subset of those roles.*

Not only are roles sometimes difficult to define, they are also blurry in their actual responsibilities. I have asked many clients if they have definitions of roles and published schedules of training and skills development they use. The situation most often mimics what Ms. Clarry wrote—they seem to be created when someone is in need of hiring a resource. And even if they do exist, most often they are not well defined.

The individuals with the greatest skill in any BI technology are the most valuable individuals in the enterprise from a *functional* resource perspective. They can also be a nightmare to deal with if a new course has been set to bring in a new set of tools or to eliminate some, and they happen to be the ones the BI super-techs love. These individuals have poured their hearts and souls into developing skills, and now they feel threatened. If you have made such a decision, have a plan for these people and get them involved.

Skills Definitions

You should make skills and roles definitions one of your highest priorities. People need to know what they are getting into, as well as what is expected of them. Ms. Clarry's article indicates that the average BI professional fulfilled 4.8 roles...that's nearly five people in one body! And, I suspect it's gotten even worse since then.

In Figure 6-2, I have added a theoretical learning curve table for a variety of end users. This is assuming you are bringing in a new tool. You may ask, "Why have you shown eight hours for those who really have little skin in the game?" Think of your experiences with Internet sites. We have all purchased things via the Internet. Not all sites offer the same methodology for checking out once you purchase. Many sites make shopping a challenge to the extent that I will abandon my intention to buy if the process is too difficult or awkward. There are some sites that I will always use, regardless of their weirdness, because of price or the quality of the product. These sites have taken some time to get used to, and others will possibly find your BI offerings (embedded) somewhat awkward as well. It is far better to set down realistic expectations and be pleasantly surprised if you have overestimated the amount of time required.

For obvious reasons, I have made the role of BI tools specialist the heaviest in resources required. These are the individuals who will be expected to know how to do the most sophisticated activities. Sometimes they have to spend hours just getting some calculation correct or getting a report formatted exactly the way it is needed.

The deep knowledge required to perform advanced tasks just takes time. I have worked with a number of BI tools, and some more than others. I have had situations where I once figured out some complex "thing" and didn't write it down, thinking it was a one-off—only to find out later (usually later than my memory serves!) that I need to do a similar thing again and just cannot remember what on earth I did the first time!

Think in terms of the tiered architecture discussed in Chapter 4, "The Scope of BI Solutions Today and How They May Relate to You." The complexity of the modern BI environment far surpasses the days when we brought in a fat client tool, attached it to a data source, and flailed

BI Roles within an Enterprise
Initial training requirements

Functional Role	BI Skill Level	Learning Curve	Activities
IT Systems support	8	128	Environmental setup (servers, access, networking)
IT database support	6	96	Data access, definition, testing, administration
IT BI Tools specialist	10	160	Understand the internals of Tool XYZ in relation to systems performance, impact, scale, sizing
Business Analyst	8	128	Ranking expert(s) in the BI components, deep understanding of package offerings, best practices Continuous skills development, primary interface to BI vendor(s)
Departmental specialist	6	96	Support departmental personnel in creating queries or building BI objects for others. Ongoing education and skills development required
Casual and non-technical users (internal)	1	16	Perform basic BI operations such as create simple reports or use objects created by others that they can modify to some extent
Executive/Managerial	2	16	Regular users who will drive initiatives and regularly interoperate with the objects created (dashboards, KPIs, etc..)
External users (B2B)	.5	8	Consumers of shared BI information. May use objects such a parameterized queries, etc.
Basic consumers (embedded)	.5	8	Gain familiarity with the embedded functions and BI features – little or no knowledge of the underlying technology

Skill range: 10 = high
1= low
16 Hours * skill level = training requirement

Figure 6-2   BI roles within an enterprise: Initial training requirements

away. In order to avoid having 4.8 jobs to do, it may be better to define the roles and expectations in an orderly, granular manner.

Not too long ago, I was solicited for the following BI architect's job. Please note the sheer variety of vendors and BI tools requiring skills while, at the same time, job-hopping was discouraged. Gee...I wonder how the individual was to gain all this experience?

Here is the description of what they wanted someone to be able to do:

Data Warehousing (DWH) and Business Intelligence (BI) Architect (Data Stage, Informatica, Ab Initio, Cognos, Business Objects, Hyperion) Architect Business Intelligence (BI) Data Warehousing Architect (Data Stage Informatica, Ab Initio, Cognos, Business Objects, Hyperion) is required for an award-winning and multi-national organization. You will be working in a strategic integration group, so there is a very good career path ahead of you.

The right Architect will have experience with translating business require-ments into system, scope, solutions, and architecture definition. This opportu-nity will offer the right candidate to further his/her career growth, and further enhance his/her experience. You as an Architect should have strong experience with architecture and solution definition in the BI/DWH area and need to have strong technical experience with Data Stage/DataStage, with strong experience with Cognos a bonus. Also, a major plus will be candidates who have experience with any of the following: Informatica, Ab Initio, Business Objects, and Hyperion. Experience with real-time integration would also be a major bonus. Finally, your CV should also reflect a solid career path, as opposed to jumping from company to company each year. The right candidate will be rewarded with a strong package and the opportunity to fur-ther progress his/her career with this leading organization

The first thing that struck me was that they obviously did not have a standard for a BI provider. The second thing that struck me was that they seemed very naïve in their assumptions about the various BI providers. All the vendors mentioned have significant inventories of function and feature. Even though they all provide query and reporting, they do not all perform these functions the same way. I count six major vendors in the list, and the description still doesn't go into any detail about which actual products are included. I would have applied for this position, but luckily I found my brain in time and, sadly enough, I couldn't find my super-hero costume to work the role.

IT Support Roles

IT roles always wind up spending more time and dedicating more resources to BI activities than they thought they would have to. The areas where significant extra time is usually required are as follows:

- Database definitions and design
- Database performance
- Systems performance and tuning
- BI tool performance and debugging

Keep in mind that many BI activities constitute, for lack of a better term, random acts of violence against data. The less-technical end user, when faced with a slow-running or non-responsive query, will simply submit a second copy and then another if nothing comes back. Ask any systems person with experience in this arena.

The sheer ad-hoc nature of BI flies in the face of the predictability and orderliness most systems support people are accustomed to. It's really difficult to anticipate how best to manage an environment where you have *no idea* what the end users will do next. I have found that many clients will not tie up their valuable IT people with education and training for a BI tool, thinking that the technical professional will waste their time or that they are savvy enough to pick it up on their own.

It is an established best practice that BI success is underpinned by proper training for the systems-support individuals. It is imperative when elements such as database design, warehouse definitions, tuning, scalability, and performance are key. Do not assume that the BI products aren't worthy of sending the IT folks off to class to learn. Make it a requirement.

A classic example of heavy IT involvement is when there is a performance issue with a relational database. The typical approach taken is to take the end user's problem query and expose the underlying SQL. In many cases, the quick solution is to modify the SQL statement to optimize it for the data. Now you have solved one instance of a query. What about the metadata design of the BI tool? Could it be that the way the data is defined causes an inefficient query to be built? If this is the case, the support individuals will have to constantly edit and adjust subsequent queries.

There are often nuances within a vendor's tools that need to be understood. Nearly every BI vendor today provides a metadata layer between the source data and the end user interface. As things get translated between the layers, inefficiencies may occur. It is not the vendor's fault; it is just the way it works.

BI Tools Support Staff and Business Analysts

"Mission critical"...if you are using this term in your statements about BI, but you do not have clearly defined roles and structure, how can this be? An old rule of thumb regarding BI coverage used to be one support individual for every twenty-five users. This is a 1:25 ratio, but it would vary depending upon the mixture of casual users and heavy users. Let's pick a number of end users in an organization today. What if we had 5,000 BI users, and we had to apply the 1:25 ratio of the past? This would equal 600 support personnel! Obviously, there is no way this would happen, but it does get your attention regarding the underpinning support requirements. In today's somewhat easier-to-use tools environment, we might think that a good support staff could handle 100 users per support staff. In the 5,000-users case, this would be 50 support staff.

Built into any of these metrics is the assumption that the support personnel are all equally skilled and their mixture of users is roughly equal. As you investigate the many roles within the organization, the various skills required, the support requirements, and the infrastructure costs, it becomes readily apparent that some work needs to be done here. In Chapter 13, I will address these issues in a bit more detail.

The net of all this is the need to define roles within and without the enterprise and map skills and coverage to these roles. It is ultra-critical that you be realistic and open with the skills development requirements for your BI tools. I have heard more than one managerial type state about one of their employees, "Oh, he is fine with this. I sent him to a class, and he has been working diligently on this ever since." I have then spent time with the employee, who is beside himself with worry and angst. Employees do not want to indicate that they are struggling after being sent off to class, but their current skills often are far overmatched with the processing requirements and current projects they have been given. In many cases, they have no one else to turn to in the organization and are really unhappy with their lot.

These people also can poison the well for others because they might be simply inept in the use of a BI tool. It doesn't make them a "dummy"; it just isn't their forte. And now that they have been handed this task, they feel exposed. In many cases, they will share their negative opinion regarding the BI tool with their peers. It's a self-defense mechanism that could have been easily avoided in the first place had someone developed a skills matrix and plan.

The Executive/Managerial Role

In most organizations, these individuals will have the greatest impact upon the enterprise's success or failure with any BI tool. They are the ultimate consumers and key motivators for BI success. As such, they need to be very intimately involved with the process. There is a very key sensitivity factor that must be addressed. The upper echelons tend to be the ones who believe the ease-of-use myth more than anyone. If product ABC doesn't seem to be what the users can utilize, they will run off to have someone look at product XYZ.

If you are one of the upper crust in an organization, it is your responsibility to ensure that you encourage and support an infrastructure that is conducive to the enterprise. Too often there is an approach like Captain Jean Luc Picard of the *Star Trek* series who often used the line: "Make it so!" It works on TV, but it is a miserable approach in real life.

Rather than become a maven or a technically savvy tools person (we thought you were an executive?!), your support of a proper alignment of BI efforts with business goals is key. If you understand that some BI tasks are easier than others and that some requests, despite their seeming simplicity, are challenging, your view of what is going on is key.

I always encourage executive/managerial involvement in BI planning sessions. We are all busy, but I am often surprised that individuals in higher positions are often invited to such sessions but cannot be bothered to show up or get involved. They are, however, often the first ones to bark about lack of progress. If you don't have a grasp on what your employees are being expected to work with, how can you set expectations?

Please understand that BI tools and infrastructures can be set up for top to bottom and back information sharing. The executive dashboard today often has capabilities to collaborate and communicate your findings and desired actions to others in the enterprise. This is where you may provide the greatest value in a BI sense. Probe for specifics on how you will be able to communicate with your staff regarding key metrics you are viewing on that shiny new dashboard.

I firmly believe the era of micro-examination of BI tools at the functional level simply must contain the elements of information sharing. If Tool A doesn't do some of the "spiffy" things that Tool B does, but it has a marvelous interface with your office system, email, drill-downs, delegation functions, and more, Tool A would get my vote.

Think in terms of how you are structured as a business. Do you have to communicate remotely to others? Do you deal with a variety of geographies and time zones? As of this writing, I have been in a position where I need to communicate extensively with individuals in Asia-Pacific locations. They are in time zones that vary from 12 to 16 hours ahead of me. Real-time communication is very challenging, and we tend to use asynchronous (email) communication most often. If either side sends inadequate information or incomplete data, we are looking at a two-day turnaround at a minimum—and most often, it is three days.

Non-Technical and Casual Users

You have nothing to complain about. You are at the mercy of the kindness of strangers based upon your level of involvement and skills limitations. This is not to say that you have no right to demand changes or to lobby for more. However, I have seen that, in many cases, the ones who drive the greatest amount of change and request the most inappropriate things are those who know the least.

One client several years ago was evaluating a new BI tool. The one they had was getting a little "long in the tooth," and it was so challenging, many users had been locked out from use by the sheer demand for skills just to perform a series of BI tasks. The client asked for a proof of concept (POC) for a new tool. They invited a mixed group into the early meetings, including their casual users.

The older tool had some report formatting capabilities that were pretty neat, albeit they were not essential to the business and the user's ability to understand the output. In evaluating the newer tool, the least-skilled individuals started demanding that the output from the new tool be able to *exactly* mimic the output from the old one. The vendor worked very closely with the BI technicians to finally beat the newer format into submission. The initial reports in the new tool were created in approximately one-fifth the time it took in the old one. However, to make the new reports look exactly like the old reports, it took hours of piddling around to get little blocks of data to appear exactly where they were required.

At the end of the lengthy exercise, it turned out that these reports were not viewed as being that relevant to the business, but a few key users "liked" the format. Several told me later that they didn't really use the reports but liked to get them weekly "just in case."

As a casual user, the most important thing you can bring to the equation is business sense and a feeling for the timeliness of the BI output you receive. If you get a report or chart that you can interpret and use, but it isn't quite formatted the way you want, live with it. If it does not convey the proper information, you have a right to raise an issue. Most important of all, if the information is not accurate or it is too dated for your view of the business, you have a significant reason to complain.

Casual users are the largest segment of any typical BI population and reap greater benefits than all others involved (along with the executives) because they receive business insight with very little skin in the game. It is more productive to ask for a new pie chart with incremental information than to badger a BI specialist with a request to move the legend over a wee bit because you find it distracting to read.

Summary

Your impact, influence, and involvement in the enterprise's BI journey will vary widely by role. It is your responsibility to understand what you can and cannot do. It is also your responsibility to properly support those around you and to not make uninformed requests with limited information and skills on your part.

An accurate, realistic assessment and definition of roles must be clearly defined and documented. As shown in numerous articles and surveys, BI has a tendency to accelerate its hold upon many who have more than marginal skills. A few years ago, job coverage (succession) was all the rage as older members of the workforce were retiring. In the BI space, this is still extremely critical. It is also an area where you need to pay attention given the more mobile workforce of today. The loss of one key BI heavyweight can cause massive disruption within an organization. It is best to document who you have, what they are expected to do, how they will be supported, and who will support them, and put it all together in a package to be approved by management and then adhered to.

Having some individuals performing 4.8 roles, as the Clarry article suggests, is not necessarily a bad thing. When others in the enterprise are not aware of this or simply let it continue, however...that is not a good thing.

Each role within a BI infrastructure is essential. Each has its place in delivering business value to and insight into elements of the business. Improper execution on the part of any of these roles can also be very detrimental to the vitality of BI usage within the organization. Let's now hone in a bit on the executive and managerial levels within the organization. We hear a lot these days about corporate performance management...what does this really entail?

7

Corporate Performance Management and the Executive View of Business Intelligence

The essence of corporate performance management (CPM) is measuring, monitoring, and adjusting to key metrics within the enterprise at all levels. You will find many definitions of, permutations of, and opinions on CPM, as I shall refer to it from now on. I get very emotional about this topic because I have grappled with this for years now, going back to the days when Executive Information Systems (EIS) were all the rage. You will see terms such as business process management (BPM), enterprise performance management (EPN), and BPM in the context of business performance management. Do not confuse process with performance.

In the early days of EIS solutions, there were many limitations in technology, and we lacked a global communications infrastructure. These systems were primarily self-contained, isolated, and insular. Data had to be loaded from a variety of sources and placed within an EIS for the creation and display of dashboards and other fancy graphical displays. They primarily were directed at executive levels to give them a view of the enterprise using a graphical user interface (GUI) that they could interpret.

When asked to define a CPM, I have heard others say, "I am not really sure how to define it, but I'll know it when I see it." Let's go a bit farther out on the limb and propose a working definition of a CPM and the executive interface with this area of BI.

Defining CPM

Let's start with this definition and explanation from Wikipedia (http://en.wikipedia.org/wiki/Business_performance_management):

Business performance management (BPM) (or corporate performance management, enterprise performance management, operational performance management, business performance optimization) consists of a set of processes that help organizations optimize their business performance. It provides a framework for organizing, automating, and analyzing business methodologies, metrics, processes, and systems that drive business performance.

Colin White describes a link between business intelligence and business performance management. "The biggest growth area in operational BI analysis is in the area of business performance management (BPM). Operational BPM applications not only analyze the performance…, but also compare the measured performance against business goals and alert business users when actual performance is out of line with business goals."

BPM helps businesses make efficient use of their financial, human, material, and other resources. The key differentiator between BI and BPM is that BPM contains the concept of a control or feedback loop that helps guide the business toward its goals. BI may provide the analytics to help the business set those goals and to monitor progress toward them.

In the past owners have sought to drive strategy down and across their organizations, they have struggled to transform strategies into actionable metrics, and they have grappled with meaningful analysis to expose the cause-and-effect relationships that, if understood, could give profitable insight to their operational decision-makers.

Corporate performance management (CPM) software and methods allow a systematic, integrated approach that links enterprise strategy to core processes and activities. "Running by the numbers" now means something: planning, budgeting, analysis, and reporting can give the measurements that empower management decisions.

Some key words I see are the following: operational, measured performance, feedback loop, goals, and alerts. These attributes indicate that there is an established set of key business metrics that numerous individuals will work in tandem to track and strive for. The missing keyword here is executive and/or managerial. There is a reference to driving strategy down (top-down) to others. BI in a CPM structure is just a tool; it is a means of placing key information within the CPM flow.

My definition of CPM would be as follows: *A well-defined, iterative process of providing accurate information for defining, measuring, and adjusting key areas of the business to keep all elements of an organization in sync and provide a clear understanding of the things they are measured upon, responsible for, and any changes in the business. All levels within the enterprise with a need to communicate and adjust any part of the plan must be enabled to do so. Feedback and adjustment capabilities are mandatory and must be adhered to.*

Elements of a CPM System

At the executive level, we often hear, "We did better this quarter/year/century than the last one"...but how do you know? And even if you did, what if the current quarter is still an abysmal 25% off of where you need to be?

Figure 7-1 addresses several issues at once. The first issue is a list of some of the things that keep executives awake at night regarding their access to information, as well as those who provide it to them. In the typical CPM cycle, what most ask for is a vision, a strategy map, balanced scorecards, and a feedback mechanism all working in tandem and providing a malleable analysis cycle accurately. This is impossible to do if the underpinning information is flawed.

With today's many choices in data warehousing technology and BI tools, it is possible to provide the four major elements of an effective CPM system if you choose wisely. Earlier, I talked about the importance of effective collaboration, and I really cannot emphasize this enough.

I have heard disturbing things from some clients in relation to their executive and managerial levels. One I hear often is: "The upper levels don't communicate effectively, but really know how to dictate changes or come down on me when something doesn't happen." Another is: "We

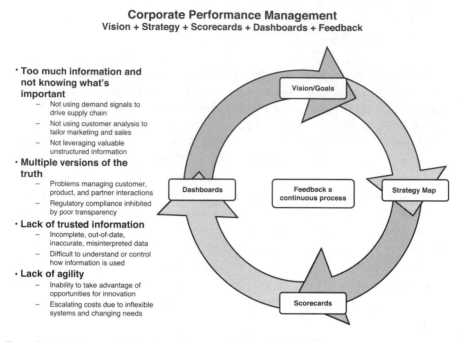

Corporate Performance Management
Vision + Strategy + Scorecards + Dashboards + Feedback

• **Too much information and not knowing what's important**
  – Not using demand signals to drive supply chain
  – Not using customer analysis to tailor marketing and sales
  – Not leveraging valuable unstructured information
• **Multiple versions of the truth**
  – Problems managing customer, product, and partner interactions
  – Regulatory compliance inhibited by poor transparency
• **Lack of trusted information**
  – Incomplete, out-of-date, inaccurate, misinterpreted data
  – Difficult to understand or control how information is used
• **Lack of agility**
  – Inability to take advantage of opportunities for innovation
  – Escalating costs due to inflexible systems and changing needs

Vision/Goals

Dashboards

Feedback a continuous process

Strategy Map

Scorecards

Figure 7-1   The Corporate Performance Management Cycle and Feedback Loop

really are unclear about what is expected of us until a time that is far too late to adjust adequately." There are technologies on the market to ensure clean, accurate information. There are tools and technologies that can deliver the information you require in time and in context, and enable open, rapid communications of business plans and changes—are you using them?

CPM systems are often the single greatest gift as well as the greatest disappointment within an organization. Even with clean and accurate data, the lack of a proper feedback loop or any ability to adjust the plan leads to an exercise in futility. I worked with an account where they had a very aggressive executive layer with very specific, well-monitored goals. Their greatest dilemma was the lack of overall funding for many of the initiatives they needed to pursue in order to survive and grow. There were definitely struggling. It's "happy ending time" at this point of the story. Their nearly flawless execution of their CPM system was very instrumental in turning around the business. They managed to convince some key investors that their game plan was as good as it gets and that their internal execution cycle and measurement system ensured everyone knew exactly what was expected and when any changes took place.

Such a scenario sounds like something out of the movie *It's a Wonderful Life*. The point is, you are never assured of success, but improper management and inadequate tracking and monitoring are a sure way to set a course for collapse. The economic woes that started to shake the world in late 2009 and beyond came on like a freight train. Many saw it coming, but many were caught unaware.

Vision

Having a vision is key to anyone's success, be it a person or a business. Where do you foresee your company in *xx* years? Where do you see your growth coming from? What will you do to make you "different" than your competitors? On a personal level, we typically envision some elevation in income, status, or possibly retirement at some future date. In the corporate world, it's all about having a sense of where you are going and why.

In a CPM sense, the long-term goals and corporate aspirations are set within the vision and are backed up by a clear strategy map of how you will get there. A corporate vision will include elements such as revenue growth, acquisitions, lines of business, and their impact on the health of the enterprise. In a CPM system, this vision is typically shared at executive levels and by the board, and is reflected in annual reports (to some degree) as well as internal information known to all employees. It is not a "trite" set of phrases printed in gold letters on a plaque and hung on a wall; it is the true, core belief held by those at all levels of the business.

Strategy Map

This is where you create and document a visual system that articulates how you will deliver the vision. Let me take IBM, where I have spent so many years, as an example. Part of the corporate vision for quite some time is to be the leading provider of hardware, software, and services. This has been clearly stated for all to see and hear throughout the industry.

However, if you look at how IBM has changed its strategy map, it has gone from a partner-centric model to one where (especially in the software market) it has executed a significant number of acquisitions. The buy versus cooperate model has been driven by the need to own and initiate enterprise-level solutions that address all facets of the business.

In a partner-centric model, there is an exposure to relying upon another provider for critical components due to the threat of a competitor's acquiring key technology and leaving a gap in the portfolio. On a grander scale, it is driven by the need to ensure that deep product integration and critical new features and functions are delivered. It's about a different span of control than relying upon others.

So, IBM has the same vision and the same philosophy but a different strategy to get there. The metrics underpinning all this have had to change, as with acquisitions comes infrastructure, personnel, and other changes. But the vision remains the same.

Balanced Scorecard

How are we doing with our strategy map and all the elements necessary to attain our vision? The balanced scorecard is where we micromanage our many components. They can be highly detailed or merely a glimpse of some of the metrics involved. The important thing is that they are accurate, understood, agreed to, and timely. Here is where the concerns about accurate information and trust come into play.

I cannot tell you how many times I have had someone within an organization state: "I just do not trust this information, but it is all I have." The underpinning reasons for this vary widely, but the result remains the same— how do you act upon information that you know isn't right? In a balanced scorecard scenario, it cannot be a case where all the metrics are wrong. If this is true, there is a serious information gap within the enterprise, and such a CPM system may as well be a dartboard.

If there are certain elements of a CPM system and its balanced scorecard that seem "odd," the most important element of all enters the arena—a feedback system. It is ultra-critical to provide a feedback system that is open, encouraged, and not a ground where others fear to tread. If there are penalties for those who question key metrics or derivations of information, the so-called system is useless. Shut it down, save your money, and send executive memos and ultimatums...it's cheaper.

Traditionally, an enterprise will rely on financial metrics to support critical decisions. This approach has proven to be less effective over time. Financial metrics only reveal the effect of decisions made in the past. Today, you need forward-looking, or "leading," metrics that are tied to the company's value drivers. Metrics, like customer satisfaction, based on cause-and-effect relationships can alert companies to problems before they adversely affect the bottom line. For example, declining customer satisfaction can point to an eventual drop in overall revenue or a loss of market share.

Scorecards are not synonymous with dashboards. A dashboard merely shows you where you are at the moment, just like driving in your car. If you are speeding, it doesn't show you where you ought to be—then you hear the siren behind you. A balanced scorecard should show you where you are, where you ought to be, and other metrics that give you some indication of how you are doing and where you fall short. These are normally used at managerial and executive levels; to others who cannot influence the business, they are of little or no value.

Scorecards help you define and monitor critical metrics. They are an important part of performance management. They typically pull data from reliable sources and employ tools that let you present your metrics in a consistent way across the enterprise—from discrete tactical projects to company-wide strategies. By translating tactics and strategies into specific, measurable objectives, scorecards help ensure that the company's goals are consistently defined, applied, understood, and communicated.

A variety of perspectives are viewed in a robust and valued CPM system, including the following:

- **Financial:** How do we meet shareholder expectations?
- **Customer:** How do we maximize our value to our customers?
- **Internal processes:** How do our operations satisfy our shareholders and customers?
- **Continuous improvement:** How do we measure, plan, and implement innovative processes?

Dashboards

Dashboards are used to convey information graphically: how much, how fast, how long, or whatever can be conveyed in that manner. They might be used to show the current sales volume or how many objects are coming off the line in an industrial sense.

I am seeing a trend today toward more real-time BI and "appliance" processing. There is also an emerging streaming technology interest as we awaken to the fact that there are technologies out there that can process real-time data feeds. Streaming analytics really are different than traditional query systems.

An ideal scenario for dashboards is in the area of streaming analytics. Figure 7-2 shows the fundamental difference between stream analytics and traditional BI. The stream concept takes data from a myriad of sources and passes it through a library of "events." Thus, the queries are in place, but the data constantly changes. Such usage is ideal for a dashboard.

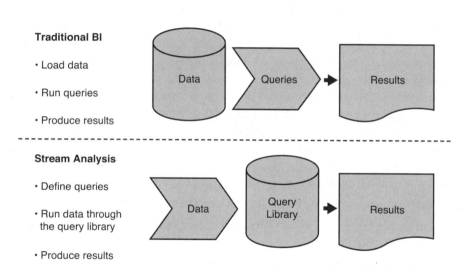

Figure 7-2 Stream Computing: a very different model

Feedback

As I have suggested regarding any BI tool, suite, package, application, or bundle, a CPM system is only as good as the data that supports it. In a CPM loop, however, the feedback mechanism is more essential than in any other BI application. You are monitoring and managing the corporation's performance against key metrics that are either on target, exceeding expectations, or in trouble. You are also trying to communicate the current status, key changes, trouble areas, areas where things shine, and so much more.

In the feedback aspect of any CPM system, the ability to flag events and provide immediate notification is key to success. As I discussed earlier regarding auto-notification of BI events, a CPM system is significantly enhanced if it provides immediate feedback when something goes awry. Whatever the mechanism may be—email, alert, flashing red, smoke signal, or your desk catches fire—it is imperative that you ensure your CPM system provides it, and that all key users understand what to do in case something happens.

I once helped a client develop a system that primarily delivered bad news, and they had all sorts of clever names for it. Most of them I cannot repeat here, but suffice it to say they were quite doomsday-like in usage. The executive users loved it as long as it didn't fall into their realm of responsibility. The internal workings of this particular client made this system very contentious and "ugly." Communication of bad news was met with immediate feedback of an unpleasant kind. The complaints and anxiety it caused resulted in it being discontinued after several months, even though the information conveyed saved them some serious losses on occasion.

If you enable a feedback process in your CPM system, consider how the communication will be handled and try to create an environment where people are not encouraged to constantly hide or defend their numbers, measurements, and results.

The "PM"s Available Today

There are a myriad of EPM/BPM/CPM providers on the market today, and all have unique features as well as common functions that must exist in any viable performance management suite. For you, the challenge is in selecting the one that most closely matches the infrastructure you have in place and the way you are organized as a business.

For enterprise-wide PM systems, it is imperative that you be able to segment areas of the business along organizational as well as functional lines. The sales department, for example, is very co-dependent upon marketing, supply chain, and more. Cross-functional areas where communication and information flow freely today must be built into your CPM model.

The major industry pundits today reference three major CPM vendors: IBM, SAP, and Oracle. This is not to say there are not many other quality offerings and vendors in the marketplace today, but in the rarefied air of enterprise CPM, these are the ones most often touted.

Your selection of an enterprise-wide CPM system will require that you standardize on some vendor's offering rather than putting a number of such solutions in place. In the critical area of information sharing, you cannot afford to have isolated and insular CPM pillars.

In evaluating CPM suites, ask yourself and others about what is absolutely critical for your organization. Some of the most salient points I consistently discuss are the following:

- Does it cover all data sources we support?
- Can we integrate it within our corporate portal?
- Does it fit our feedback paradigm?
- Can it address the many levels within our organization effectively?
- What about extranet (B2B) feedback loops?
- Is the data resilient and accurate in order to match our required planning cycle?

You can most likely add a few to the list. There are technological elements as well as business process-related elements to consider. I find that far too often, the CPM decision weighs most heavily on IT in areas they are not skilled at addressing. One area that is ultra-critical for the end users is how they will populate data if the system is one that permits the users to enter their own metrics. I have seen some very awkward non-intuitive data entry solutions handed to managerial levels and above. As most CPM solutions tend to be top-down in nature, this always seemed odd to me.

Another area that is of extreme importance is the ability to go through a planning cycle and make changes rapidly. Many clients I have spoken to tell me that their internal planning and reaction cycle can take weeks. The culprit in most cases is the latency of data. If you compromise in any area of a proposed CPM system, it cannot be in the area of timely data. If the refresh and update cycle is longer than your desired cycle, you will never be satisfied with your solution.

The Executive View of BI

The majority of executives I have dealt with seem to clearly understand the value and potential of BI within the organization. I have railed away at the need to be realistic and not naïve about the limitations as well as the potential of any BI solution.

So, the only advice I can provide at this juncture is to be involved, be engaged, and schedule regular meetings with those expected to deliver critical information to you and others. In today's stressed business environment, the last thing you need is yet another round of meetings, but if you are not engaged, the potential of your CPM, BI, and DW solutions will be significantly reduced. Rather than just have regular "chat times," it is best to set an agenda with topics of interest and importance to you. Some interest areas should be the following:

- What is our current deployment and user penetration compared to our schedule?
- Where are we in relation to our projected iterations of our planning cycle?
- What is our current skills inventory versus need for critical analysis?
- Are service levels being met? If not, what is the plan to fix this?
- How is our current feedback loop operating? You should have significant input on this, assuming you have a CPM/BI layered approach in place.
- What are we considering in the future regarding innovations in BI, CPM, and so on? New and emerging technologies such as cloud computing, stream analytics, and operational BI may be in your plans—how will they be addressed?
- What is the status of server consolidations, BI standardization, vendor relations, inventory and maintenance schedules, and more?

In a top-down BI and CPM environment, it is imperative that you be involved in thorough testing and constant validation. There is no excuse for ignoring what is occurring in your BI realm and making any assumptions about it. If we look at the true cost of any BI infrastructure, we see the following cost elements at play that can affect your bottom line:

- Software and maintenance
- Hardware and maintenance
- Processes such as ETL and CDC
- IT staff—support, training, problem resolution
- End user staff—support, training, problem resolution
- Power consumption
- Network costs
- Floor space, wiring, and so on

The most critical and insidious costs are those where inefficient or non-productive use of the technologies are in play. The number of end users hacking away at data with BI tools desperate for results is, at times, frightening. Acquisition without a plan and infrastructure is the kiss of death. You, the executive, can have a huge influence on how effective your CPM/BI solutions are, but it takes commitment and it takes valuable time.

One area where your sensitivity (or lack of) comes into play is the measurement of BI productivity and success for the individuals who report to you and your peers. Some equate BI skills with intelligence and capability, which is a dangerous view. Some people are simply not cut out to use BI tools, and it is no reflection on their business savvy or acumen.

I like to think the "exec" in "executive" has to do with execution—not by executing others metaphorically, but in ensuring execution of the proper business plan and innovation. CPM and BI solutions can be of huge assistance to you if used wisely and well.

Summary

CPM has a direct impact upon all levels in the enterprise, but the greatest is upon the executive and managerial staff. Considering the intricacies of implementing at the enterprise level, the selection must be done very carefully. Rather than hone in on the nitty-gritty functionality, it is better to concentrate on the overall effectiveness of the solution with a strong emphasis upon the feedback mechanisms in place.

Timely, accurate data is beyond critical in effective CPM and BI solutions. Even if the data is extremely accurate, if it's not updated in a time frame that makes it possible to make rapid adjustments and changes in your business plan, you wind up with some semi-relevant and quasi-historical information that may limit the scope of your decision making. Given the new and emerging technologies, such as streaming analytics, cloud, and more, the solution you choose must accommodate them or have a roadmap that supports them. If not, you will be revisiting your CPM and BI environments again. Set a firm base and then innovate.

I have spent a lot of time discussing structured information, which is critical to your success, but the vast, untapped unstructured and semi-structured data abounds. This is an area where new solutions such as streaming analytics and more will play heavily in the future.

8

Enterprise Content Management, Unstructured Data, Text Analytics, and Enterprise Search

Most of the information captured electronically exists within unstructured formats. There are documents, audio, video, emails, and many more sources of data that may be of interest to you and others in the enterprise. Rather than pontificate about the massive volumes of information, I would like to address how best to take advantage of this wealth.

There are internal sources and external sources that may be of interest and value to numerous individuals in the enterprise. Internal information is obviously more reliable and easier to control than outside sources. Information shared internally (memos, emails, and so on) provides a wealth of historical and contextual information. Past decisions and discussions that are not reflected in structured data can be invaluable in many decision-making scenarios.

External sources contain information that is dynamic, often controversial, and possibly suspect in nature. News about a competitor can be obtained in a nanosecond thanks to the global reach and interconnectivity of the Internet. Competitive sales announcements, marketing campaigns, and more are readily available to an enterprise with the proper technology and vision. We also have the legal implications in the United States, such as the following:

- Over the past five years, the concept of electronically stored and searchable information has led to a significant evolution in the law governing discovery in the United States.

- New Federal Rules Amendments took effect on December 1, 2006.

- The amendments to the Federal Rules of Civil Procedure (FRCP) represent an attempt to harmonize emerging local court practices and codify the law, rather than an effort to radically change the law that has developed over the past five years.

- Important developments involving the standards applicable to the use of search terms (for example, Victor Stanley v. Creative Pipe, U.S. v. O'Keefe).

- Headline-grabbing sanctions decisions involving the duty of counsel to have adequately searched for responsive documents (for example, Qualcomm v. Broadcom).

Today, there is little choice for any company. The law requires that you be able to store, retrieve, and produce documentation of enormous range and scope. We have switched gears from storing things we deem important to things...period. It's an attitude of: "I'll be the judge of its relevance, and you just bring me the information."

Most organizations are looking at advanced search engines in the context of both unstructured and structured information. The ability to perform analytics against unstructured information has been a recent area of interest to many, as it can provide a significant competitive advantage as well as a means to automate certain decision-making events without massive human intervention and resources.

I have found this area to be one where most organizations seem to have an avid interest. However, they have not made a significant investment in pursuing solutions in any of these areas, or they seem to have been stalled at the step where they have implemented a content management system but show no signs of using it in a BI sense.

It is perfectly understandable that this area would take a backseat to the more familiar data warehousing and BI efforts. Most organizations will say they haven't gotten their structured BI infrastructure where they want it, and it's all they can do to pay any attention to unstructured sources. However, if you have an interest in this intriguing arena, how should you approach it? What are the first steps to take? How do you sell this internally? Let's begin by looking at internal requirements and solutions.

Enterprise Content Management (ECM)

The first step most enterprises take is to implement an enterprise content management system with appropriate connectors, rules, and archiving/retrieval capabilities. The many new regulatory compliance initiatives and associated penalties drove many installations of ECM systems. It was deemed critical to be able to store, retrieve, and validate documents, emails, and more. Along with ECM, there is an obvious need to provide sophisticated search functionality such that required information is easily and accurately retrieved. I don't know about you, but I am constantly rummaging around trying to find a note or some item I need to refer to. In many cases, I am looking for a person's quote, comments, or some numbers I need to review.

It's hard enough to try to manage and organize my personal machine. I have more folders than an office supply store and still struggle to locate things. I have a desktop search engine that helps filter things to some degree, but I still need to open some things to find information. Sometimes I have to open several things. Sometimes I just quietly mumble and call it a day. At the enterprise level, content management can be a huge challenge. What is the definition of ECM?

Wikipedia defines ECM as the following:

> *Enterprise content management (ECM) refers to the technologies, strategies, methods, and tools used to capture, manage, store, preserve, and deliver content and documents related to an organization and its processes. ECM tools allow the management of an enterprise-level organization's information.*

Wikipedia also provides a bit of historical context behind ECM today:

> *New product suites have arisen from the combination of capture, search, and networking capabilities with technologies of the content management field, which have traditionally addressed digital archiving, document management,*

and workflow. Generally speaking, this is when content management becomes enterprise content management. The different nomenclature is intended to encompass all of the problem areas related to the use and preservation of information within an organization, in all of its forms—not just its web-oriented face to the outside world. Therefore, most solutions focus on business to employee (B2E) systems. However, as the solutions have evolved, new components to content management have arisen. For example, as unstructured content is checked in and out of an ECM system, each use can potentially enrich the content's profile, to some extent automatically, so that the system might gradually acquire or "learn" new filtering, routing and search pathways, corporate taxonomies and semantic networks, which in turn assist in making better retention-rule decisions, determining which records or documents to keep, and which to discard, and when. Such issues become all the more important, as email and instant messaging are increasingly employed in the decision-making processes in an organization.

Though the term "enterprise content management" most often refers to solutions that concentrate on providing in-house information, there is a wider view to be taken. The solutions tend to provide intranet services to employees (B2E), but also include enterprise portals for business to business (B2B), business to government (B2G), or government to business (G2B), and so on. This category includes most of the former document management groupware and workflow solutions that have not yet fully converted their architecture, but provide a web interface to their applications. Digital asset management (DAM) is also a form of ECM that is concerned with content stored using digital electronic technology.

The technology components that comprise ECM today are the descendants of the electronic document management systems (EDMS) software products that were first released in the late 1980s and early 1990s.

Note that the majority of the definition and explanation relate to internal information. There is an element of B2B within ECM, but it is primarily thought of as a solution suite to organize things we have in-house. In the past, we decided what we wanted to store. Older systems were designed for us to be able to retain the things that we determined were important. Now, we are required to hold onto an enormous amount of information "just in case." There are costs associated with this, as well as a growing need to wallow through volumes of information.

One area where more advanced ECM implementations improve is their enforcing of better naming conventions for documents as well as making sure emails have titles. You cannot easily provide a brief summary or annotation of a document if its title is ENU-12345-Dec 2009.doc. Nor can you easily locate information within emails when there is no subject line. I am surprised there aren't more disciplines enforced and standards applied in either area.

One other area that drives me to distraction is the propensity of some to keep appending reply and additional information to emails. Some emails are already the size of *War and Peace*, with everyone known to mankind copied on them. Then some will continue to add to the replies with additional text, no changes in the title line, and then shoot the mega-memo back to all involved. Not only do these things clog corporate email systems, but they are impossible to tag by subject other than the original text line. I have had situations where I have 20 or more massive notes with attachments and replies all with the title: "Urgent Account Situation in ___." I try to send back the least amount of text I can, as well as make some modification in the subject line.

There are many ECM providers in the market today, including IBM, Microsoft, and others. Your decision for an ECM platform and solution needs to take into account all the possible sources of information in the enterprise. Once you have identified all the possible sources, the solution proposal must include the capability to house all the information. If the solution cannot scale to accommodate your needs, it is of no value. Once the information is stored, the solution must have the capability to categorize and retrieve.

I would urge you to include in your approach to enhancing your ECM system the use of this vast storeroom as an extension of your BI strategy. Once you have your ECM system in order, the next (or concurrent) function to carefully examine is enterprise search.

Enterprise Search

Wikipedia defines enterprise search in the following way:

Enterprise search is the practice of identifying and enabling specific content across the enterprise to be indexed, searched, and displayed to authorized users.

Wikipedia also states the following about enterprise search:

> *The term "enterprise search" is used to describe the application of search technology to information within an organization (though the search function and its results may still be public). This is in contrast to the other two main types of horizontal search environment: web search and desktop search (though the areas overlap, and systems may address these scenarios as well).*

The question now arises: "What is the enterprise?" Do you define the enterprise as all that you manage "in-house," or do you look at this on a more global scale? Searching all available documents within your organization is daunting enough; adding global sources to the mix sounds impossible.

So, we all know about Google. People have started using Google as a verb, such as "Just Google this and you'll find...." If we examine the typical search (that is, Google) function, we see a list of objects that have been ranked in terms of importance, relevance, context, and more. What we don't know at this point is much detail about the individual hits. Sometimes we'll see a mini-paragraph with some details, but we are still at the point where we now must dive into the individual articles/hits and do more research.

Vendors with enterprise search engines, such as IBM's OmniFind®, offer out-of-the-box capabilities. IBM has, for example, an OmniFind Yahoo! Edition, where technologies are merged to extend the reach of global search capabilities. Microsoft® is a major player in this space as well as Google. There are others such as Oracle that play a major role in this space.

The dilemma all vendors have in this arena is the sheer volume of information required to search. Key players such as Exalead have made enormous strides in this space, as the quest for greater scalability will not cease. If anything, the problem around volume will increase perpetually.

The first order of business is to define what search capabilities you intend to implement and why. Effective use of search technologies requires planning, forethought, and purpose. It also requires some end user education as to how best to interpret results. One client I worked with not too long ago had a panic attack over a competitor's recent action. What was thought to be a serious situation turned out to be a false alarm, as the information "discovered" turned out to be over three years old. Finding information that is accurate, factual, and relevant can be a challenge.

I recommend having an enterprise search technology team dedicated to investigating the solutions available and how best to implement them within your corporate infrastructure. (Should resources from the BI team serve on the enterprise search team? Or, in your opinon, is enterprise search a standard IT function?) Once all possible and/or desired sources are identified, the next step is to determine just how they will be used. Providing a corporate portal interface that intelligently collects and presents the appropriate information in context (a "mashup") is a key to success. It may well be that elaborate meshing of information from a myriad of sources is just not practical nor justified, and a determination is made to limit the scope of the use of results returned. All of this emerges from a reasonable project designed around effective use of search technology within the enterprise.

You may decide to limit the scope of search to internal information only and just encourage people within to at least spend some time looking on the outside for critical or interesting information.

Figure 8-1 shows a diagram of what your environment may look like regarding searchable data sources. If you omit one of these in your overall search strategy, be very sure it will not come back to haunt you later. This diagram should not be interpreted as "store everything in your ECM system." It is intended to spur you on to work with others in the enterprise to map out your overall unstructured system.

For example, consider the use of BI reporting within the enterprise. The data constantly changes; thus, there are reports that may be run on a regular basis that contain some historical information that may be of use in subsequent comparisons. If the data is constantly refreshed and tends to move in time, historical reports may be of extreme value.

When such a whiteboard exercise is undertaken, it is important to ask a number of poignant questions, such as the following:

1. How do we qualify and tag our documents, emails, reports, and other important pieces of information?
2. Can we search them by title, by context, or by content?
3. If we have "legacy" sources that cannot be searched, could we use some facility such as BI reporting to at least capture key information for later use?
4. What limitations do we see in our internal processes?

White Board and ECM, Search, Text Analytics Infrastructure

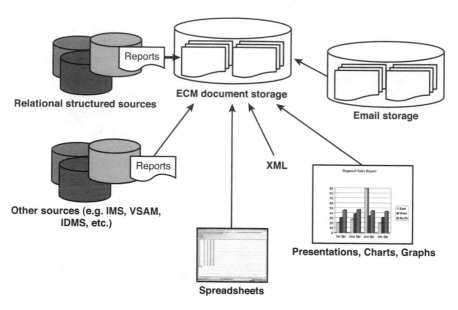

Figure 8-1   Whiteboard and ECM, search, text analytics infrastructure

5. Are there practices we need to change as a result of our investigation?
6. Are we overlooking critical information held in "odd" sources, such as spreadsheets, presentations, and more?
7. Are we positioned to take advantage of text analytics from any/all our sources?
8. Are we confident that our security mechanisms only expose information to the proper people? Do we exclude information that we should not?
9. How will we test and prove any or all of this?

I think of all the presentations I have created and received that have very critical or sensitive information in them, which I know for a fact does not reside elsewhere, that can be found. I suspect you have a similar inventory within your enterprise. These sources are often overlooked because they are regarded as quick, "point-in-time" objects.

Using RSS as a Conduit for External Information

One common and very effective means of monitoring areas of interest is to set up an RSS capability within your corporate portal. Wikipedia defines RSS in the following way:

> *RSS (most commonly expanded as "Really Simple Syndication") is a family of web-feed formats used to publish frequently updated works—such as blog entries, news headlines, audio, and video—in a standardized format.{2} An RSS document (which is called a "feed," "web feed,"{3} or "channel") includes full or summarized text, plus metadata such as publishing dates and authorship. Web feeds benefit publishers by letting them syndicate content automatically. They benefit readers who want to subscribe to timely updates from favored websites or to aggregate feeds from many sites into one place. RSS feeds can be read using software called an "RSS reader," "feed reader," or "aggregator," which can be web-based, desktop-based, or mobile device-based. A standardized XML file format allows the information to be published once and viewed by many different programs. The user subscribes to a feed by entering into the reader the feed's URI or by clicking an RSS icon in a web browser that initiates the subscription process. The RSS reader checks the user's subscribed feeds regularly for new work, downloads any updates that it finds, and provides a user interface to monitor and read the feeds.*

This is an effective means of tracking subjects near and dear to the user, as well as capturing updated information to store internally. Now we go back to our team of experts assigned to organizing and evaluating enterprise search technologies. If one group is selected as an internal test case, you have a means of testing how well the matching and merging of internal information and external information is working. Within a portal, it is quite easy to implement an event trigger that may use something from an RSS feed to kick off an alert or email or other notification. This is an area where I have not seen much in the way of setting standards or internal rules that govern and articulate how this information is to be properly used.

What if information held either internally or externally might actually provide input to some analysis that would be of value to your business?

Text Analytics

Text analytics is an emerging area where critical, numeric data or events can be of extreme interest or value to the business. For example, what if there is an article or information tidbit about a major competitor that indicates they are going to increase their marketing budget by 25% in the following three market areas: Los Angeles, Dallas, and Atlanta? There are three key indicators here:

- Marketing budget (do we know how much it is today?)
- Increase by 25%
- Three market areas: Los Angeles, Dallas, and Atlanta

The analytical part of our brain kicks in, and we ask: "What were they allocating before? What does ours look like in comparison? How are we doing in those areas? Are these areas key to us or marginal at best?" There are analytical references as well as numeric values hidden within textual sources: increase, decrease, shortfall, margin, and so on. Some deductions may be made if there is additional context supporting the text.

Text analytics is often referred to as text mining. This infers that there are gems hidden or embedded within text sources, provided you can accurately deduce the value and relevance of the information. There is a myriad of providers in the market today, including the following:

- ABNER: Biomedical Named Entity Recognizer
- ANNIE: A Nearly-New IE system, bundled with GATE
- BALIE: Baseline Information Extraction (BALIE) - Java toolkit
- CALAIS Web service
- Carabao Language Kit: A multipurpose text-to-knowledge suite with extensive customization
- CLAIR: Computational Linguistics and Information Retrieval (CLAIR) - Perl toolkit
- FreeLing: C++ toolkit
- IBM LanguageWare®: UIMA-compliant annotators, Eclipse plug-ins, or Web services

- Lingpipe: Java toolkit
- LT-XML2
- MALLET: Java toolkit
- Minor Third: Java toolkit
- NLTK: Natural Language Toolkit (NLTK) - Python toolkit
- OpenNLP: Java toolkit(s)
- RAST: Robust Accurate Statistical Parsing
- Stanford NLP Tools: Java toolkit

This is not a comprehensive list by any means, but it shows that there is a lot of investment in this technology in an era where consolidations and mergers are the norm. I turn once again to Wikipedia for a good definition of text analytics:

> *The term "text analytics" describes a set of linguistic, statistical, and machine learning techniques that model and structure the information content textual sources for business intelligence, exploratory data analysis, research, or investigation. Text analysis involves information retrieval, lexical analysis to study word frequency distributions, pattern recognition, tagging/annotation, information extraction, data mining techniques including link and association analysis, visualization, and predictive analytics. The overarching goal is, essentially, to turn text into data for analysis via natural language processing (NLP).*

> *The term also describes that application of text analysis to respond to business problems, whether independently or in conjunction with query and analysis of fielded, numerical data. It is a truism that 80 percent of business-relevant information originates in unstructured form, primarily text{1}. These techniques and processes discover and present knowledge—facts, business rules, and relationships—that is otherwise locked in textual form, impenetrable to automated processing.*

> *A typical application is to scan a set of documents written in a natural language and either model the document set for predictive classification purposes or populate a database or search index with the information extracted.*

The Search and Text Analytics Project

It is most effective if you target a specific usage and test environment to verify the effective use of search and text analytics within a control group. For example, in a customer project in the automotive industry, a defective part was receiving a lot of attention. With the implementation of a search/text analytics solution, the client discovered that it was a secondary effect caused by another part that had not been identified as the culprit. There were numerous reports and memos available describing the failures, and these were the primary source of information used in the discovery phase.

There is a fine balance between being too narrow in your data sources and opening up the application to a more global but nearly unmanageable volume of information, such as external sources. The first order of business is to validate the value-add of such solutions, as well as learn a bit of craft in targeting additional, non-structured data to analyze. Text mining can uncover a wealth of additional information, but it may not be of use to users unless it is framed within the context of their role in the enterprise.

What if you uncovered a significant glitch in a competitor's marketing strategy? The logical thing to do would be to expose this to the proper individuals in the organization who might be able to take advantage of this. If your firm already had a distinct advantage due to this flaw in the other guy's plan, would you take actions to expose their shortcoming to gain an even greater edge? Or would you make some minor adjustments to press your advantage without making them aware that they had a serious flaw?

Most organizations would do the latter but might immediately add a watch element to their RSS bucket and make it a point of monitoring the competition for any adjustments. As part of this, you may be able to pinpoint some numerical metrics that you would monitor and add to your BI layer from your RSS feeds or other sources. It is common to use text analytics to enhance a dashboard with information of this nature. If you do so, you must clearly make the users aware that this data is not rock solid but best effort in usage.

Text analytics and accuracy of search follow the same rules as other elements of BI. Any assumption made without validation of results or proof of technology is made at your own risk. Once there is a comfort zone established with the marriage of search and text analytics, the expansion of use and additional value of the information uncovered increases.

Most organizations find that areas such as customer fraud, sales and marketing campaigns, and competitive analysis are sweet spots for text analytics. Manufacturing operations such as the automotive example I referenced earlier also may benefit from seemingly disparate data or events. So, in the case of our project team, we need to identify an area that is both of keen interest to the corporate advancement as well as verifiable by the business organization.

Text Analytics as a Part of the Complete BI Picture

Most BI vendors are spending considerable focus upon the integration of search technologies, unstructured information, and text analytics as necessary elements to effectively compete. IBM, for example, has acquired SPSS due to a perceived gap in their BI portfolio. IBM had invested in both data and text mining technologies in the past, but the acquisition provided a means of rapidly filling in a missing piece.

Seth Grimes (Intelligent Enterprise—June 10, 2009; Text Analytics Summit) stated the following:

> *The number and quality of end-user presentations at this year's Text Analytics Summit prove that Marti Hearst's 1999 observation, "The nascent field of text data mining (TDM) has the peculiar distinction of having a name and a fair amount of hype but as yet almost no practitioners," is definitively no longer operative.*

Some of the influential players have awakened to the fact that unstructured sources and structured sources may have a high degree of affinity. The challenge is to somehow join the information accurately. If the values held in the disparate sources are misaligned or not able to be matched, we have only expanded the overall BI, warehouse, and ETL dilemma to an entirely new array of data.

I would encourage you to view the inclusion of unstructured information as part of a more holistic BI picture. If you opt to create a project/team for the unstructured elements of your BI infrastructure, make sure they do not go off on a tangent that satisfies the overall goal of using unstructured information as an adjunct to your overall analytics strategy.

The Impact of XML on BI

There has been acceleration in both interest and implementation of text analytics in the last decade. Much of the recent interest has been spurred on by the acceptance of XML as a rich data source. Not too long ago, XML was a convenient standard data format for web applications. It was soon found to be a perfect vehicle to house data of a variety of types: numeric, text, contextual, and so on. The revolution has begun whereby the concept of data warehousing is beginning to change from the rigid, structured formats to a more open, rich XML storage and retrieval facility. Given this enhanced warehouse view, we may find that our ability to store and access more current information becomes easier.

You may be familiar with the term XMLA. XML for Analysis (abbreviated as XMLA) is the industry standard for data access in analytical systems, such as OLAP and data mining. XMLA is based on other industry standards such as XML, SOAP, and HTTP. XMLA is maintained by the XMLA Council, with Microsoft, Hyperion, and SAS being the official XMLA Council founding members. In addition to having an XMLA standard, it was necessary to develop a different means of querying XML data. SQL queries may be used against XML data but are not efficient and need to have the data "shredded" (parsed) into components. Thus, XQuery evolved.

XQuery is a query and functional programming language that is designed to query collections of XML data. XQuery 1.0 was developed by the XML Query working group of the W3C. The work was closely coordinated with the development of XSLT 2.0 by the XSL working group; the two groups shared responsibility for XPath 2.0, which is a subset of XQuery 1.0. XQuery 1.0 became a W3C Recommendation on January 23, 2007.

The mission of the XML Query project is to provide flexible query facilities to extract data from real and virtual documents on the Web, therefore finally providing the needed interaction between the Web world and the database world. Ultimately, collections of XML files will be accessed like databases if the literature and multitude of commentaries are accurate.

Summary

The areas of unstructured information, enterprise search, and text analytics are all beyond the point of being "emerging" technologies. All have numerous solution options and have proven to be of extreme value to forward-thinking organizations. The stumbling block for many appears to be in trying to tie these offerings within their enterprise infrastructure to specific business problems.

It is highly recommended that specific, targeted business areas or application areas be thoroughly tested and validated. The linkage of information among disparate data sources and rapid identification of key information must be proven. Portal integration and collaboration functions (notification, alerts, and so on) must be a part of the process as well.

A project team and executive business sponsor will be very instrumental in developing a corporate strategy once an initial project has been completed and verified. There is usually a significant change in attitude and internal interest once one business area has been able to employ these technologies to their advantage. The user community contains interest areas and uses of information that are highly diverse. Given the unique attributes of these technologies and the challenges of the traditional BI environment, how does one segment the user population into meaningful categories?

9

Key Influencers in the Enterprise

I wanted to separate this discussion from the discussion regarding roles within the enterprise covered in Chapter 6, "The Impact of Business Intelligence on Roles within the Enterprise." BI end user segmentation should be viewed more from a business area perspective rather than that of functional roles. From a role-based perspective, anyone who will perform as a BI technical specialist will have to spend a significant amount of time learning BI tools in-depth. Those who are mostly passive recipients of BI functions and processes will have little say in the matter, other than commenting on how well the solutions meet their needs.

I prefer to look at end user segmentation from the angle of the value and impact the users have on the business. There are high-value segments, and others who benefit from BI but do not have a significant impact on the enterprise as a whole or within their own functional area.

User Segmentation Reality Check

As I mentioned earlier, one of the top agenda items, if not THE top one listed by Corporate Information Officers (CIOs), is Business Intelligence. However, the role of the CIO today often involves a set of paradoxes that make it difficult for IT to succeed. Martha Heller (*CIO Magazine*, 12-15-2009) describes the plight of many CIOs. Much of the inherent trouble stems from the perceived value of IT by the business community within the organization despite the effort IT makes to align itself with delivering business value. Later in this chapter, I will get into end user segmentation more thoroughly, but one key segment to identify is the significant individuals in IT who have a good deal of business acumen and quality contacts throughout the organization.

Another area that Ms. Heller touches on is the technology arena. She states, "The CIO paradox can be as profound as this: Bad technology can bring a company to its knees, yet corporate boards rarely employ CIOs as directors." As we'll discuss, the identification of key influencers and the ability to connect them at the enterprise level can have a profound influence upon corporate BI success. Her statement points out the importance of both the technology and the organization. A bad choice of BI technology will be a disaster—enough said. Poor organizational structure and poor interaction could be even worse. This would be akin to giving a caveman an M-16 rifle broken down into its individual components and expecting him to evolve his hunting techniques with no instruction or context.

Within any organization, there will be those who contribute more to the business and bottom line than others. This does not devalue the roles of those with less impact; it's just how businesses operate. In the world of BI, as already discussed, there is perception, and then there is the reality of how useful and to what degree a BI solution will have an impact on the bottom line.

I would look at a role like the CIO and make few assumptions that BI solutions would have an impact there. As I mentioned before, the CIO surveys typically show BI as the top priority among most of these folks. However, the driving force here is what they perceive BI to be able to do for their critical end users. Now if you had a measurement system in place to provide the CIOs with a dashboard of the impact their BI implementation was having, they would be a true beneficiary of BI in their own right.

In determining how best to serve the end user community as well as the business, it's best to identify those in the organization who would have the greatest impact upon key business operations as the primary recipients of BI output. Identify those who benefit the most from analysis and other BI output. The impact players may reside at various levels within the organization, and thus a reality check is in order.

I have been involved in endless BI solution implementations where the overwhelming numbers of users are those who create and/or receive reports to be able to explain some data to those higher up. In many cases, the output is merely a replacement for or slight embellishment of production reporting.

The dilemma in 99% of all organizations I have worked with is that the internal politics get in the way of being a bit more creative and dynamic as a business. Quite often, I use sales organizations as a key example because that is where I have seen endless attempts at improving processes and reporting. If the recipients of sales results and/or forecasts merely want to defend their position or bring down the hammer on others for not producing, what's the point? The better solution would be to augment a sales information system with accurate customer profiles and realistic projections of how much can be expected from the customers, as opposed to a dartboard quota thrown because a specific set of figures must be met.

Another area where significant attention should be paid is with inter-organization synergy points. There are business-related areas where cross-functional information flow is critical. At the enterprise level, you are better off ensuring that there is a proper flow of information and cross-pollination of results among interested parties than saturating an isolated part of the organization while others are left in the dark. Without naming a customer or industry, I can cite numerous situations where one functional area learns about another area's dilemma or progress very late in the game when there could have been enormous mutual benefit attained by sharing BI information.

I simplify my BI user segments by narrowing the categories to four major types of individuals, as follows:

- **Executives and senior management:** Those who must be worked with and kept informed regardless of their degree of involvement.

- **Key influencers:** Those who have significant impact or may have potential impact on the overall enterprise BI strategy and success.
- **Marginal players:** Those who are involved with or use BI technologies but have little overall impact one way or another.
- **Others:** Those who are of no consequence to BI solutions, either from the technology or business view.

Of these groups, the ones with whom to spend the majority of the time working are the key influencers. Without their enthusiastic (I hope!) buy-in and participation, there will not be anywhere near the impact accomplished. You cannot boil the ocean, but you can heat up some of the water molecules and let them radiate the heat.

Identifying the Power Brokers–Key Influencers

In any organization, it is possible to map out the influencers (also known as power brokers) where it is to one's advantage to enable or enlighten them. One of my many roles over the years has been as a technical software sales representative. I have had this role on a local as well as a worldwide basis. I very quickly learned to have the account teams provide an influence diagram of those I would have to call upon and converse with. In these conversations, it has been nearly universally the case that some key individual either couldn't make the meeting or would have to be involved later.

In these scenarios, it has often been the case that the missing ingredient (individual) wasn't a senior, high-level executive but someone who was known, respected, and called upon in key decision-making events. Some of these folks were part of IT, and some were a part of the business user community. When I performed this function on a worldwide basis, it was rare that I would have a chance to return to the scene of the crime, so I would spend additional time with those in my company trying to recommend a quality follow-up with the missing link(s). From the perspective of a vendor, this was a safety feature. From the perspective of providing quality customer service, I wanted to make sure the missing person(s) would get an accurate update that pertained to what their interests were.

You know your power brokers and you know your organization. If you were asked to create an influence map of the areas within your enterprise, could you do it? Would you be able to tie key end users from multiple areas to data sources as well as shared information requirements? The hardest question to address is: "If I show this to the management and/or executive team, would they agree?"

Figure 9-1 shows an influencer's map drawing to illustrate a type of consultant's tool used in BI planning and guidance. Note that connections are identified as established or desired. If you look at the data access, you'll see that Business Unit A wants or requires access to the same data that Business Unit B has, yet there are not effective communications links between them. Business Units A and D both access the same information, yet we do not see an effective communications link between them either. Business Units B and D have effective communication between them, even though they do not share the same data.

Key Influencers Map

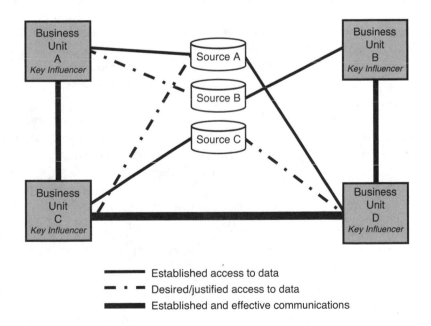

Figure 9-1   Key influencer's map

You can find an endless number of examples of diagrams and formats in use. The objective is not to create the perfect illustration; the objective is to map out a sense of reality. When you identify a critical path that is incomplete or disconnected, you have uncovered a potential major flaw in the business itself. The emphasis needs to be on information access and sharing, interconnectivity, and collaboration.

This diagram is obviously a small portion of any enterprise and may not be in a form that you like at all. However you draw such a schematic, it behooves you to take a hard look at your organization and identify key influencers, their access to data, and their communications and connectivity with others. I have been involved with some rather "wild" sessions, where working on a diagram similar to this has resulted in some harsh realities being addressed as well as some potential gems uncovered.

As an outsider, I ask those who have invited me in to please provide an audience with the key influencers in both areas to see if we can enhance their internal synergy. Sometimes this request is met with awkward silence or stammers. I can usually guess what is coming next: "They don't exactly see eye to eye."

Sometimes, when you have to deal with the body politic, a "testy" situation simply cannot be overcome. I often see this where a client wants to make a strategic change in their current BI strategy, such as moving BI functions and data warehousing back to the mainframe, but there has been a stake hammered in the ground to follow a distributed processing path regardless that cannot be uprooted. No amount of justification or rationale can change some of these scenarios.

But going back to our map, the exercise here is to document and discuss whether the correct dots can be connected or an approach created to fill in any missing links. A key influencer must be looked at from different perspectives. Are they a key influencer because:

- They will use and benefit from the BI information?
- Without their OK, nothing happens?
- They are most effective at building internal bridges and communications?
- They are visionaries and understand the added value?
- Of all the above?

I am not talking about being a key person because someone has the funds to pay for the BI technology; I am assuming BI is already in-house, and we are now trying to make it more effective internally. Ownership of data is also a key factor. Some lay claim to data because it provides an internal "edge" or power they can wield. I find this to be distasteful and counterproductive, as there is more at stake than someone's individual fiefdom; the enterprise view demands that such attitudes be stifled and put to rest.

Attributes of Key Influencers

I tend to look at key influencers from both the technology angle as well as the business angle. Some of the significant attributes I find valuable to identify include the following:

- The BI role as discussed in Chapter 6—how much BI technology will they be exposed to and have to deal with?
- How instrumental are they in making technology recommendations?
- What corporate revenue responsibilities and impact do they have and control?
- What impact will they have on their own part of the organization given enhanced BI capabilities?
- What is their expanded sphere of influence within the enterprise? Are they impact players outside their own realm?
- Can they be viewed as a visionary and open minded, or do they tend to adhere to single-threaded ideas and concepts?

One client I worked with several years ago had delivered an inordinate amount of analytic value by using an OLAP engine to its fullest and most creative extent. They did very little traditional BI reporting and charting. They chewed up an inordinate amount of CPU cycles building and maintaining their OLAP cubes. Their major complaint was that they couldn't build the cubes large enough or update them as rapidly as they wanted to. However, they were one of the best examples of intra-corporate BI synergy that I had ever seen. They linked cubes and business processes across the enterprise and had an extraordinary degree of collaboration developed between segments that was the best I'd ever seen.

This particular client scenario demonstrated that selection of an adequate technology and connecting it to a superb business strategy can take an enterprise as far as it wants to go. I don't wish to downplay the advancements many BI vendors have made in their wares and sound as if just any BI tool will do. However, if a particular tool can be applied to its full potential, many small inadequacies can be overcome. This example is also another reason why I am somewhat biased toward BI standardization and having the fewest tools possible. When an enterprise has nurtured a strong skill base among the users, the effectiveness of any tool will increase exponentially. In the case of this client, the one tool was all they knew and all they used with the exception of spreadsheets.

In discussions with numerous individuals from different departments, they all said the same thing for the most part. The technology and the processes used to build and maintain their OLAP environment were very clearly understood by all. They had spent a significant amount of time developing and sharing skills in the technology. They had made the end users very comfortable with the information available and how it might be used. They had a unified approach to their BI strategy that allowed them to maximize their chosen tool's potential.

What does this example have to do with end user segmentation? Their key influencers were absolutely wired together across organizational boundaries. Every discussion involved at least two functional areas. They had evolved an internal discipline of looking at how BI applications (in this case, OLAP cubes) interlock within the business. If they are operating the same way today, then any change or additions in BI technology will, no doubt, be looked upon in a more holistic manner than in most organizations.

Extending BI Beyond the Enterprise

Extending your BI environment to external participants (B2B and so on) will certainly require that you have your processes and infrastructure tightly wired. Everyone you touch will have their own set of key influencers and connections. A bad experience can alienate an external participant for a long time. It could mean they never return to do business with you. They also have their own connections to other firms where they might spread the bad news rapidly.

Think of some of your early experiences with the Internet and how many sites and sources you may have abandoned. The typical reason for turning away from sites then was the poor performance of a site or connections dropping. This sort of thing is rare these days, and it's now all about quality of data and breadth of service. The emerging cloud computing technology providers all understand this and find that their greatest challenge is to convince potential customers that their services are cost-effective, easy to implement, secure, and scalable.

Connecting your BI environment to others outside can only be effective if the recipients value your services and will act as internal sales folks on your behalf. When you operate outside your own box, be sure to identify the ambassadors willing to promote you. Many conversations and opinions regarding your services will abound when you have no involvement. You may be able to mask internal inadequacies from others for awhile, but in the long run, exposure is inevitable.

Summary

You cannot parse the entire end user population within the enterprise into segments that have any meaning in the long run. You know the various roles people will play and the depth of their commitment and involvement with BI technologies and processes. As far as end user segmentation is concerned, the most effective approach is to identify key influencers in the organization and make sure they are serviced, monitored, connected, and extremely satisfied.

If there are missing connections within the organization (data, collaboration, and so on), this needs to be addressed effectively or there will be far less overall success and BI maturity. CIOs, for example, get pounded about their cost containment and overall budgetary aspects but quite often are kept out of the loop at key levels within the organization.

Connectivity and collaboration within an enterprise for its BI strategy and growth is essential, or you will spend a lot of cycles and funds for a marginal return. If you think about it, lack of a cohesive BI strategy is probably why you may be sitting there wondering why you have so many BI tools in-house.

We've looked at user segmentation, BI tools selection, and many more elements of enterprise BI. Let's assume we have made some very good decisions and have constructed what we feel is a solid approach everyone agrees to. How do we continue to justify and measure our BI efforts?

10

Justifying Business Intelligence Solutions and Measuring Success

Everyone wants to hear a success story. The methodology of building a BI justification strategy varies wildly from organization to organization. Potential clients always ask for references from a vendor as a means of justifying and validating their impending investment in a tool or technology. One way to provide this is to create a justification tree for BI.

Justification cannot be based on a loose, moral goal; it must be hardwired to some sound and defensible metrics. Jeff Gentry was quoted in *Enterprise Journal* (December 1, 2001) as saying the following:

> *Justifications for business intelligence projects are as varied as business strategies and vendor product claims. Many are good, others not. I'd say that the most common and absolutely worst justification ever concocted for data warehouses and data marts has been this one: "To provide better information to the business."*

Though the article dates back several years, I hear many pundits echo this sentiment more and more. The reason Mr. Gentry makes this statement is its simplistic view of BI and the fact that generating better information may not have any bearing upon the health and vitality of the business, despite people receiving "better information." How do we justify BI in our enterprise? How do we measure it? Let's look at justification first.

Justification Scenarios

One simple way of justifying a BI solution is to create a simple roadmap for advancing the cause internally and for having an action plan that supports it. I also suggest going back to review your vision statement and your strategic goals to tie into any justification scenario. If a situation arises where there is internal conflict, it helps to be able to pull out an agreed-upon statement and remind everyone of why you are on a BI path and how you intended to get there.

BI Roadmaps

What would a BI roadmap look like? It could be a highly detailed "How To" diagram or as simple as jotting down a few salient points that everyone can agree to. For example, here are a few simple steps to follow in creating a roadmap:

- Create and maintain a compelling and pragmatic business case for leveraging BI for setting goals such as reducing costs, acquiring/ retaining profitable customers, achieving operational excellence, increasing campaign effectiveness, meeting regulatory requirements, delivering more robust management and financial information, improving strategic performance, and driving top-line growth.

- Identify and make plans to overcome common BI challenges, risks, and barriers to success with the support of key influencers.

- Develop a comprehensive, actionable BI roadmap (or program plan) for delivering high-value BI applications that deliver targeted business process improvements and fulfill the business case.

- Identify an individual who will be responsible for tracking the project and for providing a comprehensive summary of progress as well as results.

I want to remind you that we are looking at this from the enterprise perspective. When I mention the concept of "agreed-to" plans, I mean that cross-boundary issues have also been addressed. If one part of the organization sets a phenomenal plan in place but later finds it conflicting with another area's strategy, you are setting yourself up for a possible major conflict.

Some folks who have a passion for BI will put forward extremely complex scenarios for justification. If a justification process takes too much time, you are just taking away critical cycles from other areas. The key here is that there is a realistic business case that includes measurable goals.

An example of a completed roadmap might have the following steps associated with it:

[Project name] is intended to deliver a new solution designed to increase the ability of our sales and order process to reduce the number of returns that are currently xx% of our total sales and are costing us approximately $xx per quarter.

The target for reduction is xx% with a savings of $xx over a period of [period].

Ongoing measurements and reporting of losses will be provided for comparisons with metrics on the completed project.

[Individual] will be team lead on this and will report to [management and/or team] on the progress weekly at Thursday's project tracking sessions.

The following technologies [list] will be implemented on [platform information] at a cost of $xx. (Note: all associated costs need to be listed including software, hardware, skills development, power consumption, staffing, administration, and floor space required.)

The project will commence on [date] with a target completion date of [date]. Please refer to the following timeline charts [charts inserted here].

Project started on [date].

Training and skills development started on [date] and completed on [date].

Initial testing and implementation completed on [date].

Production commenced on [date] with current losses reported to be [metric].

Initial results showed a major contributing factor for returns to be [factor such as product quality issues, etc.].

Final analysis [overall cause and effect including initial cost estimates and final actual costs].

Action(s) to be taken [actions].

From here you can set up milestones and expand upon the project. When it comes time to compare the cost/benefits there will be a very realistic view of what the actual project costs were. Many clients will take elements such as training and just ignore the costs by acting as if it was just a thing they had to do to get started. True enough but it is still a cost factor.

It becomes awkward when the only considerations are pure costs. In our outline above we are trying to examine returns of merchandise and see if we can reduce the flow of articles back into our stores. I use this example because it is one I am very familiar with. There are many aspects to this problem. Perhaps the issue is simply poor product quality. It may be less expensive to continue buying from a particular manufacturer in the short run, but the impact on continued business from your customers could be significant and this is not reflected in the returns metrics but in overall sales.

I am the type of buyer who is fanatically loyal when I find a provider who consistently offers reasonable value and quality products. I tend to pay a bit more in order to get a consistent quality of merchandise. I am also the type who will walk away from a provider never to return when I have been 'burned' by someone. It may take more than once but never more than twice and you will not get me back.

In our scenario of building a roadmap it is as important to fine comb the results and the causes of the problem as it is to set up the project to begin with. It isn't just about the cost of returns but the overall (secondary) effect this has on the business as a whole.

Articulating Potential Benefits

Much of the emphasis should be placed on the area within the BI roadmap where the actual benefits and hoped for results are identified. You may have, for example, a new BI project where the recipients of the BI processes are going to be handed a series of new reports and charts within the corporate portal. What exactly do we expect from this new capability? For fun, let's assume it is also a case where a new BI tool has been proposed.

First, you describe the problem: "Our ABC department has requested a new set of reports and graphs that provide [metrics] for the period from [start] to [finish]. Their goals of [measurements, etc.] dictated by [corporate sponsor, initiative, etc.] have not been met because they cannot adjust their current goals within the desired timeframe [timeframe] due to data latency. Their current reporting system takes [current time scenario] to provide adequate information. We estimate our current loss of [productivity, revenue, etc.] to be [$$$] given our existing scenario."

Next, you describe the solution: "We are installing [BI tool] at a cost of [$$$] to be in operation by [date] for the purposes of delivering the required information in a new timeframe of [timeframe]. We anticipate we will improve our information flow to meet our goal of [desired timeframe]. There are incremental costs identified [people, hardware, software, etc.] with this project."

Finally, you describe how you will measure success: "Our project leader [name] will perform the following tasks to provide critical feedback on our progress and success by [dates, ranges, etc.]. Success will be measured by [criteria – improved reports etc.]." This may seem a bit elementary, but when I ask if justification scenarios and project tracking are part of a client's DNA, many times I am told, "No."

This trend is one of the curious anomalies of BI today. Because it is far easier to justify due to its emergence as a key corporate strategy element, too often I see clients playing a bit loose with justification scenarios. If you were to follow the example I described previously and had such a justification statement documented, the next step is to get the appropriate approvals for the plan. I am a fanatic for getting people to sign agreements at least in principle. It's probably a residue from my consulting days, but too often I was the victim of a client changing the scope of the project such that justification and defense of a project were moving targets.

Business Unit Impact on Justification

The business units gaining the benefits from any BI project are the first line of validation. They may have a lot of technical skill in the game or perhaps none. What they do have are a set of expectations and desires that are either met or unmet. You cannot possibly have a claim on success if the critical end users find the solution of little value or far less than expected.

I return to my comments about key influencers in Chapter 9, "Key Influencers in the Enterprise," where I tried to drive home the need for interorganizational coverage. I was involved in a couple of client scenarios where there were at least two parts of the organization involved. In the first case, one of the key influencers in Department X was very pleased with their new BI usage. Their counterpart was not and complained that they were not getting what was agreed upon. In a meeting where we had all interested parties sit down and rehash the statement of work, the disgruntled party proved to be an irrational, unreasonable, and quite wrong individual. This person exposed himself to others for all to see, and it resulted in an executive action not in this person's favor...awkward, but reality.

With another client, I had a similar situation, but the aggrieved party quickly realized that all work items agreed upon had not only been met but were exceeded. They had been fed some erroneous information from another within the organization. They had mistakenly been told that some of the BI output from a later phase had not been delivered and that a deadline had been missed. When pressed a bit further, the disgruntled individual actually came up with some radical news about what he required in his part of the organization. It would have resulted in significant data warehouse architectural changes down the road that were easily incorporated into the budding solution before major rework was required. Is there a possible solution you can implement that helps validate a BI scenario with less commitment and involvement? Yes. Look at establishing dashboards as a first step for user buy-in.

Lindsay Wise wrote the following for BeyeNETWORK (September 23, 2009):

> *With industry hype surrounding the use of dashboards to visualize defined metrics and identify overall performance while being able to drill into the cause and effect of issues related to these metrics, dashboards have become one of the most popular ways to access business intelligence on the front end. In addition, dashboards can become a company's first line of access to business intelligence in lieu of implementing a full-scale solution as a first step. In these cases, many options exist when looking at dashboards or other subsets of business intelligence. For instance, organizations can use hosted solutions and pay a monthly subscription fee. Depending on the option chosen, it may be realistic to pay $100/month for a departmental deployment. Alternatively,*

organizations can deploy solutions for an average of $6,000–$10,000 for an average of 10 users (these numbers are based on overall averages provided by a series of dashboard vendors regarding the average cost of their deployments). These prices do not take into account additional costs. Mark Flaherty, VP of Marketing at InetSoft, reminds organizations that, "It is important to remember to take into account 20% over and above software costs for software maintenance."

Taking a dashboard approach as a first step may make perfect sense for any organization wanting to initially justify and verify BI solutions before diving in too deep. This approach provides a means to deliver BI output to business units with little or no skills required on the part of departmental specialists. If we use this approach to start our justification process and to tie key influencers together, we have a solid foundation of BI value with far less investment in skills and time.

Business users need to be content with the solution, possibly excited, and talked to on a regular basis. Sometimes justification is simply the fact that some critical individuals now feel that they can do their job better, are more productive, are better informed, and are able to deliver better results faster. If they will provide this feedback to the appropriate executives and management, you are in great shape

So, I return to the concept of providing a roadmap or project plan with agreed-upon goals and metrics as well as accountability. I have been on the receiving end of poor BI decision making where a corporate decision had been made, a large volume of BI software had been acquired, and the resulting usage was a disaster. I call such phenomena "big purchase...no plan."

Big Purchase...No Plan

Clients like to feel as if they have gotten a great deal. If they feel like they really milked a vendor for all they're worth, it sometimes makes them almost giddy. BI tools are often acquired in extremely large quantities, yet the average deployment rate touted is normally 20%. Stephen Swoyer wrote an article for *TWDI* (published May 20, 2009) that deals with BI deployments and the myth of BI usage. It is based upon a 2009 BI survey.

Mr. Swoyer writes:

Take BI adoption, for example. Business intelligence vendors like to talk up a 20/80 split—i.e., in any given organization, only 20 percent of users are actually consuming BI technologies; the remaining 80 percent are disenfranchised. According to BI Survey 8, however, most shops clock in at far below the 20 percent rate. In any given BI-using organization, notes Nigel Pendse, a principal with BARC and the primary architect of BI Survey, just over 8 percent of employees are actually using BI tools. Even in industries that have aggressively adopted BI tools (e.g., wholesale, banking, and retail), usage barely exceeds 11 percent.

That's a far cry from the 20 percent figure, yet the 20/80 split remains a mainstay of BI vendor rhetoric. Many tout their own (typically self-serving) spins on the issue, using figures as high as 30 percent. No matter what figure is quoted, most BI products rarely reach one-fifth of a user population, yet vendors will claim that their product breaks through that barrier, penetrating to the remaining 80 percent.

There appears to be an inordinate amount of blame thrust upon the BI vendors here, although the figures are accurate. It is not the fault of the vendor that a client does not deploy an acquired tool to their end users. The client decided they were going to service *xx* number of users; does the onus now fall on the vendor to glue people in their seats and make them use it? "It's too hard to use; therefore, we haven't had a lot of success deploying this tool!" I've heard this many times and am tempted to ask, "Did you buy it sight unseen? Were no users involved? Can I sell you beachfront property in Antarctica?" Come on now!

It goes back to the plans, goals, and effective communication you have or may not have in your BI strategy. If a few sterling individuals have decided that Tool XYZ is easy enough for everyone else and no one else was involved, this amounts to organizational stupidity. There is no kinder way to put this.

You cannot discuss a BI strategy and prospective tools with everyone in the enterprise. But, you can involve a subset within each functional area to be a part of the evaluation and justification work. You can tie in the key influencers and use them as ambassadors and filters within their own realms.

Remember Mr. Gentry's comment that I mentioned at the beginning of this chapter? He suggested that a poor justification argument would be: "Providing better information to the business." I have railed about making assumptions about BI throughout this book and will continue to do so.

Let's look at a hypothetical BI purchase. Originally, we were going to buy a BI tool for 100 known users in 8 departments located in various areas. The tool we were looking at has user-based and role-based pricing, so the average cost per user came in at roughly $250 per person. The initial cost of this solution was $25,000 plus 20% annual maintenance. I won't go into incremental costs of hardware and support, and so on.

Somewhere along the way, we decided to take a more holistic view of the enterprise and decided this tool was, indeed, one we could standardize upon as well as deploy across the board. We decided we really wanted to acquire 15,000 seats, and with the vendor's discount of 40%, we ended up paying $2,160,000 (not counting maintenance). This is $250/person * 40% discount * 15000 = $2,160,000. At the end of year 2, we had deployed the mythical 20% of users.

The cost evaluation would look like this:

Year 1 cost of software	$2,160,000
Year 2 cost of maintenance	$432,000
Total cost	$2,592,000

If we now factor in the 20% deployment figure, we get the following metrics:

Year 1 effective use cost	$432,000
Year 1 ineffective use	$1,728,000
Year 2 cost of maintenance effective use	$86,400
Year 2 cost of maintenance ineffective use	$345,600
Total cost of ineffective use	$2,073,600

By our calculations, we have spent roughly $2,073,600 for software that is warming the bench. Our original plan to service 100 users would have cost us $30,000 for the first two years. You can argue volumes and rates and ratios, but these scenarios exist in the BI space. I have been involved in some client situations that far exceed these numbers. In Chapter 3, "The History of Business Intelligence within Your Organization," I provided a table/matrix of a BI standardization agenda with similar figures. No matter what the numbers may be, most organizations pay too much for BI solutions and then whine about how it's the vendor's fault.

ROI, TCO, and TCA

How do you measure your return on investment (ROI) for BI? You do not want to get into a scenario where you burn up lots of cycles and time trying to justify your BI efforts with high ROI numbers, unless you have a consensus that BI has delivered some value that everyone agrees upon with minimal effort to produce the figure.

If your justification roadmap is done well, your ROI scenario should be easy to articulate. For example, if the results of a new BI initiative have resulted in increased sales of 5% and/or a reduction in hours spent by individuals by 15% (multiply this by their cost and overhead), you have a handle on your ROI. In the example of ineffective deployment of a BI tool, if we finally agreed upon a cost figure of $4,345,000 for software, hardware, personnel, and so on for our BI solution, but also discovered that we had increased sales by $25,000,000 the first quarter and increased customer satisfaction by 8%, then the "wasted" costs are almost a moot point. OK, so we bought too much and had a lousy plan, but what we did do was well worth it.

I have mentioned two cost numbers in this hypothetical situation: $2,592,000 for software and an additional $1,753,000 for other costs associated with the software. This new figure of $4,345,000 is not the figure typically used in reporting the total cost of acquisition (TCA). TCA would typically be reported as the original $2M+ figure.

Total cost of ownership (TCO) is often equated to the TCA figure, which is a serious error. TCO should reflect the total cost of all facets of such a purchase. It would include the cost of all hardware, personnel, cycles used, training efforts, and so forth. TCO also includes the elements no one feels comfortable reporting upon, such as loss of time while users took stabs at learning the BI tool(s) but failed.

One area where this is particularly onerous is the data warehouse arena. Clients today are reexamining their platforms of choice for data warehousing. Many are looking at the mainframe as a better option for them due to its many enhancements and benefits. But, as I have stated in earlier chapters, this platform discussion breaks down at the TCA level far too often. Little regard is given to the TCO figures. I discuss platform selection in more detail in Chapter 11, "Platform Selection, Technology Biases, and Other 'Traps'."

If you are being a realist about your BI infrastructure, you will bring all known factors into the equation and use them in a typical ROI formula. One cited by Gwen Thomas in a whitepaper made available from BeyeNETWORK (Understanding Data Governance ROI: A Compliance Perspective 2009) is this:

$$\text{ROI} = 100\% \times \frac{(\text{Total Benefit}) - (\text{Cost of Benefit})}{\text{Cost of Benefit}}$$

In Ms. Thomas' example, she mentions "degrees of separation" from quantifiable benefits as such: Projects that are just "one degree of separation" from money are easy to understand. Direct-mail campaigns, for example, are always based on ROI. Conduct the campaign, and you can expect a certain amount of revenue. Divide the revenue minus costs by the costs, as shown previously. On the other hand, consider an effort to clean up customer data before conducting the campaign. This effort is "two degrees of separation" from the ultimate benefit. It should result in a higher return for the campaign, so it's probably worth the effort since it will improve (or protect) the ROI of the main activity. Now consider a data governance effort to establish data standards and data quality rules. This effort has to take place before the clean-up; it is "three degrees of separation" from the ultimate benefit. It is still important, but just a little farther removed from hard dollars.

The paper deals mainly with data governance and is an excellent read. However, the point she makes about degrees of separation offers a new perspective on some of our efforts. I think we all tend to look at tasks such as data cleansing as costs associated with producing accurate results. Seldom do we turn around and attribute a benefit amount associated with this effort. Where the data is used in other ways beyond the scope of the immediate project, we then reap additional benefits at no cost.

If you have some internal processes and/or metrics for justification scenarios, take a careful look at the specifics behind them. If you have a means of identifying actual dollar amounts that all parties agree to, that should be sufficient. The worst case is where there are no measurable goals, no criteria for success, and no agreement in place for justification. In order to meet any justification scenario, you must have a before and after picture of your BI environment. How do you measure success?

Measuring BI Success

I find this quite simple to do if you have individuals assigned to collecting the appropriate metrics. If you have an organization that supports a BI competency center (BICC), for example, the task of measuring success is built into their key measurements. Successful BI endeavors are directly tied to the corporate vision and definition of BI. They are also tied closely to justification scenarios. Somewhere in your definition statement there needs to be a definition of how success will be measured.

If we think about my example of under-deployment of BI technologies, attaining a sub-standard deployment certainly flies in the face of declaring success. Simplistic goals such as providing better information to people say very little and certainly aren't defensible to senior management or the CFO. I would recommend establishing a set of measurements for success and tie every one of them to revenue or some high-value aspect of the business. Some criteria I have used and have seen others use are as follows:

- New reporting/charting solution—target was to increase or decrease some business factor by x%.
- Increased customer satisfaction—identified x% improvement resulting in $yyy revenue.
- Budget/planning cycle decreased by x%, resulting in greater business agility and yyy fewer hours utilized in the process.
- New BI user group brought online with an increase in productivity of xx%.
- Reduction in fraud and/or wasteful spending amounting to $yyy within the following time period.
- Reduction in BI spending (consolidation play) of $yyy with an increase in BI deployment of [metric].

You can undoubtedly add to this list, but please ensure that the measurements used tie back to specific business goals and dollar amounts. In most cases, you have access to a known set of end users. As such, it is highly advised to survey this set of individuals from the perspective of their roles regarding BI and their position within the enterprise.

Lack of any ability to measure success usually occurs when BI technologies are just thrust upon people with the expectation of producing wondrous results with unspecific goals in mind. If you are going to engage in BI measurements, here are some elements you should identify by individuals, contrast them with stated goals and objectives, and check them off as you go:

- What were you doing before the new solution was made available?
- What are you doing now that is different?
- What new information do you receive today that has made a difference?
- What dollar amount can you attribute in terms of revenue, savings, or other?
- Who within the organization have you communicated this to?
- What other functional areas do you communicate with, and have they seen improvements due to this new functionality?
- What does your management chain think of your measurements? Do they agree? If so, may I verify with them?
- What next steps do you want to take to increase the value-add of BI in your functional area?

If you cannot complete such a survey, your BI environment and success is suspect at best. In the early stages of BI implementation, there is always a flurry of activity and communication. However, once it gets to the production phase, people seem to lose interest and taper off in awareness and focus.

Dorothy Miller wrote the following in Information Management Online (October 19, 2007):

> *There are some classic definitions and discussions concerning business goals and requirements that are entirely appropriate to the current BI arena. It may be worthwhile to repeat some of these very well-known ground rules. Most of the players in the business world are familiar with the concepts. However, these obvious rules are not necessarily followed. For BI assets, that*

is crucial. The money and other resources dumped into these BI systems can be astounding. Consultants and others in the industry for any length of time have personal experience or knowledge of major BI failures that have cost jobs and even crippled entire companies. So, understanding the concepts is not enough. It is imperative that management take the very hard road of defining and then regularly revisiting and redefining the strategic and tactical goals for their organization. This also means ensuring that the BI assets conform to those goals.

Though a bit dated, this is an excellent article that discusses the pitfalls in effective BI measurement.

BI Clouds and Outsourcing

The latest trend in BI implementations is to give them to others to worry about. There are a number of "software as a service" offerings (SaaS for BI), cloud solutions, and the option to outsource your BI to others. This is a very dicey proposition for many. To begin with, the overwhelming numbers of these solutions are merely looked upon as a means of cost containment and potential scalability at a lower risk. The attitude prevails of, "Let's set up a provider who can have our users subscribe to a set of services and pay as they go, and we wish them well."

On the other hand, the April 1, 2010 issue of *CIO Magazine* contains an article where IT professionals responded to a poll of what was on their radar screens today. Cloud computing came in as being of greater interest than Business Intelligence (48% compared to 35%). The driving factor behind this was the need to provide easier, more effective deployments of all solutions including BI.

There are also options for internal clouds whereby the infrastructure of on-demand services are made available to the organization but managed in-house. It takes quite an effort to set up such solutions, but some providers, including IBM, have made major inroads into delivering a solution suite and methodologies to address the greatest stumbling block in BI—deployment to large groups of end users. These solutions also help address the issues with scaling to the proper size with far less pain than before.

The dilemma of measuring success does not disappear with the embracing of such alternate solutions. The one area of improvement is that of identifying the costs associated with BI. External providers will let you know what you have spent at the lowest level of detail. Measuring success is still up to you. Environments where others are constantly adding or changing BI services, such as we see in cloud computing, are very difficult to track without having a constant dialogue with all users across the enterprise. You may have 1,000 users registered with a provider this week with a total bill of $15,000 for the previous month. The following month, you have 857 registered users but a bill for $22,000...what changed? How do you track these variations in usage?

You simply must be prepared to ask such questions and to provide defensible measurements. Because much of BI usage is ad-hoc in nature, you don't have a hard and fast usage and benefits analysis as might be seen in a typical OLTP application. You might see a ton of activity (queries, reporting, and so on) but very little measurable success. In a BI world, activity does not equate to success.

Summary

Both justification and measurement of the success of BI usage take work. Without well-understood goals and measurement criteria, you might as well throw a dart at a board filled with numbers. BI isn't about launching a myriad of new queries and generating countless reports; it is all about working smarter and providing new business information that can be positively identified.

The previous chapters and associated topics come together here, with my urging you to have a plan, establish a vision, create a clear definition of BI within your enterprise, and then establish goals and measurements that will provide feedback to all that your BI strategy is working and produces a return everyone is pleased with.

Justification is more about establishing a solid infrastructure that delivers the vision and far less about keeping down the costs of BI. There are some major factors that can affect your BI success, such as platform selection, technology biases, and other known "traps." We will cover these issues next.

11

Platform Selection, Technology Biases, and Other "Traps"

"Our direction for BI and data warehousing is to move away from the mainframe and onto distributed platforms." I hear this again and again. Now we see a movement back toward the mainframe due to several new factors that have not been available before. This is not where I inject my own prejudices around the mainframe, but where I simply want to point out that there are new factors to consider that have made others reexamine their current environment. The purpose here is to stir your thought processes about the true motivation within your organization when it comes to BI solutions selection criteria. For example, I have heard numerous accounts indicate they are, "Getting off the mainframe"..... for 15 years or more.

Business Intelligence solutions have absolutely no bearing on the enterprise's success if there are prejudices built in from a technology perspective. They should always be driven by corporate objectives and business impact. I also hear numerous clients spout software biases such as database selection simply because someone is impressed with a recent benchmark white paper. Regardless of speed, feed, and all, delivering gibberish faster has little if any value.

The first and foremost change is that many new technologies have been ported to the mainframe environments that were not available a scant two years ago. Data warehousing packages including BI clouds and enablement suites now provide the same ease of installation and maintenance that were only previously available on distributed platforms. In addition, new hardware enhancements, such as specialty processors and faster engines, have spurred this renewed interest.

Where to start? I suggest beginning with examining where your data resides and its current shape and accuracy. BI processes today are becoming more focused on near real-time data access and operational BI. One of the key factors has become: "How close in proximity are my BI tools to the data they need to access?"

Platform Selection for BI Tools–The Database View

Where does your BI data originate from? Is the majority of it stored in mainframe repositories and databases? In nearly every case, source data must be manipulated in some manner (ETL processes, moved to a relational source from older file formats, and so on). The prevailing attitude appears to be, "Well, if I have to massage the data and do things to it, I may as well store it on another platform because it is cheaper than hosting it on a mainframe." In my current role, I wallow through these arguments endlessly, as the prejudices toward mainframe technology are deeply rooted in ignorance and urban legend biases in a majority of the cases.

Remember that we are trying to establish an enterprise approach to BI. The interconnectivity of data and elements of the organization must be considered in doing so. Depending upon where you capture your data and the need for up-to-date information in your organization, the recommended solution may well be to offload to a distributed platform. If, however, you ascribe to the belief that a mainframe must be rejected out of hand because they are most costly, I strongly object.

There are a number of TCO studies available to provide a very different view of mainframe costs compared to distributed solutions, and I will not take up space to discuss them or reference them. I suggest you follow the data and determine how best to set up BI data for analysis and access by end users that is secure, reliable, and accurate. The more real-time the requirement, the less time you have to move and schlep the data all over the place to get it into a new format for BI access.

Figure 11-1 shows a diagram of the two platforms most commonly used for data warehousing in support of BI. In the mainframe environment, it is possible to provide a self-contained environment for data, from capture to loading and updating a data warehouse. Regardless of where you decide to install your BI tools, this approach is the most secure and most tightly controlled environment. There is less delay in doing so, and typically new information is more readily available than having to re-host it.

BI Data Access and Flow

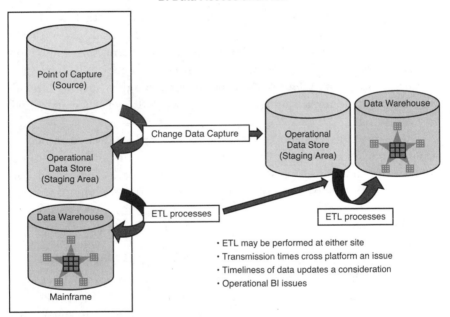

Figure 11-1 Data Access and Flow

If the ETL processes are not required or performed at point of capture as some clients do, the loading of the Operational Data Store (ODS) is extremely fast and provides a platform for Operational BI applications. Data held in many an ODS is more detailed and granular than that of many data warehouses. Thus, we have a means of delivering data in a near real-time manner, as well as having an effective staging area for feeding the data warehouse.

If your data is captured on a non-mainframe platform, this discussion is of no consequence unless you are one of the new breed who are examining a mainframe option possibly for the first time. In the 1996 movie *Jerry Maguire*, Tom Cruise was heard yelling, "Show me the money!". In my data warehouse and BI morality play, I have to shout, "Show me the data!". Latency, delays, lengthy updates, and other negative factors do not have to be tolerated if you are willing to explore all options.

Platform Selection for BI Tools—The Tools View

So where do you install and support your BI tools? Until recently, the only modern options were always on distributed platforms, with the exception of a couple of BI vendors offering mainframe solutions. Now we have new BI tools on the mainframe, such as Cognos 8 BI, that take advantage of specialty engines and newer technologies, such as Linux®, thus keeping the impact on traditional cycles (MSUs, as they are called) to a minimum.

The typical installation of BI tools in a distributed environment is usually done on servers that are separate from other processes so as to not conflict and contend for resources while BI work is being performed. The normal distributed BI environment will allocate some of the processing power for production, some for testing, and some for peaks in usage. I have heard a number of figures discussed when clients determine when to add additional capacity to their BI server farm. The average seems to be around 20%, with the rest providing a "pad" of processing power.

I contrast this with a mainframe environment where the goal is to utilize every cycle if possible. It is not unusual to run a mainframe in excess of 100% capacity. Regardless of where the data resides, if you implement a distributed BI tools approach, you will have to monitor and adjust to increased usage by adding servers to the mix. Along with this approach comes additional cost in the form of software, power, and personnel. There is nothing inherently wrong with this implementation; it is just how things are.

Figure 11-2 illustrates the two platform options from both the self-contained mainframe environment and the distributed or client/server model. Today we are seeing a number of server consolidations from distributed back to the mainframe, which offers greater security, greater availability, and lower costs for power and support.

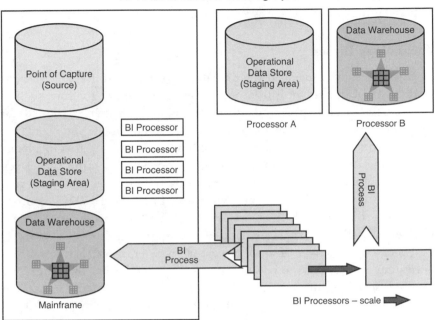

Figure 11-2 BI Tools Processor Hosting Options

Some have started viewing the mainframe as a massive, enterprise server capable of hosting all processes there. Again, the primary determinant is the location of the data. Hybrid implementations are quite common and are often the best solution. In cases where data latency is not an issue and people are performing heads-down analysis, it may be best to house the data and BI processes on the distributed platform.

Without knowing your environment, it would be foolish to suggest that any particular platform option is best for you, and to toss out a blanket statement such as, "I always recommend a distributed environment for BI projects," is arrogant and inane. Biases are just that—biases—and they have no place in the realm of BI.

Understandably, there are corporate standards that must be met or your technology world would be overwhelmed by total anarchy. It is, however, a dangerous practice to dictate a set of standards without performing the underlying diligence to back them up from a BI perspective. The majority of enterprise standards have been established based upon trends set in the past and often do not change as the industry adjusts.

Technology Biases

I have already mentioned the distributed versus mainframe argument that has been in play for quite some time. Others enter the fray, such as the embracing of a specific database technology no matter the cost or deployment options. Some will say, "We are an all-Oracle shop" or, "We only support DB2® or Teradata." I have long ceased trying to win anyone over to an alternate solution for databases, but keep in mind that given the recent mergers and acquisitions, there will be some internal favoritism given to the vendor's own wares. In a mixed DBMS environment, the BI approach is to try to select a tool that covers all data sources, as well as provides a federated data approach.

There are numerous BI appliances out on the market that many find appealing, as they tend to be self-contained "black boxes" that offer low-cost and scalable solutions. You still have to populate their databases as well as support them, but a number of clients believe them to be the next great wave of BI.

Some have biases for specific BI vendors and will argue incessantly, if not irrationally, that they are the only BI provider they will embrace. I cannot help in such scenarios nor will anyone be able to dissuade them from their viewpoint. This is different than the client using OLAP technologies I discussed in Chapter 10, "Justifying Business Intelligence Solutions and Measuring Success." In their case, they found a solution that worked extremely well for them and were open to suggestions. They simply had not found anything else that would enhance what they were doing at the time.

There are often severe cost biases driven by internal initiatives to keep costs low by any and all means. Here we tend to see a number of clients embracing open-source "free" BI tools. It's difficult to argue against free in a situation where cost containment is everything. I submit that in such environments, there is not a serious enterprise BI commitment. Maybe this is the best you can do given budget constraints, but in such cases, the organization is pretty much on its own to figure out how best to implement and use the tool(s).

In the January 4, 2010 issue of *Computerworld*, Mitch Betts comments on open-source BI offerings as "going mainstream for routine uses." He states that million-dollar development, support, and labor costs are not uncommon in large-scale deployments. If you explore the open-source venue, be prepared to provide a substantial amount of labor and skilled personnel at these options. He also states that the lack of trained developers will slow a project and increase overall costs. Note the use of the key word "developers" here. This is a strong indication that the average end user is not going to play well in this case.

In my current position, I have to spend a great deal of time discussing platform options and associated costs. It surprises many to find the following metrics associated with a mainframe versus a distributed (x86) option. On the mainframe side, it has the following cost advantages:

- Up to 80% saving in IT cost
- Up to 96% less hardware—760 x86 processor cores versus 26 IFLs
- Potential for dramatic reductions in software expense for processor-based licenses
- Reductions in power and cooling
- Up to 93% savings in KWatts and energy costs in this scenario
- Up to 46% less space
- Up to 89% people savings

The cost differences between the two may cause you to take notice. However, if a mainframe option does not fit your business model, then it's an interesting fact, but so what? In cases where a mainframe option is rejected out of hand because people assume it is more expensive, there is a different lesson to be learned.

A common solution today is a BI appliance. Now if the application warrants a standalone appliance and it really is pragmatic to isolate this solution for well justified reasons, then such options are ideal. There are situations where a set of data needs to be beaten senseless for a group performing heads-down analytics. The data need not be very current and the users would potentially provide a significant business value ... absolutely perfect. If, however, the driving factor is the appliance is perceived as a low-cost, inexpensive way to provide some BI without any thought of how it will integrate later ... not such a good idea.

Other BI "Traps"

Sometimes I see a client whose view of BI solutions is that they must have particular bells and whistles in order to be considered. I normally encounter this where the client is a bit naïve about BI but has been exposed to some technology that captures their interest and imagination. They may not be sold on a specific vendor but will hold a stake in the ground regarding some functional aspect or behavior they have seen, and any vendor worth listening to had better support it!

The majority of BI tools today have very similar characteristics. One of great worth is the support of a thin client interface. I can acquire a powerful BI tool that only requires that the end user has access to a browser. There is no hardware upgrade involved in most cases. The software on the user's desktop need not be upgraded or enhanced other than to support the appropriate browser, connectivity, and so forth.

I often see some situations where an unrelated product must be supported, such as Microsoft Excel or some office automation tool. These are not unreasonable requests but are sometimes a problem. Product A only requires one click to put a report in the current office system, but Product B requires two clicks. Product A is a bit dated and requires software on everyone's workstation, but it only requires one click. Yes, I have seen such arguments. I cannot believe anyone sits down and spends all day, or much of a day, clicking their mouse until their fingers get tired from adding BI output to an email. Such positions are frivolous at best.

It's about keeping your eyes on the overall business impact. Executives often fail to ensure their view of BI is understood and a vision is established. The only ones who maintain a constant enterprise view are those at the top positions within the organization. The rest of the employees are driven by the closer, immediate things that affect them. Top down directions in BI and corporate vision are essential to providing guidance that will assist in avoiding traps.

Handling Biases

I suggest there be a negotiator and project specialist assigned to such situations where technical savvy as well as tactful negotiating skills are needed. If there is any bias injected into the corporate ecosystem that does not have a solid, defensible basis for support, this must be squashed as soon as possible. It is unacceptable in an enterprise BI culture and becomes a counterproductive sticking point.

The process of BI platform and tools selection begins with establishing the business requirements and impact, not the platform. This is not a "Fire! Aim! Ready!" exercise. For example, if there is a significant need for up to the minute data for a number of key users or business processes, then this takes precedence over anyone's technology view. If it is deemed critical before you begin, it will become even more critical if you ignore it and then do not deliver later.

If you have issued a BI RFP or RFI lately, it helps to examine the checklists associated with specific BI functions. One thing I do not see in the typical RFI/RFP is why a particular feature or function is deemed valuable and who thinks it is so. For example, let's list a couple of items that I've seen in RFI/RFP requests and expand upon them a bit:

Feature/Function	Importance
Cross-tabulate reports	High
Interface to MS Excel	High
R/W support for OLAP (Essbase)	Med

The first two items are very similar in that cross-tabulations can be achieved with either solution or both. R/W access to an Essbase OLAP cube can be done with MS Excel as well as a variety of other BI tools. MS Excel is probably the most common interface to Essbase, so is it imperative that the new tool be able to provide this, or is it a "nice to have" feature? Have you ignored the usual suspects, such as: "Does the tool support a full range of chart types: pie, bar, Venn diagram, and so on?" Internally, all these check boxes may make sense, but quite often I have found that many of them emerge due to the range of features being used today, as well as some that people believe would be nice to have.

Few, if any, RFP/RFI submissions articulate the anticipated business value expected or why a particular feature rates an importance of "high." This is not to trivialize any effort at creating a comprehensive RFI/RFP, but I believe it to be of extreme value if you match the business processes to the BI functions and not the other way around. Within the enterprise, there may come a time when every icon in a BI tool has been selected and every little feature and function is used by someone. The best approach is to identify some users or part of the organization with the need for any of the desired features.

In the example of an interface to MS Excel, the driving force may be that a segment within the marketing department has a series of reports that contain some sophisticated calculations. They would like to be able to transfer the results of these calculations to Excel rather than having to recreate them in a spreadsheet. It may well be that the volume of data used to create the metrics is too large for effective use in a spreadsheet; therefore, the use of a reporting solution as an intermediate step provides an advantage to one group. Here we have a use case that makes sense, does not represent a bias, and may be of incremental value to some. It may also be the case whereby the need to utilize this output can be accomplished faster by providing direct access to the data via Excel. If the majority of the "math" was performed in the query, the report may be an unnecessary step.

There is no substitute for aligning business processes and requirements to any and all BI efforts. It can provide tremendous assistance in identifying how best to service the enterprise and eradicate some of the internal biases that can be very frustrating and counterproductive. Piling every little wish and request into your BI evaluations can also be less than effective. When you prioritize any BI feature/function as high, make sure you also articulate why it is categorized as such.

Summary

Platform selection today is a bit more demanding to investigate than in recent years due to numerous new technology offerings heretofore not available. The shift in BI from looking at static piles of data to a more fluid environment forces us all to examine what is best for our organization and set aside biases if we possibly can.

Tying all BI efforts to the needs of the business and clearly articulating why a particular platform, data base, tool, feature, or function is required will often remove some of the internal "ugliness" when trying to reach a consensus on some technology.

Those who put stakes in the ground over some particular element without a clear and sound reason for doing so are putting themselves first and the organization second. If there is a good reason to require some technology nugget, it should be obvious to all concerned as to why it is important and documented. BI today is being viewed more and more as a means to enhance specific business processes. Most organizations are moving away from throwing BI technologies at their end users and seeing if it will stick.

I mentioned RFP and RFI discussions, as well as a PoC (proof of concept) as part of the BI acquisition process. What is the best way to handle such activities? How can we best address our BI technology quest? Please read on....

12

Intelligent Responses to an RFI/RFP and Setting Up a Proof of Concept/Technology

Most of us have been involved in exercises in product/solution selection and evaluation. We see requests for information (RFI) or requests for proposal (RFP) issued to a selected set of vendors/providers, where they begin a frantic effort to outdo the others in a race for your business.

Many times, the result of such efforts is an invitation for the vendors to prove their claims and to use this bake-off or beauty contest, as it is sometimes called, to determine the best solution provider. I have a number of RFI/RFP forms saved but will not bore you with the massive checklists contained in them. I would rather discuss the elements within a BI RFI/RFP that are of greatest value.

To me, a POC is a "given" in any BI vendor or product comparison. However, most I have seen seldom hit the mark in really proving the concepts set forth. From the vendor perspective, these things are sometimes a nightmare and seldom provide an opportunity to really showcase a solution. Let's take a deeper look at the RFI/RFP/POC processes.

Creating a Better RFI/RFP

The first order of business is to determine the scope of usage within the enterprise. Any RFP/RFI at the enterprise level will require a massive checklist to ensure that the many features/functions necessary to all users will be included in the solution. However, the more important aspect of going through this exercise is to determine which of the vendors invited to the dance can map their solutions to your uppermost business needs.

Get into the Details

One of the criteria we always include in an RFI/RFP is the ability to create specific charts and chart types. You'll see some line item that looks something like this:

Business Charts and Graphs—The product(s) selected must be able to support all of the following graphical styles and types. Check all that apply to your solution:

- Line chart
- Bar chart
- Pie chart
- Venn diagram
- Stacked Bar chart
- Mixed charts

I discussed this somewhat in *Business Intelligence for the Enterprise* (Upper Saddle River, NJ: Prentice Hall PTR, 2003) and would like to revisit it again. We all have assumptions about what a line chart looks like and what it does. However, we have all had experiences with different software offerings that provide variations on options for charts. With line charts, there are often unique features such as an X, Y, and Z axes and more. You cannot list all the mini-features desired, but the end users certainly have some specific ideas about what is needed, and if due diligence is not enforced, you may find people trying to force a BI function to do something it cannot do.

12: Intelligent Responses to an RFI/RFP and Setting
Up a Proof of Concept/Technology
177

In the case of line graphs, one feature that is commonly desired is the ability to have gaps in values so the line doesn't drop down to 0 and then back up again. It may come under missing value options or other such heading—trivial little thing, eh? Well, if you're the user and, for whatever reason, the line graph function has to act that way, you will jump through some pretty amazing hoops to try to mimic this function. So, there are those pesky assumptions made about BI features and functions.

At the enterprise level, an RFI/RFP project needs to be broken down by individual parties; potentially there will be multiple providers of input. Those functions that are deemed critical by any key influencer need to be addressed in more detail. Having a 300-page RFI isn't the answer, so what might you do?

For example, IT will always be a part of the process but it is essential to provide critical input from the key stakeholders and their department heads. Executive and management understanding of what will be delivered versus what they believe the solution provides is often far apart. In many cases business requirements have changed or key objectives either ignored or overlooked. If I were a key player in the enterprise (e.g. Sales VP) I would like to know how the overall solution will merge with other areas of the business. If there is information I believe to be highly critical and shared with other parts of the organization it is imperative that I put my stamp of approval on the project based upon accurate and up to date information being fed to the RFP/RFI process.

Figure 12-1 displays a diagram of how you can extend an RFI/RFP item to specific end users who have all declared business graphs/charts to be of high importance. Three individuals (for the sake of illustration) have listed six different charts as being of high value in their responses to the RFP. They all have very specific features and output styles in mind. Many such desires have been embedded by their use of other tools.

You cannot list all the features in the RFI/RFP that they may desire, but you can perform a quick survey to get samples from them, as well as a list of their required features as a reference for discussions with the prospective vendors. As I mentioned earlier, if you do not do the proper diligence on items at this level, then when the selection is made and people begin to use the tool, someone will have to spend a lot of unnecessary time trying to mimic a feature they "assumed" worked a particular way.

Cross-referencing RFP/RFI Information to Additional Details

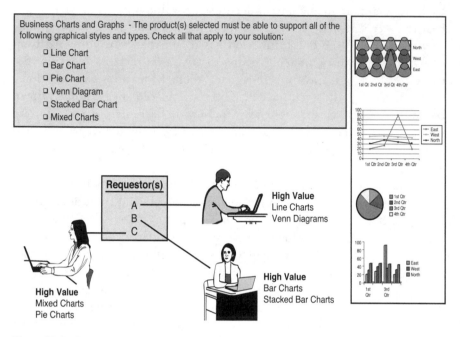

Figure 12-1   Cross-referencing RFP/RFI information to additional details

Going back to the line chart example, what if missing or zero values were not a feature of the chart? Let's also suppose that all other charts and graphs were deemed best of breed among the vendors, but the line chart features were not quite what the key users wanted. There may be a work-around for this the vendor can provide, or they take this under advisement and add the feature to a future enhancements list (try that with open-source providers!).

The users involved in developing the criteria for the RFI/RFP can be very helpful in providing examples of their desired output or feature request. Sometimes such information gathering uncovers requests that are trivial or borderline unreasonable. Nonetheless, it is important to know what the potential users deem significant.

Coordinating IT and Business Users—Ranking the Proper Criteria

As I have suggested, there will be user involvement in the process; I also want to make it clear that the various elements in the checklist must be driven by required business needs. Putting a stake in the ground to support some feature simply because an end user or someone else happens to really like it but cannot link it back to the business justification happens far too often.

We've covered some of the pratfalls of injecting prejudices into BI efforts in Chapter 11, "Platform Selection, Technology Biases, and Other 'Traps'," as well as in other parts of this text. Every single item on an RFI/RFP needs to be equated to business factors and needs to have involvement from IT as well as the business. Any time you are involved in a BI "beauty contest," the vendors will display a dizzying array of features and functions. Many of them will never, ever be touched by human hands in your enterprise.

Every RFI/RFP I have been involved in has some element of ranking or classification involved. High, medium, and low values are sometimes applied. Sometimes we see attributes such as supported, unsupported, requires additional hardware or software, and so forth. Without tying these back to part of the business processes, what is the use in ranking any of these things? Some criteria are "given," such as the data that needs to be accessed. This sort of item is a simple fact of life. However, what does the check in the check box imply? Most of the elements are in response to a yes or no mode of questioning. It is equally if not more important to then understand how these elements do what they do.

Data Access and Performance Aspects of an RFI/RFP

Far too many times, I see extremely important elements of an RFI/RFP covered with simple check boxes and find out later the prospective buyer didn't delve into the details about exactly how a particular element such as a query actually works.

"Does your product support the XYZ database? OK, good. How does it access XYZ? JDBC? Great!" In BI, any tool will offer extensions to an end user's query. Because the mission with relational sources is to issue efficient SQL against the database while hiding the SQL syntax, quite often there is a "mystery" behind what is actually occurring. For example, if a particular calculation or function is not supported by the source DBMS, it is quite common for the BI tool to cache the result set and perform extensions upon the data by creating an internal file/buffer/result and using it to complete the work. There is nothing wrong with this; it is a perfectly acceptable process. But, many clients never dig that deep.

It is important to understand the mechanics behind the BI tool. If a particular DBMS is supported to the fullest extent, and it is just a fact that the calculations outside the DBMS are necessary, fine. But, do you know how your BI tools process data? When a query returns a large result set, where is this stored? Is the DBMS locked or in a holding pattern waiting for the BI tool to process all rows? Does the toll provide a means to process a subset of rows? If so, does it release the results or is it a convenience for the tool to be able to throw a small set of rows up quickly but keep a lock on the data?

Once you understand exactly how data is handled, you can decide upon the viability of any solution. This exercise becomes extremely critical in scenarios where you are performing data federation. Are you looking to join disparate data sources from different platforms or some such exercise? If so, it is imperative that you understand the process and potential pitfalls of doing so.

There are two aspects of most RFI/RFP items. First, the primary question is: "Does the tool provide the following function?" This one is always included and typically follows the checklist pattern. The second and most important one is: "Precisely how does this particular function work?" An effective approach is to have a vendor walk you through the process in-depth and document it. It is a means of making sure your decision for any particular solution is well understood and diagrammed such that anyone can understand the inner workings (at least in theory). It also helps you begin a chronology of vendors and their support of specific functions and features because, if you are like most clients, this may come around again.

If you have a clear understanding of how a particular offering works, it will help later on in scenarios where performance may not be what was expected. I have seen numerous BI implementations where the BI tool is blamed for poor performance, when all along it was the database, or the application server, or perhaps the network. I have also seen many cases where the database has been held at fault when it was really some of the inner workings of the BI tool that were at fault.

The RFI/RFP process is usually not pleasant and requires significant resources to complete thoroughly. Because you are going to go through the exercise, why not do it well with the future in mind? How about creating a rich document as well as a summary of the findings for future use?

Documenting RFP/RFI Information for the Future

Why does this help? If another exercise also known as RFI/RFP comes around and you have thorough documentation, it provides a significant amount of leverage to use. "I am sorry Vendor X, but the last time we went through this, we found the following features lacking and cannot support your inclusion into the process." You may find out that things have dramatically changed from the last time you looked at them. Let me cite an example in my own world. Cognos was a powerhouse BI vendor for years. Their portfolio had been enhanced over the years and culminated in a bundle called Series 7.

There were excellent features as well as some loose connections among features in Series 7. Then, in 2003, Cognos announced ReportNet. This was a radically new BI platform that shook up the BI world. It has been enhanced continuously since then and is now called Cognos 8. If you had evaluated Cognos pre-ReportNet and now wanted to take another look, you would be stunned at what had transpired in their portfolio. If you kept minimal information about them (Series 7 et al) and now wanted to re-visit, you are starting from scratch. If you had documented any perceived shortcomings, your current view and evaluation would give you a solid basis from which to start.

People move on. It is typically the case that many individuals who were involved in an RFI/RFP in the past are either not with the company anymore or are in different roles. We all have heard of endless discussions about capturing an individual's expertise so those who follow do not have to start from scratch. Why not apply some wisdom and discipline to your RFI/RFP knowledge?

I cannot tell you how many times in my sordid career I have had clients tell me they aren't interested in one of my wares because it doesn't perform some function, only to find out that we fixed this one or two releases ago. The onus is on the vendor to keep a client informed, but it is far more difficult when a client has rejected an offering due to some previous shortfall. I don't keep abreast of many things that I am not directly involved in or have a need to track. I suspect you are the same, as we are all working at maximum capacity. A well-documented BI RFI/RFP is also a good starting point if you are looking at reopening one or issuing a new one and want to have a checkpoint for a particular vendor.

The features that you know they support are documented, as well as the shortfalls, if any. Now you have a starting point with justification, as well as a deeper understanding of where everyone left off. Don't make your own people work themselves to the bone every time one of these things comes up. Put the heat on the vendor with information to back it up. Stop reinventing the wheel in the RFI/RFP space.

Let's assume we have our fully developed RFI/RFP in hand, and we have decided to invite one or more vendors to the dance. How do we fill out their dance card? How do we validate their claims and satisfy our curiosity, as well as build the confidence of our end users? I recommend a thorough proof of concept or proof of technology exercise. I also recommend one that isn't just a brief walk-through of some bells and whistles with a clever little demo. Every vendor can make their product look wonderful—don't be naïve.

The PoC/PoT Scenario

The most commonly used differentiation between a PoC and a PoT is that a PoC is typically a vendor's session where they have worked with others in your organization to create a "Dog and Pony Show." A PoT is typically a vendor-orchestrated session where the client's users perform hands-on tasks with the tools to get a sense of how they function and how applicable they are to their own needs.

One significant difference between them is that in a normal PoC, the vendor is granted a bit more leeway when showing off their wares. In a PoT, the presenters and facilitators had better *really know* the BI tool, as the client end users are going to go any which way—and possibly make a ton of errors along the way. Some PoTs I have seen are tightly controlled ones where a script is provided and the users are only there to walk through the steps to see if it feels comfortable to use. There is nothing wrong with this other than the fact that they provide little value in demonstrating a specific user need unless this is built into the script.

If you have created a thorough RFI/RFP set of documentation, the next logical step would be to ensure that the key elements are covered in a PoC/PoT. Going back to my example of business charts and graphs, in the majority of cases, there are individuals involved who know exactly what they want to see. Put the onus on the vendor to produce these results. Tie the lesser RFI/RFP document to the expanded version where you have identified specific things your users want to see and make the vendor show you exactly how these things are done. Maybe they aren't done at all and you have some hard decisions to make.

I make a distinction between a "localized" BI decision and the enterprise level. One of the reasons many clients have a variety of BI tools is the quest to fill in missing parts. Tool A was good for Department A but not for Department B. If the solutions implemented have significant differences and do not overlap, a dual BI tool decision is justified. If there is significant overlap and we are dealing with a preferences scenario, this leads to the situation many face today where they have too many BI tools and too few users.

I have seen many effective PoC/PoT efforts where the client has a decent checklist of what they want to see. Hopefully you are one of those and are very comfortable with your process. I always caution people not to accept an answer from a vendor where the associated function or feature is not shown. I might hear a question such as: "Do you support the feature _____we want to use?" The vendor replies: "Yes, we do. I can't show you that right now, but we put it into our responses." OK...is that good enough for you? If so, then don't be shocked if later on, you discover it doesn't work quite the way you "assumed" it would.

NOTE

I highly recommend that you always, always use your real data in all events where an end user or others touch a keyboard in your shop. Every vendor has sample databases used for demos. They have to do this, as demos are a normal part of any vendor's activities, and they have to have something they can use. However, at this phase, it is not acceptable nor should you permit this to happen. This also extends to all training and skills development exercises provided to your end users later on. The harsh realities of what your data really looks like need to be interjected as early as possible. Sometimes the shortcomings of the shape of your data will emerge as part of this process. It is infinitely better to know this early on. Please keep these efforts real!

Matching RFI/RFP Checklists to a PoC/PoT and Documentation

In our business charts scenario, I am assuming that the RFI/RFP checklist has been expanded upon and the key users requesting these functions have been involved in the PoC/PoT process. If you use this approach and thoroughly test your vendors, you will never be unpleasantly surprised.

So, we have an initial RFI/RFP with the usual checklists and disclaimers. We have a set of key users or advisors, or whatever you want to call them, who are involved in refining the items listed in greater detail. We have some documentation and examples regarding the many RFI/RFP items, with special emphasis on the ones marked "high" in required function/features, and we have arranged a PoC/PoT with the vendor to verify and validate the technology.

Prior to this, we may have weeded out certain vendors and documented this such that others may be able to review this later or in future evaluations where a BI RFI/RFP goes out again. We have completed the process and have created a summary of it all that provides justification for our decisions that we can present to the appropriate parties.

Following such a series of steps and processes provides us with an intelligent approach to BI acquisitions. We have a document with known requirements, we have individuals involved with specific requests that have been verified, we have concrete evidence that the proposed solution works as substantiated by the PoC/PoT, and finally we have summarized information that is available for review.

There is a quantum leap from a local POC and an enterprise BI implementation, but you have to start somewhere. If you involve at least two inter-connected business units that will be sharing information later as part of this, you will have at least two proof points. The articulation of the business processes in the POC will go a long way to ensure you are on the right path. One clear example of this would be to tie a real-time BI application and process such as a Customer Service Rep application to a sales tracking and forecasting element. Improving customer service is a key initiative to any sales organization but how does one measure the cause and effect? If you clearly understand the interrelationship of the two and how one affects the other, you have a POC with some teeth in it.

Most POCs are, of necessity, a brief exercise in technology such as producing some reports the end users have been asking for and ensuring all the little widgets and options are actually within the prospective tool. Sometimes it is far more effective if you take a holistic approach such as adding the collaborative elements within the POC. If a critical factor is the ability to exchange and share results to enhance the business, this MUST be a part of the vetting process and it takes the POC out of the narrow, parochial view of the solution being tested.

I do not know what your process for RFIs and so forth may be. There are a number of websites that offer RFI/RFP counsel and advice and examples of how to write one. My BI roots have shown that far too many of these efforts become mad scrambles behind closed doors both on the part of the requestor as well as the potential providers. They require work regardless, and the work is usually not perceived as pleasant. I would argue that such activities can be turned into a very positive experience and set a new standard for the enterprise. If such experiences are always treated as pedantic, tedious, and a necessary evil, such endeavors will be looked upon as objects of dread and loathing.

Summary

There is a great deal of potential synergy between RFI/RFP activities and associated PoC/PoT projects. At the enterprise level, it is difficult to satisfy all end-user requests; thus, honing in on specific business requirements helps ferret out aspects that are essential to immediate requests.

In your activities within all this, keep in mind the need to document, document, and document. Use all this to your advantage. You can gain an upper hand on the vendors that come calling on you, provide a thorough weeding-out process, and build a better mousetrap when evaluating potential BI solutions.

When you take on these projects at this level of depth and thoroughness, your prospective vendors will treat this quite a bit differently than being confident that they can run in, do a razzle-dazzle demo, and hope they meet your requirements. I am not suggesting vendors are nefarious or not well-intended, but they will respond according to the weight you put into the evaluation. Poor software decisions can be disastrous.

So, once we have made a decision and forged ahead with our implementation, what should we do to ensure that we provide proper end-user support and increase our collective productivity?

13

End-User Support and Productivity

I once heard an exchange in a class given by a BI vendor that went something like this. The potential end user commented, "Gee, I was told this thing was easy to use...I don't get it." The vendor instructor said, "It is. The more you use it, the easier it gets!" This is a true story and may make you chuckle, but I sat in stunned amazement. Unless the individual attempting to use a particular tool is a total nitwit, of course they'll gain more knowledge and comfort with continued exposure. The question is: Do they have the time, and are they really charged with dealing at this level of involvement to accomplish what they set out to do?

I shudder to think of how many hours I have spent working with and learning to use the many BI tools I've been involved with over the years. It's probably better that I don't know! An even more depressing number would be the hours I have spent supporting others in situations where inadequate support was creating problems.

In the world of BI, when there is a usage problem that is not a product defect, the issue boils down to someone knowing enough about the tool to be able to experiment enough to get the right answer. If the person making the attempts stumbles upon a method, they heave a huge

sigh of relief and hopefully tuck away this knowledge for future reference. What if there was a better, easier way that is more efficient to perform the same task? Chances are, the user will never know. In addition,
quite often they will share their knowledge with others out of kindness,
and thus begin an internal level of misunderstanding and sub-optimal
product knowledge that will spread throughout the organization.

Why not begin with an understanding of what effective support looks
like and making sure we all meet corporate objectives with the proper
amount of skills and knowledge regarding our BI portfolio?

WYNTK–What You Need to Know About BI Support

BI tools require skill to use. We discussed roles in Chapter 6, "The
Impact of Business Intelligence on Roles within the Enterprise," as well
as key influencers in Chapter 9, "Key Influencers in the Enterprise." No
matter what skill level you possess or are aspiring to, there will be
things you need to learn to be more effective. Unless your role and mission is to become a BI tools guru, you will probably never spend the
time you would like to in honing your skills. Regardless of your role,
what do you do today if you get stuck? Who do you call or schedule time
with to work through an issue? How do you verify if a particular function is the best option to use?

One way to look at a support infrastructure is to create a "straw man,"
whereby the IT and business users sit down and develop a support strategy based upon "what if?" scenarios. Let's take the case of a casual user
who intends to create some BI output of their own, but they have no
intention of getting too deep into the weeds with any tool.

Figure 13-1 shows a simple view of the various individuals who may
be involved in a typical BI implementation. The solid lines are how this
installation has set up support and how they require the various roles
interact. It is not acceptable to have an end user contact a vendor and
bypass their "formal" support (BI specialist) unless they don't have one.
There is nothing wrong with seeking additional information, tips, and
techniques, and so on (dotted line), but it is not acceptable to be the
only one in the organization with newfound knowledge. Hopefully, the
initial BI item of work came in the form of a documented request, and
thus we have an audit trail of the request.

BI Support Infrastructure – Lines of Connectivity

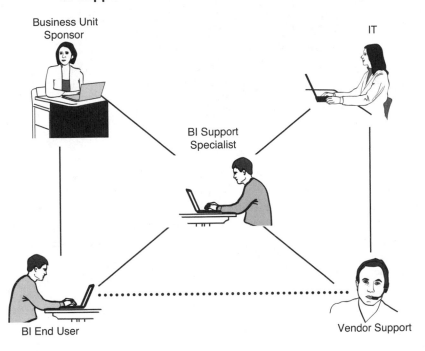

Figure 13-1   BI support infrastructure—lines of connectivity

The user probably has some idea of what they are trying to accomplish and, if so, they can take some time to document their request. End-user work request forms were all the rage and were a means of identifying the scope of work within different parts of the organization.

Today, I see BI efforts mostly as ad-hoc activities to fulfill business or functional area requirements. In *Business Intelligence for the Enterprise* (Upper Saddle River, NJ: Prentice Hall PTR, 2003), I discussed how you should document and identify BI work elements. I don't want to rehash this now, but suffice it to say that you need to put some discipline into identifying queries, reports, and other output. For example, during the writing of this book, I have had three distinct situations where clients wanted to evaluate, and possibly replace, one of the products I support. It is a good, solid offering but has aged somewhat, and alternatives (modernization) are under consideration.

The first questions I ask are these:

- How many users do you have, and who are they?
- How many stored objects are you keeping?
- Which of them are active and/or used by multiple people and/or multiple functional areas?
- What do these objects do?
- How many are critical?
- How many use platform-specific functions?

The typical responses to these inquiries is, "We really aren't sure." So, how would they begin the process of replacement? I always ask if they have a centralized support organization such as a BI Competency Center and rarely get an affirmative reply. I find that this doesn't just apply to my products but other BI tools in-house. The typical approach is to have a loosely coupled set of people who have found that they can rely upon each other when there is an issue or someone needs help.

Let me cite an example where proper support and infrastructure make a significant impact on your overall BI success. As I mentioned in Chapter 11, "Platform Selection, Technology Biases, and Other 'Traps'," on platform support, there are additional issues within a BI platform that must be understood and attended to. When any BI query and/or output are executed, some of the work takes place in the DBMS and some within the BI layer. Depending upon the particular bit of work, extensions to the calculation(s) may exist solely within the BI object. If, for example, this is a report, the extensions in logic and "math" only reside there. If the BI tool provides a metadata layer where calculations can be defined, such objects may be used by all and are separated from the specific BI object.

Taking this a step farther, it may be that a more efficient way of handling this is to push the math even farther back into the DBMS itself and reduce overhead as well as be able to share the calculation among multiple tools and applications. How would anyone even know to do this or that it may be needed?

This is where the implementation of a BICC and providing a core competency group that specializes in a portfolio of tools can bring enormous value to the enterprise. Lessons learned, best practices, tips and techniques, and other shared information evolve from proper support organizations. Such an organization also offers a career path for individuals who enjoy going deep into technology, working with end users, building a proper support infrastructure, and the others challenges associated with BI.

To me, without a BICC, anything else calling itself a BI support organization is a poor substitute. The problem is exacerbated when your BI reach is extended to external users. I didn't even add them to the preceding pictorial; you have to get the internal processes in place first.

Centralized Support–A BI Competency Center (BICC)

Without a formal support plan, BI success is a matter of luck at best. I often wonder at the paradox where a client has stated that BI is "mission critical" or a CIO says they have it as a top priority but cannot articulate how the internal support and infrastructure will work. Thus, we need to look seriously at a BICC.

Discussions about the BICC concept and value are readily available. One of the earliest ones was by Gartner Group (Kevin H. Strange and Bill Hostmann, July 22, 2003), entitled "BI Competency Center Is Core to BI Success." It states the following:

> *Business intelligence (BI) can enhance and extend an enterprise's business applications, resulting in a better-managed enterprise. Choosing and implementing the right BI tools and technologies is only one part of the formula for success. Most BI projects must integrate the requirements, data, and priorities of the IS organization and multiple business units, which requires unique skills. However, most enterprises have difficulty finding people with the right skills, situating them in the right place or leveraging available skills across projects and business units.*

> *The BI competency center's (BICC's) role is to champion the BI technologies and define standards, as well as the business-alignment, project prioritization, management, and skills issues associated with significant BI projects. In "The Business Intelligence Competency Center: An Essential Business Strategy," we explored the many challenges of planning and aligning the BICC in an enterprise.*

BI success depends on the formation, organization, and staffing of a BICC. As BI projects continue to gain strategic importance, we again explore the issues surrounding the planning, staffing, and politics of the BICC. Two case studies show how the BICC can deliver a business solution to a business challenge.

Even mega-vendors like IBM have implemented large-scale BICCs as they understand more than anyone that BI is an amalgam of technologies as well as business processes. There are best practices and proven techniques available for any product, so how do you ensure they are clearly understood and shared within and across the organizational boundaries?

TDWI posted this online on January 8, 2010:

A business intelligence competency center consists of a relatively small team of BI experts (typically fewer than 10) with well-defined objectives, roles, and responsibilities. Their overarching charter is to promote the optimal use of business intelligence across the organization. A BICC's focus could include data integration, data stewardship, delivery of information and analytical services, and vendor relationships.

The scope of your BICC is determined by your organization's priorities, its business objectives, and the skills of your business users. For instance, if your organization decided to focus on analytics, then your BICC would consist of a team of business analytics experts who understand the predictive-modeling and forecasting technical domain, and how to structure and maintain the required BI environment to enable delivery of analytical services to business users.

The executive team establishes a formal organizational structure to bring together this group of experts and defines their focus and responsibility. In addition, the executive team defines the interaction between the BICC, the business units, and the IT group.

I am not totally comfortable with this definition, as I don't believe it addresses the BICC at the enterprise level unless the number of employees isn't very large. However, I do agree that the connection points and responsibilities are spot on. The role a BICC plays and your overall success will be determined by your level of commitment to BI. The less you place under the span of control of the BICC, and the more you leave to chance, will diminish your ROI.

The primary purpose of a BICC is to provide a centralized, clearly understood, and well-executed BI plan. When I left IBM in 2003 to join Cognos, the BICC concept was beginning to develop. Today, you can find endless articles, papers, consultant reviews, and more about building an effective one. In my 2003 book, I discussed them in part. Now my view is that a BICC has evolved from being a very good thing to have to a position of being mission critical.

Business intelligence provides historical, current, and predictive views of business operations. As BI and reporting have become increasingly more critical to organizational success, IT departments have begun looking for ways to use standardized technology to manage and support BI deployments that span divisions, regions, and functions. Getting more from your investment in data is the key value of the business intelligence competency center. More enterprise clients have begun to reach out to a larger community to glean ideas and practices. This even extends to competitors in many cases.

Today's global BI community explores, discusses, and gathers resources about business intelligence topics, with a special focus on business intelligence competency centers (BICCs). BICCs provide the centralized knowledge and best practices needed to make broader BI initiatives that address your specific challenges.

I don't want to get into making recommendations as to how to structure your BICC. There are endless sources available for you to do this with lots of guidance, examples of what works, and so on. The question I have is: Do you have or intend to develop a BICC? They provide a wide range of services and benefits, including the following:

- Interface between business users and IT
- Interface and liaison with BI vendors
- Central point of BI expertise and knowledge
- Collectors and disseminators of product knowledge
- Education and tips/techniques providers
- Product evaluators (RFI/RFP/PoT, PoC)
- Closely work with IT to determine technical best practices
- Key architects for new BI applications and growth areas

- First line of defense and interface with external end users
- Performance and scaling advisors
- Deep product knowledge expertise
- Tracking business value and reporting to executive and management levels
- And more...

One of the key functions a BICC provides is a methodology of obtaining product information and tips. I have seen BI blogs, wikis, newsletters, alerts, and so forth implemented as information providers within BICCs. For example, if there are registered users for a BICC blog or forum, critical new information can be broadcast to the user community, which can save some folks extraordinary amounts of time.

What if someone uncovered the fact that use of a particular BI tool against a database or a certain type resulted in an undocumented error? What if this error was not apparent, such as faulty calculation results? How is such a situation handled in your organization today? Does someone broadcast a severe error alert (email and so on), or do many people discover it the hard way...one by one?

Many BI issues or glitches or errors are unique to a particular environment or usage. It is an area that is very frustrating for IT. IT can apply fixes and maintenance to applications and systems quite handily. However, dealing with nuances that surface within BI tools, such as peculiarities in execution, are not things they normally deal with, nor should they have to.

Here is another section from the Gartner article referenced earlier:

Most organizations lack the skills and organizational commitment for managing, implementing, and supporting significant cross-functional BI projects. If they have the skills, they're spread throughout the organization, with priorities placed on efforts other than BI. The results are projects that do not achieve their full potential and that cause a great deal of organizational strife.

Many enterprises have found that a BICC increases their likelihood of success with BI projects. The BICC helps IS organizations understand the BI technologies and applications that users will need to meet their varied analytical needs of BI. In addition, the BICC plays a critical role in managing the alignment of "BI activism"—that is, the ambition and determination of the enterprise's desire to promote BI by providing communication across lines of business to prevent the creation of new BI application "silos."

I like this article for the simple fact that it reflects my own views. Although it dates back several years, its truth remains and resonates even louder in today's world of BI. The BICC is designed to reduce costs, maximize potential BI use, minimize risk, and provide a fountain of knowledge to all those interfacing with any of the internal BI portfolio.

Methodology of Work Submission and Success

I am not suggesting that every query and report needs to be formally submitted and processed, but I am suggesting that every piece of work needs to be documented. This is a huge shortfall in the majority of clients. "We have a lot going on in BI, but we aren't sure of all that's being done" You can bet that IT doesn't have any of its staff writing Java™ or COBOL programs willy-nilly. Someone has assigned the work and someone is tracking it. Part of the problem is that there typically isn't a database created to enter any BI information. How hard can that be?

In Figure 13-2, you see a simple workflow diagram used in a fictional organization. The most important elements are a database to house BI work and a methodology/process behind BI work. The majority of clients don't have extreme difficulties with BI until something goes awry. Typical scenarios include the following:

- Under-deployed seats after a period of time that have come to the attention of the organization
- Consistent performance problems
- A major shake-up, such as loss of a critical resource or decision to standardize
- System resource evaluation points out unacceptable usage
- A decision made to replace or eliminate a BI tool, and no one has a grasp on the extent of its use
- New leadership that wants to know the value and effectiveness of the current software inventory

BI Request Workflow and Tracking within a BICC

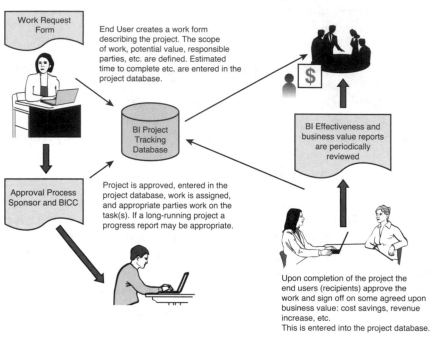

Figure 13-2   BI Request Workflow and Tracking within a BICC

One of the most significant benefits of a BICC is that it brings verification of the value of the enterprise's BI strategy. It can provide a measure of the most elusive quantity requiring measurement—productivity.

Vendor BICCs

Vendors such as IBM, SAS, SAP, and others offer their own best practices and BICC offerings. If you are on the verge of making an enterprise-wide BI decision and standardizing on a particular vendor, chances are they will have their own offering including best practices. What they cannot do for you is to create the internal communication processes that are best for your organization. They will have significant expertise to lend regarding their own products as well as some general rules.

If you create a framework along the lines of what I have described so far, it should be applicable to any and all BI tools and solutions. Once you have a well-understood process in place, you can make adjustments to accommodate specific vendor concepts and ideas.

Productivity—A Valuable Offshoot of Effective BI

When you have enterprise-wide BI activities, there will be a number of people assaulting data and stomping around the BI space, trying to make some magic happen. Without setting standards, enforcing education requirements, determining the skills of the users, and more, productivity becomes more of a game of darts than a well-executed plan.

Keep in mind that every moment someone is playing with a BI tool, but not producing something of value, is a loss of productivity. Ignore the fact that they are also incurring costs with the resources they take while experimenting, as well as their own personal cost to the enterprise. This is why I hammer so much on pragmatic evaluation of potential end user's skills and the need to minimize their frustrations with efforts that yield no results.

What Is End-User Productivity?

We usually define productivity as the amount of work or benefit received from performing a task with the least amount of effort or energy. In today's business environment, we tend to equate productivity with being able to get people to do more with less or in shorter periods of time. So, look at this from a BI perspective.

Sometimes productivity can come from existing BI systems simply by refining what some of the end users are doing. In one client situation, I discovered that they were pumping out a ton of reports where the query values were hard-coded. They would have a report for each month where the month was entered as a specific value

I have seen endless situations where an end user is given access to some data and use of a BI tool, and they are convinced they will be able to crank out those pesky reports and metrics they have been craving but couldn't get before. The proper amount of vetting of their skills and training required has not been done, but they're off on a quest.

Their initial interaction with the data and the BI tool was simple, as they found it easy to click on some data items and drag them to a palette, resulting in a little report displaying some rows and columns. Then, they take the next step, where they try to apply additional features and functions, only to hit a wall. After several hours of frustrating play, they finally go to others for some assistance. Now we have two or more people involved in this project, and the primary user realizes this is beyond his or her skill. Another kind soul steps in and offers his or her help to complete the reports.

Now the initial user is at a crossroads with their degree of BI skills, knowledge, and desire to further engage with their data and their tool. When the next task comes along, they may spend more time learning new features, or they may come with their hat in hand back to those who may have assisted them the last time. They may mature in their skills later, or they may just remain a peripheral player. I have heard many of these people say, "Oh sure! I work with the XYZ BI tool all the time." Realistically, they are nothing more than a drain on others and may reduce the productivity of their peers.

True BI productivity occurs when a required BI task or business request is documented, deemed to be of a certain value, and matched to an individual with the appropriate skills who can complete the task in a minimum time frame. Critical analyses and valuable BI output often dramatically reduce costs, provide an exciting new information stream, increase revenue, deliver faster results, improve customer satisfaction, and can increase productivity. It does not increase productivity whenever there is a mismatch of skills and requirements.

Quality BI output can increase the overall productivity of several layers of end users within an enterprise or part of an organization. Many seem to forget that the importance of BI is what you do with it, not who does the work. I once implemented a critical measurement application with a home-grown alert function. This was before the days when we had such sophisticated functions built in. Prior to this, the client was in the habit of periodically looking to see if there was something out of order. They would make it a point of running the same process again and again during the day just to be sure. It was used by a series of brand managers in a manufacturing account and dramatically cut down their constant looking at the data "just in case."

Today, we would (hopefully) utilize our BI tool's built-in event detection and alerting capabilities. In the scenario I described, the productivity of the end users increased as they no longer tied up personal time looking for a problem "just in case." There was far less overhead on the system, as I ran the analysis once for all brand managers and notified those who had a measurement out of range. In the past, they had all been executing the same query and producing the same report.

So, productivity has both personal aspects as well as system elements. If, for example, you find ways to reduce the overhead of queries, you can instigate continuous improvement in BI processes. Offerings that enhance BI query performance or control such as Teleran, Appfluent, Guardium, and others provide features that a DBMS may not offer.

When an enterprise is pulling their BI efforts down the same path and not at odds with a cluster of BI tools, overall productivity will increase. You will find yourself looking for ways to enhance your infrastructure and add additional ingredients that are fresh and new instead of supporting three, four, five...nn query and reporting tools.

If you perform a web search using BI productivity as criteria, you'll receive an impressive number of hits. There is no doubt that BI efforts can be extremely productive. What you need to understand is the quest for productivity with BI usage should be a never-ending effort when there is a mission to deliver continuous improvement and refine the value and impact of BI upon the business.

Summary

BI software brings unique value as well as unique problems to the enterprise. You have non-technical individuals wrestling with technology that they may or may not be ready for. If there is no formal support structure or overall skills development plan, you will be in trouble quickly.

If you have already experienced this, it is time to set a different course. It is not acceptable to allow random acts of BI work to be produced and used without any record of who, what, why, and how long. If you implement a BI project database, it is imperative that you make it simple to use and do not require a ton of input. The process of data entry and tracking will have to become a part of the emerging BI culture within your organization.

The most effective means to track and manage your overall BI investment is the implementation of a BICC with a charter to make BI successful. The

BICC should be chartered to provide a wide range of activities within the enterprise. Executive sponsorship is critical. Most of all, it should not be permitted to be bullied by anyone in the enterprise regardless of their status.

Let's assume we have a BICC, we have selected our BI tool(s), and we are starting anew with BI in the organization. What might the implementation process look like?

14

Implementation of Business Intelligence Solutions

Now we are finally to the point where we are proposing to do some actual BI work. I want to make a few assumptions here before we begin. First, this is a new BI project with a new BI tool that we are using for the first time. Second, we have a BICC in place with responsibilities that extend beyond product evaluation and recommendation. Third, I assume this to be a new group of end users and not some who've become disenchanted with another tool...no built-in prejudices here. Fourth, I assume that the product has been properly evaluated, and we know that the necessary features and functions have been verified by the vendor and BICC. Finally, we have a series of processes and procedures in place as well as a BI project database within which to store our proposals and results.

In the realm of assumptions it is a good idea to jot down every aspect of the potential solution as a large checklist from both IT and the user community. In numerous working sessions I have found it interesting when any organization does this a a regular part of their solution selection process. Pitfalls, gaps, and erroneous assumptions often get exposed and new directions taken due to a meaningful multi-way communication exercise.

Keep in mind that this is how you will set the standard for the rest of your corporate BI efforts. If you have new procedures in place and a new way of providing BI support, this will be far easier than with an experienced group. I get very grumpy when I hear people say: "Oh great, now we have to do some new process. As if we aren't busy enough. We never had to do this before." If you are a shining beacon of BI success, perhaps this is warranted. If not, please remain quiet.

The first order of business is setting the end-user expectations. This is the critical point where expectations are set and from which success or failure will take form.

Setting User Expectations Early and Coping with the First Project

Your end users have arrived at the BICC for a kickoff meeting and have brought their rough sketch of the BI work they have in mind. The BICC will expect the following outcome from the initial meeting:

1. The scope of the project will be laid out and the key end users will be identified.

2. The BICC will determine the depth of involvement required by the end users as well as assign a point of contact for the project.

3. Critical resources such as database access, target recipients, and other systems resources that may be required will be identified.

4. The BICC will explain the processes involved for the following:
   a. Entering project data
   b. Reporting on progress
   c. What systems will be utilized and how
   d. Educational expectations including setting a schedule for the end users who will perform the work
   e. How support works—who to call, what will happen, what is expected of the users

5. The initial steps will be clearly documented and agreed upon. One of these will be the commitment of the end users to developing proper skills required and meeting the education requirement set forth by the BICC.

Some of these steps may have been established during the initial evaluation and PoC phases, but they must be discussed again. For both the BICC and the end users (not to mention the vendor), there must be some boundaries and understanding. Both good and bad activities are part of any learning process. The BICC may find that they have to provide far more resources initially as they may not be as technically proficient in the new tool as they would like to be. In such cases, a quality vendor will often oversee the first project.

One of the major reasons for demanding documentation (Hey!... maybe using an internal blog!) be a part of this is that you really want to capture the entire learning process as well as pitfalls and pratfalls along the way. If you do this (for example, blog), you will need to have someone monitor the events logged lest a run amok and disgruntled end user unbuckle it all with inappropriate comments.

At the end of the initial meeting with all parties, someone needs to transcribe notes into a summary and send it to all parties for agreement. It's a nice bit of documentation for future use. If someone later on contests the scope, the value, the process, or any other part of what was agreed upon, let them chime in now. After awhile, and with everyone settling into a more familiar rhythm, these processes will become far easier to adhere to and will take far less time. The important thing to remember is that we have defined a formal process. Do not let personal familiarity and comfort with others make it easy to sidestep the process. It needs to become part of your BI DNA.

How to Scope the First Project

If the initial project is too expansive or grandiose in scope, you are asking for trouble. It would help tremendously to break down the project into steps and see if it is possible to identify an initial phase where you can contain the work in a more controlled environment. Let's say, for example, the entire scope of the project involves accessing a variety of databases, possibly some unstructured data access, and you are looking to deliver new reporting initially but have a plan to extend the analysis to include OLAP sources that do not exist yet.

There are several elements that are new to your organization, and thus, you are, "boldly going where no one has gone before." To date, you have no idea how the BI tool is going to be accepted by the end users beyond the agreements received when you performed the PoC weeks ago. The euphoria phase will quickly fade once any difficulties arise...and they will if the project is too large or complex right out of the box.

One very commonly employed method is to identify a subset of reports or other output as the initial deliverable of a BI project. I would suggest that you not tackle the most difficult reports as step one. If you have done your PoC/PoT homework, you will know that the more difficult items can be produced. Maybe you already have some of them completed as part of your PoC/PoT. Put a block of work in front of the end users that takes advantage of their current skill level. I will assume that they have been through training at this point and a quality match has been made between their skills and the scope of work.

If you are in a situation where the BI work is mission critical, and you really need people who are deeply skilled in the technology and you cannot afford to watch users "experiment," I recommend one of two approaches in order of preference, as follows:

1. Hire skilled individuals as part of the project. You should know this far before the initial project is started.
2. Engage the vendor or a qualified partner to complete the project as a services offering.

The reason I place hiring options first is that you will not only bring invaluable experience in house, but you will have the opportunity to spread and evolve these individuals throughout the enterprise. The best placement for them is within the BICC and, secondly, within key departments engaging in BI operations.

Figure 14-1 depicts these options, as well as some of the pros and cons. If you are going to hire BI expertise, you must have clearly identified the roles and responsibilities, as we discussed back in Chapter 6, "The Impact of Business Intelligence on Roles within the Enterprise." Where this really comes to bear is when you have not made a particular BI tool your standard and thus are looking for deep but well-rounded individuals. I have seen resumes of people who list skills in a number of BI tools. This is not impossible, as there are some very bright people out there. However, it does raise a couple of red flags in my mind.

Initial Project Scope, Skills Acquisition, and Actions

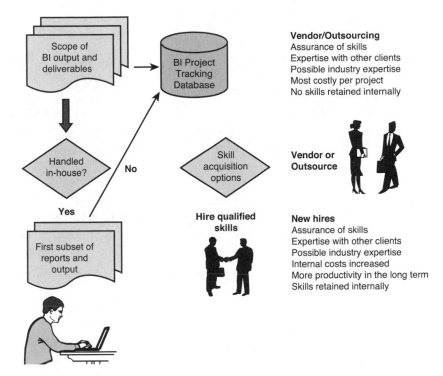

Figure 14-1   Initial project scope, skills acquisition, and actions

First of all, are we looking at a highly versatile and possibly quirky individual? Have they changed employers often? If so they may come in like a house on fire, get everyone energized, and then leave you in the lurch. Sometimes this can be prevented by ensuring that they have a growth path within your organization. It is a rare individual who can be satisfied with a position where they endlessly work on any set of BI tools. It gets very boring after awhile, unless there are rewards and incentives for growth in place.

BI Skills Required

The implementation of a BICC and your corporate infrastructure will be elements that will attract highly qualified BI specialists. Here is a description I used when I was working for a BI consulting firm as the practice leader. Note that the majority of these elements were directly tied to client requests; thus, an in-house specialist would be expected to fulfill these requirements.

Title—Business Intelligence Specialist

The business intelligence specialist's role is to strategically design and implement BI software and systems, including integration with databases and data warehouses. This includes selecting, blueprinting, gathering requirements for, and designing BI solutions and then rolling them out to end users. The business intelligence specialist is also responsible for ensuring high levels of BI availability through support functions and in-depth testing.

Responsibilities

- Evaluate/cultivate long-term strategic goals for BI development in conjunction with end users, managers, clients, and other stakeholders.
- Organize and lead projects in the implementation and use of new or existing BI software tools and systems.
- Lead the integration efforts for merging BI platforms with enterprise systems and applications.
- Design, code, test, and document all new or modified BI systems, applications, and programs.
- Develop the semantic layer, metadata, reports, and report definitions.
- Develop graphs and portal interfaces.
- Lead in the design of databases and data warehouses to ensure interoperability with BI solutions.
- Analyze user requirements and, based on findings, design functional specifications for BI front-end applications.
- Develop ETL design guidelines to ensure a manageable ETL infrastructure for the BI system.
- Work with project managers to ensure that data entry, retrieval, change, and delete functions meet business requirements for project completion.
- Design and deliver end-user training and training materials; provide technical support as necessary.
- Troubleshoot BI tools, systems, software, and performance, and provide tuning expertise as needed.

- Act as evangelist for BI benefits across the organization; promote BI usage to relevant departments.

- Evaluate and select database/data warehouse components, including hardware, relational database management systems, ETL software, metadata management tools, and database design solutions.

- Conduct research and make recommendations on BI products, services, and standards in support of procurement and development efforts.

The list goes on and on, but you get the point. When you peel back the list of requirements, it starts to sound like you are asking for a BI super hero—and you are. All the elements of this list are part of most BI projects, and someone has to cover them. If there is a weak link in the chain, it will create problems upstream or downstream.

The depth of skill presented here is far beyond the typical end user request. Many will state: "I just want to access my data and produce some reports and output. I need to do my job better!" This is not a frivolous request by any means, but it must be couched within some degree of reality.

End-User Provisos

No matter who is involved, from the BI novice to the BI specialist, you must provide some boundaries and provisions to which they agree. BI specialists know what they don't know and are typically quite adept at filling gaps. BI is a point of pride to them, not just a job. It's the new or novice end user I am most concerned with.

Given that we have a BICC in our example, there will be some agreement with the end users as to what is expected of them. If the proper assessment of the difficulty levels of a particular set of tasks has been made, the BICC will be able to submit a comprehensive list of "to do's" for the end user that will include education and skills development, as well as how to report problems and bugs, and how support works.

After years of dealing with BI issues, I would be a rather harsh taskmaster as part of a BICC. I cannot tell you how many times I experienced an end user going into some defensive posture where it was everyone's fault but theirs. No one had an agreed-upon document or record of the scope of work as everyone was getting along in the early stages. Now the end user has turned into my worst nightmare. One problem with these situations is that in many cases, no matter what you do from that point on, they'll never be happy or say anything positive about their experience to anyone. They often go out of their way to poison the well for future BI success.

If we take personality quirks out of the equation, the first thing needed is an agreement between the end users and the BICC. "If you do this, we will do that." Many end users try to circumvent the required education and training steps because they are too busy and will sit down and flail at BI projects. If you allow them to get away with this, then you deserve whatever you get.

I am not suggesting that you establish a set of BI commandos and grumps in the BICC. I merely suggest that part of the BI philosophy and execution involves checks and balances. I would recommend that part of any BICC include some discussions about how to handle difficult end users and objections. You are selling the BI strategy internally, and whenever you are involved in sales, you will potentially have disgruntled customers. In this case, the customer is *not* always right.

If you provide a document of work effort and responsibilities within your BICC, you interject a layer of formality that may come in extremely handy later on. Once there is a level of trust and rapport developed over time between end users and the BICC, you will see your productivity and value-add from BI absolutely soar.

BI Solution Elements–Query, Reporting, OLAP

Depending upon the specific BI functions being applied in the project, there will be varying elements that will have an effect upon your success. Given the huge scope of BI possibilities and functions available, there is often a propensity to want to fire on all cylinders at once. I suggest you take a deep breath and get your toes in the water first

Let's hone in on two key areas of most BI scenarios: query and reporting, and OLAP analysis. There are different issues involved with both of them, as well as a common thread of data access.

Query and Reporting Application Elements

Beyond the scope of using the BI tool targeted, we have to set up several things in order to use the tool to begin with. Modern BI tools provide a metadata layer that offers the capability to rename underlying data definitions with business terms. It also provides the capability to create calculations that combine several data elements and calculations into one definition such as Profitability.

A path to the data (ODBC, JDBC™, direct connection, and so on) must be established and tested. One element most competent installations will examine is the quality of the SQL generated by a BI tool. We discussed this in our chapters on platform selection and executing a PoC (see Chapter 11, "Platform Selection, Technology Biases, and Other 'Traps'," and Chapter 12, "Intelligent Responses to an RFI/RFP and Setting Up a Proof of Concept/Technology"). If the proper amount of homework has been done and verified in a PoC, this step will be rudimentary. Have you verified that the SQL generated is optimized for your use? If not, then every new query will be suspect if it does not perform well.

The validation really becomes a validation of the interplay between the DBMS, the BI metadata layer, and the tool itself. If you know in advance that a considerable amount of the data manipulation must be done in the BI tool's application server layer, and the setup is optimized for your use, everyone will have a clear understanding that this is how things are going to be.

Sometimes a report writer will return a subset of the result set's rows as a means to provide the end user with immediate feedback. There is also an option to return all rows once the user is satisfied. The resulting overhead and wait time may surprise folks if this has not been understood during earlier steps in the evaluation process.

Rather than treat your users as lame brains, make sure they understand what is happening under the covers of a query and reporting BI application. Sometimes this alone helps fend off complaints later on. Every step of the query and reporting process should be tracked and measured in the early stages. Any BI vendor worth doing business with will have a suite of administration, tracking, and measurement functions. The DBMS vendors have their own utilities and functions to assist with understanding what's happening behind the scenes.

Once you have the various elements covered and clearly understood, you can evaluate whether or not you need to make adjustments later. Perhaps performance issues surface that you hadn't identified before. It's a lot easier to perform some technical surgery and corrections at this stage than later on when additional end users pile on and you have to scramble.

The two elements, query and reporting, have separate but common issues. Both have implications of performance as dictated by the inner workings of the DBMS and the BI layer. Once the query layer is felt to be reliable, accurate, and efficient, you can concentrate more on the end user's interaction with their data. If there is an option to reduce the number of rows returned while a user is beginning, but it is not the default, you either try to reset the default or make sure they understand that this is the most efficient way to interface with the reporting tool. If you covered this requirement in your RFI/RFP and PoC/PoT processes, everyone will understand that there is a best practices approach to creating and executing queries.

The early stages of a query and reporting solution will require far more close monitoring than after you gain more expertise. The greatest reason for this is there is a high probability things will change. While you are in "learning mode," you will not want to document many of the activities. You will want to take copious notes and write a summary of reality later and weed out the missteps.

OLAP Application Elements

In OLAP scenarios, there is a consistent set of steps and issues depending upon whether you are implanting a pure MOLAP (multi-dimensional OLAP), ROLAP (relational OLAP), or hybrid solution (some of the data is held in MOLAP form and provides a ROLAP drill-thru extension).

In pure MOLAP instances, the data used to build the "cube" must be accessed and loaded at the lowest level, and then the cubes are built using a calculation engine to create the higher aggregation levels. Depending upon the data source, you may have easier access paths to the data and some may be difficult. Once the data is loaded, the next step is to process the cube builder. This is typically done in batch for most MOLAP applications, although today there are significant improvements in technology that may lead you to examine a ROLAP or hybrid solution.

Once a cube is built and made available, the amount of user training and skills required is far less than that required for the traditional query and reporting applications. The values and calculations have been built, and all you need to do is learn how to query the cube, drill-down, slice, dice, and play.

Depending upon your OLAP solution, you may have a series of user interfaces available to access the cube (Excel, Lotus®, vendor-provided, and so on). The more of these you allow to be used, the less efficient the end users will be. Most OLAP interfaces have common functions but are not always implemented the same way.

The time required to build a cube will determine the size of the OLAP source(s) you can provide. This will also have a bearing upon the timeliness of the data itself. Load, build, and use scenarios have an implied lag time. ROLAP solutions offer a better "cubes on the fly" capability but may not provide as many mathematical functions as a pure OLAP application. Here we go back to setting the ground rules and understanding of the applications phase.

If you have a choice between standard query and reporting or OLAP applications as part of the initial phase, I always recommend beginning with the OLAP applications first. This assumes that there is no priority of one over the other and the OLAP application has equal or greater value right out of the box. The reason for this is that you will be able to put data in the hands of end users that has been calculated, verified, and built for speed. There is far less end-user training and associated confusion with OLAP applications and far less systems overhead, as the users will be beating upon a proprietary data source that is built entirely for speed and supporting BI.

Another aspect of OLAP that I covered in-depth in my 2003 book was that the data contains a single version of the truth, as well as all values calculated and completed. Assuming there were no errors in logic, the users hold in their hands all possible values and have free rein to explore, compare, and play at "What if?" scenarios. It is a way to get initial BI acceptance for a wider range of end users in less time.

In Figure 14-2, I have diagrammed some of the query, reporting, and OLAP architecture. Note the dotted line where some providers allow a reporting engine to access and produce more traditional BI reporting on top of OLAP data. This has not been commonly available in the past.

Query and Reporting versus OLAP Projects

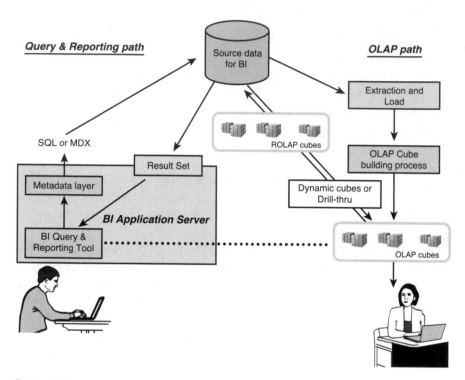

Figure 14-2   Query and reporting versus OLAP projects

System Sizing, Backup, and Recovery Issues

No matter what you have been told by others, your system may not provide the amount of BI throughput nor deliver the amount of processing you thought based upon input from the vendor. Having been on both sides of that fence, I can understand the frustrations. From the vendor perspective, all measurements and estimates are done on a best-effort basis. Standing in front of a customer and telling them they will get *xxx* amount of throughput or work from a customer's environment is a very "iffy" proposition. One of the attractive things about the new wave of BI appliances today is their promise of performance at low cost. Let me just say that BI usage and requirements will wildly vary over time.

As part of your new BI venture, you will learn things about your system and BI usage that will lend beneficial metrics to accurate sizing and usage planning later on. Even if you have a system that is very similar to another customer, very seldom are two systems alike. The data may vary in size and complexity, as well as the details of what your queries and BI work look like compared to another.

As a part of your initial implementation and learning period, be sure you take accurate measurements of your BI environment. The numbers of queries, their relative complexity, query reuse, average result set, largest result set, and smallest result set are all important measurements to obtain for DBMS usage.

The end-user behavior also needs to be looked at with the proper perspective. Early on in BI application usage, there tends to be a flurry of activity due to the newness of the system. In most cases, this will settle down into a consistent level that is possibly not as daunting as you first believed.

System Sizing

Your choice of platforms and BI tools architecture will have a lot to do with your sizing and scaling options. If you are implementing on a distributed platform, it is most likely you will have a set of dedicated servers in play. If you are running your BI processes on a mainframe, you will be sharing resources with other system applications (OLTP, batch, and so on). Regardless of the platform selected, there are established ways to measure usage and modify resources.

Let's assume you have installed a new set of distributed servers for your BI application. You have connected it to the network and the source data and have started your BI venture. In the early going, there will be lessons learned and possible missteps corrected.

In initial testing and sizing efforts, the best thing you can do is to use a set of queries that all have the same characteristics. For example, if you have a group of users who tend to ask very similar questions, such as "Show me all the sales totals for the ___ district," and they vary their query by district, you'll have a relatively common request. It will also provide some indication of how well the database responds to such queries. If the DBMS has been properly configured, contention, locking, and so forth should be kept to a minimum.

The best BI sizing paradigm I know is to build, test, measure, understand, adjust, retry, measure again, and then agree. If you begin with a cluster of disparate queries and users and run into trouble, where do you begin to unravel the issues?

In a recent client scenario, a BI environment was proving to be a disaster to scale. The client loved the BI tool, but was not pleased with the performance and throughput they were getting on their platform of choice. They asked to have their exact environment duplicated on another platform to see if it would be better. The testing resulted in the new platform outperforming the old one by a ratio of 400:1. This is no exaggeration. I will not go into the details of the environments, but think of the reaction on the part of the client.

In another scenario a client opted to keep all their data on a series of distributed platforms but move all their BI seats to a centralized mainframe which proved to be more secure, easier to deploy, and far less costly as their previous configuration requiring a constant flood of new BI servers.

And yet another client found that a thorough analysis of a mainframe versus distributed implementation reduced their overall costs by 80%+. I am not trying to bang the mainframe gong and come off as a platform bigot. What I am saying is that all potential platforms and solutions are not the same from a systems and sizing perspective. Many solutions under consideration do not take into account the fact that elements such as hardware must be upgraded and the associated cost of this natural growth.

It is not feasible to test your BI options on all available platforms, but it is wise to keep your options open. Chances are you'll have greater success when you have done the proper diligence in developing your testing and sizing scenarios.

Think of the many recent stories about how some website was taken down by some huge surge in usage. Sometimes it is just the result of an incident that drove an inordinate number of people to visit a site that could not possibly be anticipated. Sometimes it is a result of poor planning and lack of foresight on the part of the provider.

Backup and Recovery

You will have well-defined backup and recovery options and functions provided by any BI vendor. These procedures should be thoroughly tested in the initial phases of your BI implementation. Loss of data is bad enough but to lose the associated BI objects the end users created and rely upon is disastrous. In many cases, the users have created works of art that they don't remember how they created.

Some BI technologies provide self-defining documentation (options, data accessed, calculations, and so on). If this is the case, the end users should be trained to use these features and, worst case, print the output to paper and keep it somewhere. One product I supported for years had a marvelous documentation capability that dumped everything you could possibly want to know about the current object or procedure. I used to publish a tips and techniques newsletter about this product that was distributed and used worldwide.

One tip that got a tremendous amount of use was the ability to document this product's procedures and actual lines of code to a file. The file could be used later to rebuild entire applications. The users also had the ability to easily back up their own work. In some situations where IT didn't provide adequate support, this proved to be a lifesaver.

Regardless of what processes and procedures you have in place, they mean nothing if they fail when you need them. Sometimes one of the most unpleasant discoveries you can make is to find that a vendor's backup/recovery features have a problem. Maybe there was some missing maintenance needed at the time of backup, and the procedures fail. Failure to test these options is a common error and can result in a huge loss of productivity.

Summary

BI implementation in its early stage should be looked upon as a well-crafted, cautious, multi-step process with the goal of gaining all appropriate information in the initial phase. By limiting the early interactions to work that is simple, consistent, and measurable, you have a solid basis for expanding the use in a shorter period of time.

Performance and tuning aspects must be understood. Capacity and usage measurements from a known set of inputs offer a means to fine tune or drastically modify options if need be. Making sure all parties are involved and understand the many processes is imperative. Testing key elements such as backup and recovery procedures had better be tested in the beginning, not at a critical point of failure later.

All elements of a BI infrastructure need to be tested, examined, verified, and adjusted if need be. I think of these projects a bit like time trials at a major automobile racing event. The cars are held back from driving at maximum speed while the track and support teams are being evaluated and all conditions affecting the race are understood. Once the day of the actual race arrives, the activity goes from an orderly set to that of breakneck speed and sometimes chaos. If you have to wave the yellow flag in your BI efforts, it will impact all the prospective players.

Let's now begin to examine some of the more esoteric aspects of modern BI solutions. Today there is a keen interest in how BI solutions play in an enterprise SOA (Service-Oriented Architecture) environment. Is an SOA important to a BI infrastructure?

15

The Impact of Service-Oriented Architectures (SOA) on Business Intelligence Solutions

Wikipedia defines SOA as follows:

There are several different definitions of **service-oriented architecture** *(SOA). Generally speaking, SOA is a flexible set of design principles used during the phases of systems development and integration. Upon deployment, an SOA-based architecture will provide a loosely-integrated suite of services that can be used within multiple business domains. SOA also generally provides a way for consumers of services, such as web-based applications, to be aware of available SOA-based services. For example, several disparate departments within a company may develop and deploy SOA services in different implementation languages, and their respective clients use a well-understood, well-defined interface to access them. XML is commonly used for interfacing with SOA services, though this is not required.*

SOA defines how to integrate widely disparate applications for a world that is web based and uses multiple implementation platforms. Rather than defining an API, SOA defines the interface in terms of protocols and functionality. An endpoint is the entry point for such an SOA implementation.

Service-orientation requires loose coupling of services with operating systems and other technologies that underlie applications. SOA separates functions into distinct units, or services, that developers make accessible over a network in order to allow users to combine and reuse them in the production of applications. These services communicate with each other by passing data in a well-defined, shared format, or by coordinating an activity between two or more services. One can envisage SOA as a sort of continuum, as opposed to distributed computing or modular programming.

BI and an SOA converge when one views BI as an integral provider of business information. If BI is ingrained in an enterprise's "DNA" we see the natual drive toward integration of BI elements into an SOA. One example would be to create a common query with a BI tool and ensure it is used in all business processes that might require its results. Each BI element with an SOA becomes an object that offers a single version of the truth. We might also see the same thing done with a complex business report. It is created once, embedded into an SOA, and becomes the standard, common report for anyone wanting a view into the business produced by this report.

SOA...So What?

In the realm of BI, an SOA has several major implications that could be of great use to your implementation, corporate strategy, and the end users, as follows:

1. A BI service may provide a reusable component, such as a calculation or module, that enables consistent and well-defined attributes to be used across the enterprise.

2. It provides a set of standards, such as XML, that may be used within an overarching infrastructure, making BI elements easier to incorporate with other non-BI functions and applications.

3. SOA components are often characterized as embeddable objects, thus providing the capability to enrich other applications (for example, portals) with BI processes.

4. It provides a better integration platform for loosely coupled applications or, in the case of BI, where multiple BI tools may exist and could benefit from interoperation.

Every BI vendor has information on how they define and implement an SOA. As standards emerge and are refined for the exchange of information and services, it opens up a wide array of choices for you in your BI strategy. Being able to call upon a suite of services and interoperate them or replace them with a new function is a very powerful capability.

There are various degrees of service and depth of embedding capability available. Some BI architecture (platforms) offerings provide a comprehensive, extensible, and integrated suite of functions built from the ground up. Some have taken the approach of rapid acquisitions and a loosely coupled suite. Some provide the capability to create modules as services that can be easily embedded into other processes (web applications) without having the entire infrastructure installed. From an SOA purist's view, the smaller, embeddable architecture is more attractive, as they offer the option of dispersing a particular BI function with far fewer systems resources involved.

This is an area that is primarily the responsibility of the IT department. The end users will usually go comatose during the first few sentences of an SOA discussion. So, if BI is a joint venture between IT and the business units and end users, does an SOA aspect have that much relevance in the end? The answer is yes, but someone must present the elements that an end user needs to be aware of and possibly be excited about.

For the end user, the fact that a service can be isolated, embedded, and widely used can be a huge benefit. The capability to perform a mix and match of functions within a variety of interfaces such as a corporate portal can be another huge benefit. Rather than try to win the end users over about the esoteric aspects and technology advantages of implementing BI as a part of an SOA, show them some examples.

IT has been keen on modularity and distributed applications for years. Those who dwell in the IT world for a living and have a hand in programming understand the advantages of being able to write reusable code. For the end user of BI applications, they need to understand why such a feature plays well in the long run. We discussed the concept of pushing calculations as close to the DBMS as possible. The BI user does not want to try to maintain a collection of objects (queries, reports, and so on). Once they realize that isolating a piece of BI logic within a single object is inefficient, they will begin to look for better ways to deliver a consistent BI layer.

If I have created a very efficient query and have tied it to a very valuable report that is of benefit to a wide range of users in the enterprise, I would deem it quite advantageous to be able to use it within a variety of other applications and scenarios. In this situation, the query/report is used as a service—a unified object. If there is a need to modify any part of the "object," you make one change and it is immediately applicable to every instance where it is used.

What I have found is that the advantages of a BI SOA implementation are more readily understood and appreciated by a more mature account that has more experience with BI, regardless of what the current mix may be. They have been there, done that, and have learned the pratfalls of having their BI processes too widely distributed and having key functions too deeply embedded in the BI objects.

Is SOA Practical for BI?

Mr. Lyn Robison of Burton Group blogged on October 20, 2009 in an article entitled, "Is BI Destined to Be Like SOA?":

Business Intelligence is a hot topic. Enterprises are spending large sums on BI initiatives. Unfortunately, BI projects are failing more than they are succeeding. BI initiatives typically do not deliver their promised benefits. I just saw a survey that says almost two-thirds of companies that employ BI are being barraged with complaints that the system isn't doing what they need it to do. Another survey undertaken by the National Computing Centre found that only 13% of BI projects undertaken in the United Kingdom lived up to expectations. This figure is mirrored by a number of other studies.

There are vendor SOAs and then those that clients try to implement on their own. For client SOA implementations, I agree that the majority of their efforts are shaky at best. Mr. Robison's article offers some hope as well as other opinions as to what causes BI failure. The client has the daunting task of trying to integrate a suite of applications, databases, and platforms with a widely dispersed set of users and preferences. It would probably be easier to enforce world peace than to pull all this together in some installations.

I will go way out on a limb here and suggest that the reason for the majority of these failures and shortfall is the lack of a corporate vision, lack of BI standardization, absence of a BICC, and the myriad of assumptions we've discussed so far. If you have a solid plan and infrastructure, a limited set of BI tools, and a competent support group, you can begin to rein in some of the anarchy and disjointed BI efforts within the organization.

SOA can be extremely valuable to an enterprise's BI strategy if they have a clear understanding of what the services actually are that are required. Dispersed and disconnected sets of users and BI applications are nearly impossible to organize as a set of services. Think of the commonly used credit card and/or bank account validation provided by so many vendors and institutions. Everyone who does any banking or purchasing on the Internet can relate to such functions.

In the BI realm, a service may be an embedded data mining scoring function or a customer sales summary. Much like the BI checklists we discussed in Chapter 12, "Intelligent Responses to an RFI/RFP and Setting Up a Proof of Concept/Technology," BI services need to be identified, agreed upon, and planned for. If you have three different sets of reports for a particular area that are created using three different BI tools, and there is no common ground, which of these, if any, do you target for a service?

I would opine that BI is only pragmatic for a vendor who is looking to provide a stack of tightly integrated features and functions, making their overall development efforts considerably easier. This is regardless of how successful the vendor's customers are with their vendor's SOA capabilities. For any client expecting a BI SOA to be their savior in providing a better approach to BI, it will not work if there is no tightly knit organization.

Getting Started with a BI SOA

An article and proposition that is far more positive than Mr. Robison's is one by David Besemer in *Information Management Magazine*, May 2007. Although it predates the more pessimistic viewpoint, Mr.

Besemer emphasizes the slow but emerging adoption path of SOA in the context of BI. In his article, he states:

> *Michelangelo once said, "Genius is eternal patience." For those of you who believe that service-oriented architecture (SOA) is genius, your eternal patience is about to be rewarded. According to software industry analyst David S. Linthicum, "Most activity around SOA has been limited to discussion, study, planning, and small projects. 2007, however, will witness a significant surge in SOA spending, as early adopters evolve proof-of-concept implementations into more robust deployments and late adopters buy into the architectural shift. SOA for business intelligence (BI) is following a similar adoption path, moving rapidly from prototypes and single projects to broader, enterprise-wide deployments. Where is your company on the SOA for BI journey? Have you done your planning and proof of concepts? Have you advanced your learning curve for both front-end BI services, such as reporting and analytics, and back-end BI services, such as connectivity, transformation, and integration? Do you have strategies for taking SOA for BI to the next level where SOA's interoperability and reuse benefits accelerate? Or, are you like many companies that are still unsure where to start?*

The questions he poses in the last sentences are extremely important. The last comment about being unsure where to start probably applies to the majority of enterprise accounts I have met with. First of all, if IT doesn't have a strategy for the overall corporate SOA, it is ludicrous to bring BI into the conversation. If IT has a strategy, it will heavily affect a BI decision. The most poignant element for the business and end-user community will be the corporate BI interface. I assume everyone reading this book has some opinions about and understanding of portals and user interfaces. As mentioned several times already, modern BI tools provide a variety of deployment options, including thin client interfaces with services and BI interaction using a browser.

In thin client architectures, the capability to embed services, mash them together, and otherwise provide a common means of connectivity are inherent to the overall framework. All functions and applications are rendering to a browser via an application server; thus, the very fiber of these interfaces involves a set of services. If you are using a BI tool and accessing it via a browser today, you are already using some of the basic elements of an SOA.

To quote more of Mr. Besemer's article:

> *SOA for BI covers both the front-end (visible to users) BI services and back-end (visible only to IT) BI services. More than half of the survey respondents planned to implement front-end query and reporting services by October 2007. In addition, approximately one-third of the respondents planned to implement other front-end services such as analytics, dashboards, and alerting during the same time period. Regarding back-end BI services, also known as data services, more than half of the survey respondents planned to implement data services for source connectivity by October 2007, closely followed by transformation and integration data services.*

In the two years between the two articles cited, there is a great disparity in opinion as well as enthusiasm. If I weigh in with personal experience, I have to take somewhat of a middle position. The uptake of BI SOA technologies is less than most would like. However, we have not seen the death knell of BI or SOA, as some would have you believe. The problem has been no strategy, no plan, no buy in, and hence no BI SOA.

To continue with a little more of Mr. Besemer's opinion, he suggests that a narrowed focus for a BI SOA is the best approach. I wholeheartedly concur. He states that the best way to avoid known pitfalls is to narrow your focus. This includes looking at it from several angles, as follows:

- **Department focus.** Do not try to make SOA for BI work for the entire company out of the gate. Focus instead on one line of business or department (customer operations or finance), which has been listed as the highest priority. Once this department or line of business is successful, others will happily follow.

- **Project focus.** Within a department, pick a project or two that you can slightly overstaff, providing enough slack to work through your learning curve. Again, once you have several successful projects, other project leaders will apply this new, now-proven approach.

- **Staffing focus.** Select team members who like to try—and later evangelize—new technologies and approaches. Because the BI for SOA technology is relatively easy to learn and use, these attributes are more important than specific technical skills. And make sure these pioneers can stay focused on SOA for BI for at least 18 months to allow their expertise to develop and evangelism to spread to other projects and departments.

- **BI services focus.** Do not try to execute on both front- and back-end BI services at the same time. Although the survey seems to show a slight preference toward front-end BI services, focusing on the back end first is actually the best place to start.

In Chapter 14, "Implementation of Business Intelligence Solutions," I discussed implementation concepts and recommendations. If you are setting a course for BI SOA implementation, the same rules apply. You have to prove that your concepts work and that they have value.

Scott Morrison is quoted in eBiz on the "SOA in Action Blog" on September 20, 2009, as follows:

> *The handkerchief is a great idea; you can wash it and reuse it over and over. But despite this, nearly everyone—myself included—uses Kleenex. It's just more convenient. The only handkerchiefs I own go into the breast pocket of my suit.... Software reuse is also a great idea and a worthy goal. The truth is, though, it rarely happens in real life. Copy/paste/edit is just too fast and convenient, even though it's easy to make good arguments against doing so. I suppose it's a sad reflection of the disposable mentality that runs throughout modern society. I see a similar pattern in SOA all of the time. Everyone leads with a story of reuse; but reuse takes a lot of discipline, commitment, communication, process, organization, and even time to do well.*

Discipline is lacking in the majority of BI activities. One way to get a tremendous boost in creating and evolving a BI SOA is to build a tighter partnership with one of your approved BI vendors. As I mentioned earlier, BI vendors are all committed to their own SOA as a means to develop a modern, extensible platform. They will have been through many of the steps required to deliver an effective SOA and will have a set of best practices, service offerings, and procedures.

This is different than having a BI vendor come in and perform all your BI work for you. This is a case where they will provide invaluable expertise on how best to set up your BI environment, establish guidance for BI services, and set up BI components for reuse.

BI SOA Frameworks

Originally published on November 19, 2007 in BeyeNetwork, Richard Skriletz wrote the following regarding a successful SOA/BI convergence:

How then should the BI/SOA convergence be visualized? Every organization should diagram a reference architecture that shows the critical objects, relationships, and associated technologies within the IT environment, including legacy and emerging technologies. Looking solely at SOA and BI and data delivery, this reference architecture should include the framework for:

- *From an SOA perspective, the services, services management, and services integration broker components should be included.*

- *From a BI and data delivery perspective, the enterprise reporting, dashboard and metrics, data quality management, data integration, master data, and enterprise data warehouse components should be included.*

- *From a convergence perspective, there are critical areas where SOA and BI and data delivery come together: (1) the meta-libraries for metadata and meta-processes; (2) the business rules engine repository of data and application rules; and (3) the enterprise data structures of the single, highly normalized, enterprise transaction data store and, where this is not the only application data store, the organization's master data.*

There has always been a tension between process and data, and SOA and BI are no different. To be successful, the proper vision of how SOA and BI complement each other and how they can be managed successfully must be developed and reference architecture produced. Without one, one or both of these technologies can be misused and impair the IT organization and its support of the business.

I opted to cite a number of others in this chapter as there are widely varying opinions and articles on BI/SOA. I agree that there is a reason to be cautious about SOA implications regarding BI, but I also feel there is enormous potential. I encourage you to explore this venue while treading with caution. Think of the typical BI environment where there are a slew of BI objects created but not tracked or managed. How many of these objects are valid or accurate? Would you like to make it easy for the creation and embedding of a series of BI services throughout the enterprise that have not been validated or may be suspect as a service?

On the other hand, some BI work is very complex, and when a particularly challenging calculation or object has been completed and is worthy to be shared and reused, why not do so and increase the value of your BI investment?

As much as collaborative efforts among individuals within a BI framework is of extreme value, collaboration among BI objects may be of equal or of greater value. In situations where you have multiple systems, multiple tools, and multiple outputs that will all be in existence for some time to come, does it not make sense to provide them as a service such that they may all be used as well as viewed within a common interface?

Sometimes we forget that beneath all the glitz and glamour of BI tools and solutions, we are dealing with the normal computer issues and elements as much as anyone else in IT; we just have an easier way to access the system and its resources. We also have the opportunity to either create havoc or to provide extreme value for many within the enterprise to take advantage of.

One example of a well-established BI/SOA is the acquisition of Cognos by IBM. The portfolio keeps expanding thus an illustration here would be of little value due to the dynamic changes that have taken place. However, the concept of an SOA by both IBM and Cognos (pre-acquisition) was one of a well-defined, layered approach with key elements as follows:

- Data layer: at the base of the stack we must be able to define, access, and expose all possible data sources such as relational, OLAP, unstructured, and more.

- Metadata layer: there must be a common definition and view of the underlying data with a clear differentiation between the technical definitions and those exposed to the end users.

- Application and Services layer: all the functions one might wish to use. In a BI context this would include the query interface, the reports, etc.

- Presentation layer: once any BI process has created meaningful output, it is essential to deliver it to any user in a wide variety of formats and styles.

From an SOA perspective the stack is composed of a set of services that deliver BI results. The single query I mentioned earlier is an executable service. It may be used by a variety of reports or other output producing option but is, in itself, a self-contained entity ... a service.

Summary

The merger of an SOA and BI services makes perfect sense. However, we are treading on new ground in many cases, where we are beginning our new BI quest while we are trying to define, refine, and implement other enterprise technologies, such as our SOA.

In the definition and implementation of a BI SOA, we find the need for more collaboration than ever before among all key players. We have the business units and end users trying to build BI solutions in cooperation with IT, as well as dealing with the vendor(s) delivering BI tools and possibly services.

Opinions regarding the current state of the art in implementing BI SOAs and customer successes widely vary. I would suggest paying more attention to the success stories and less to the statistics about success or failure. Obviously, there are some very productive and well-done BI SOA examples, so the quest is to see if you can model one of these.

An undated article on eBiz by Christina Torode states the following:

> Companies are missing the boat on SOA success if they're spending millions of dollars on a service-oriented architecture only to use it for application integration alone, analysts and practitioners say. Rather, today's SOA success stories are in wider-reaching business process management (BPM) initiatives where, in some cases, even IT becomes organized along business process lines.

I have mentioned portals, mashups, and end-user interfaces as key elements of an SOA as well as any BI solution. Let's get out of the deeper functional areas of BI and take a look at user interface styles. The typical BI user is mostly concerned with what appears "on the glass."

16

Enterprise Portals, Mashups, and Other User Interfaces

A portal is considered an entry point into some area or world. In the technology world, we view an enterprise portal as a window into a myriad of points that could reside anywhere in the world. Touch points could be internal or external and provide a wealth of information from a wide variety of sources.

Wikipedia defines an enterprise portal as this:

> *An **enterprise** portal, also known as an enterprise information portal (EIP) or corporate portal, is a framework for integrating information, people, and processes across organizational boundaries. It provides a secure unified access point,{1} often in the form of a web-based user interface, and is designed to aggregate and personalize information through application-specific portlets. One hallmark of enterprise portals is the de-centralized content contribution and content management, which keeps the information always updated.*

When you have been provided with a window on the world, what would you point it toward? If you could use it as a collection point that may provide connectivity to systems that have a number of things in common or a reason to tie them together, what might that look like?

The Enterprise Portal—Its Purpose and Potential

A portal might be considered the most intelligent and useful application of Internet technologies. Today's modern portal interface is through a browser. In the realm of BI, we look at a portal as the potential integrator of a wide variety of data sources, BI functions, and collaboration services. All BI vendors offer a portal in some shape or form. The major players—IBM, Oracle, Microsoft, SAP, and others—offer significant interoperability within their own stack and frameworks.

Portals have become commonplace and widely used in recent years. A few years ago, they were still considered a bit on the fringe of technical society, but just like web browsers are so universally accepted, portals don't have to be thought about very much...they just *are!*

Most BI tools have morphed from the days of having a closed and proprietary interface that seizes the entire screen. Today, although most offer their own portals, they also provide the capability to use their services within an array of portals and support a variety of web browsers.

I refer back to our discussions on BI standardization and want to emphasize that a standardization project extends beyond the BI tool itself and encompasses other technologies such as portals, browsers, application servers, and office systems. If you have set a hard and fast standard in one area that your BI tools are required to support, this criteria must be part of the evaluation process. The best BI tool on the planet is of little use if it does not interface with the other enterprise technologies.

In the Wikipedia definition of an enterprise portal, there is a reference to portlets. These are "pluggable" user interface software components that are managed and displayed in a web portal. They are reusable web modules that run on a portal server. Portlets have predefined roles, such as retrieving news headlines, searching a database, and so on. I think of them as just another web service.

You will also see the term "applets." These are programs designed to be executed from within another application. Unlike an application, an applet cannot be executed directly from the operating system. I think of them as applications within an application.

I have used the term "embedded" with BI services. It is possible to provide a BI portlet or applet that may be reused and embedded within another application or as part of a portal. If the BI service is deemed "enterprise ready," it may be added to a growing library of rich functions providing a service to many users and applications.

I mentioned Operational BI a few times. In an operational sense, you might embed a report that profiles a customer's buying record and more to present to a customer service representative within a portal. If the report contains some sophisticated metrics and calculations and is deemed 100% accurate, you now have a valuable BI service available for use globally.

There are portals that capture the entire screen and those with a variety of elements (windows) presenting many areas of interest. To reference two that I work with closely, in IBM, we have Cognos with its own portal called the Cognos Connection. It provides an open interface to other web services but is intended to provide a collection and launch point for Cognos objects. IBM also has WebSphere® Portal that can also be used by Cognos and others to provide a collection point for a wide variety of services that have no product or functional centricity.

Figure 16-1 shows a few portal examples. There is no magic about these particular images; they are just to illustrate a portal can take on nearly any shape, size, or content. Key words such as embeddable, linkage, and so on are associated with portals due to their capability to partition the glass and present a wide variety of output and objects upon it.

In the Web world, there is often an enriched view of many other sites that may or may not be related and cross-references used from site to site. This logical (and sometimes illogical) collection of sites and information are very common today. What I see emerging within many clients are portals that extend beyond internal borders, as well as extensions on intra-organizational borders. Many organizations offer self-service portals that allow the users to define what they want to see within their own, customized view in order to either connect common objects or simply for convenience.

However, let's think about what we would like our BI portal to be able to do for us and how we would like it to function to optimize our interactions with BI tools and other technologies. In a more perfect portal world, we would be able to tie together common functional threads, such as being able to track a competitor as we develop and launch a new sales campaign.

Portal Examples

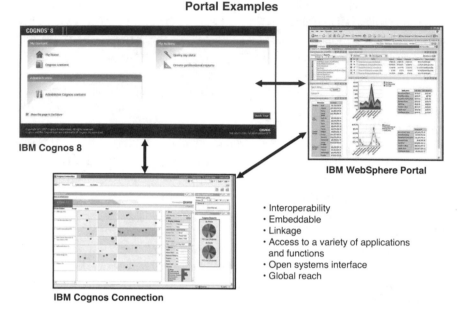

IBM Cognos 8

IBM WebSphere Portal

IBM Cognos Connection

• Interoperability
• Embeddable
• Linkage
• Access to a variety of applications
  and functions
• Open systems interface
• Global reach

Figure 16-1 Portal examples

Looking at the objects in our "ideal BI portal" (see Figure 16-2), it would certainly be nice to have all of these items wired together or "mashed" into a cohesive application. Perhaps we want to have our RSS feed monitored to send us any news item on the competition by email. If the situation warrants it, have an alert posted in our portal.

We have an event being tracked that performs a periodic search on not only our competition but other key business factors. The search results are posted interactively by level of importance. If we need to schedule a meeting, we have a live calendar to view and interact with.

Our personal interaction with BI is centered on the screen, and we've given it a bit more space than the rest of the desktop. Other BI feeds are active but created by others, and we have just embedded them within our personal portal. More and more effective and creative use of portals is being made by clients who view these technologies as a means to provide the ultimate application integrator without having to write interface code. If a value presented in the pie chart shown in the upper left of Figure 16-3 can be used to feed the graph in the middle, why not "wire" them together?

The Weather Underground Portal

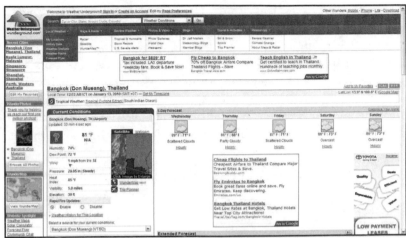

Figure 16-2   The ideal BI portal

The Ideal BI Portal

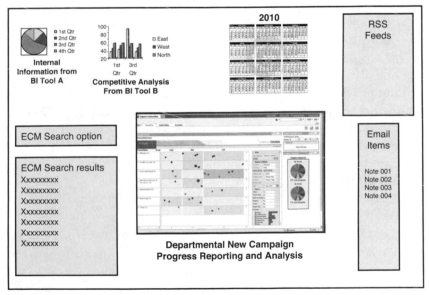

Figure 16-3   Mashups compared to portals

We used to be excited about object-oriented programming, where individual objects (services) could be defined independently and then wired together later. Wiring today is the capability to take one object and connect it to another without having to be a programmer. BI offerings today enable you to do things such as drag a query result on top of a chart type and instantly generate a graph based upon the values. I still think of object-oriented types of applications when I ponder wiring today. The end users can create their own connectivity given the proper application architecture. We often refer to this capability as a "mashup."

Mashups–A Perfect BI Delivery Model

Wikipedia defines a mashup as follows:

> *In web development, a **mashup** is a web page or application that combines data or functionality from two or more external sources to create a new service. The term mashup implies easy, fast integration, frequently using open APIs and data sources to produce results that were not the original reason for producing the raw source data. An example of a mashup is the use of cartographic data to add location information to real estate data, thereby creating a new and distinct web API that was not originally provided by either source.*

Mashups are considered a step above and beyond the traditional portal architecture as much of the new functionality is based upon Web 2.0 capabilities. I have heard people use the mashup term and portal capabilities interchangeably. This is technically incorrect, but what they are trying to convey is the sense of putting two or more things together and presenting them within a common interface.

To explore Wikipedia's definition a bit further:

> *Mashups and portals are both content aggregation technologies. Portals are an older technology designed as an extension to traditional dynamic web applications, in which the process of converting data content into marked-up web pages is split into two phases: generation of markup "fragments" and aggregation of the fragments into pages. Each markup fragment is generated by a "portlet," and the portal combines them into a single web page. Portlets may be hosted locally on the portal server or remotely on a separate server.*

Portal technology defines a complete event model covering reads and updates. A request for an aggregate page on a portal is translated into individual read operations on all the portlets that form the page ("render" operations on local, JSR 168 portlets or "getMarkup" operations on remote, WSRP portlets). If a submit button is pressed on any portlet on a portal page, it is translated into an update operation on that portlet alone ("processAction" on a local portlet or "performBlockingInteraction" on a remote, WSRP portlet). The update is then immediately followed by a read on all portlets on the page.

Portal technology is about server-side, presentation-tier aggregation. It cannot be used to drive more robust forms of application integration, such as two-phase commit.

Wikipedia also provides a handy table to highlight the differences between a mashup and a portal, as shown in Figure 16-3. So, I have beaten the formal definitions topic senseless. What does this have to do with your BI strategy?

Portals, mashups, embedded applications, applets, portlets, and all the "modern" web-based technologies will play a huge role in the future of BI. In many clients, I do not see a great deal of cooperation between the BI support folk and the Web and infrastructure team. This is a big mistake.

Understanding BI in the Context of Portals, Mashups, and Collaboration

I recently had a client ask me if I could provide any references for customers who had successfully implemented BI within a portal environment. I must admit that I looked at him as if he had two heads and a large wart on his nose. You really do not have a choice here. This is where technology overall is going and where you have to spend some time in research.

Several years ago, one of the early ventures into the mega-collaborative portal space was IBM with its IBM Workplace. This isn't a book about IBM, but I use their examples because I have spent the majority of my professional time in IBM and have been intimately involved with IBM technologies.

IBM Workplace began in 2002 when IBM announced its Java EE-based "NextGen" initiative, which evolved into the Workplace initiative in 2003. The first Workplace component announced was Workplace Messaging followed by more Workplace applications.

Then, Workplace 2.0 was announced in 2004 with a myriad of features and both rich client and thin client (browser) interfaces. The continued evolution was driven by the customer desire to integrate applications with collaborative services. IBM has made so many innovative moves in this space that Workplace has become passé in favor of going back to the roots of its core brands, such as Lotus and WebSphere, where these integrated and collaborative functions are part of the overall infrastructure. This led the way to even greater innovations, such as cloud computing, where clients sought to not only deploy large numbers of BI end users but also wanted a full-function collaboration suite (email, messaging, integration of BI and events, and so on).

This is what all major BI vendors are striving to deliver. So, from your perspective, it is essential that you take a survey of some of your technology stack and decide how best you will meet your portal, mashup, collaboration, and BI co-requisites.

Here I go again with another checklist, but sometimes it helps to have a list of topics or items to ponder as you move forward with any project:

1. What is your corporate portal strategy; are you committed to a single vendor or suite?
2. Are you exploring Web 2.0 and its advanced features, such as mashups?
3. Do you consider your portal strategy, DBMS strategy, web-enablement strategy, and BI strategy to be parts of a common, interlocking infrastructure?
4. Do your BI tools support your current web browsers and vice versa?
5. Do you have a documented support plan and roadmap from your vendors?
6. Would you willingly change any of the associated components (application server and so on) if they did not support BI, or do you not consider them to be co-dependent?
7. How well does your current email and collaboration software (instant messaging and so on) interoperate with your BI tools?
8. Does your existing portal infrastructure support your office and collaborative software?

9. Can you easily merge and interoperate your BI tools with collaborative services?

I raise these issues due to the emerging awareness by many that due to the way we work today, there is a crying need to make collaboration far more interactive and real-time. In the BI realm, we see a drive toward data delivery that is as up to date as possible. In the world of collaboration, we strive to provide immediate feedback systems rather than rely upon the phone or even email.

Instant messaging systems have gone from being "quaint" to where they are a necessity. In my current role, we use a piece of collaborative software where I can see if people are online (provided they haven't managed to define themselves as hidden) and send them an interactive bit of text. If I have an urgent need to talk, I can do so in a few clicks and short bits of text. If I see they are not online, I can send off an email or call and leave a voice message. If someone is in Do Not Disturb mode, they still see my message and can ping me back if they want or do so once they are fully available.

I have had a worldwide responsibility role for years now. I had to learn to be very creative in dealing with others in different geographies, time zones, and so on. It used to be a personal art form to do such things, but now I have the tools I need. I have ways to access others on a global basis interactively. I can attach notes or place objects in the chat window for them to review and much more. Without such functions, I would not be able to do my job.

In your environment, it helps to map out how you want BI to operate. Once you have produced a bit of information that must be shared, do you want to immediately notify them yourself? Would you rather have some sort of trigger or alert set on their end so when new or changed news arrives, the onus is upon them to review it? Do you want to receive notification as to whether they have bothered with the information or not? Do you need an IM in order to provide real-time interaction? If so, how well do your BI tools work with this facility, if at all? The list can go on and on.

The point here is that BI today is no longer about creating reports, charts, and other output with no linkage to others. Information that is relevant to the business must be shared. You will see this emphasized more and more as people awaken to the new synergy paradigm emerging within BI.

Jeff Kelly posted this on DataManagement.com on July 7, 2009:

From Facebook to Twitter, social networking has changed the way people communicate in their private lives. And with the continued adoption of collaboration software in the enterprise, it is starting to do the same in their professional lives, letting workers share documents and brainstorm new ideas.

The next frontier for collaboration software could be its convergence with business intelligence (BI) applications. Web 2.0 tools like blogs and wikis, vendors and industry analysts agree, have the potential to dramatically expand the reach and effectiveness of BI and data analytics throughout the enterprise.

Technical challenges lie ahead, but so do potential benefits, such as giving workers the ability to easily share and interact with BI reports and analytics. Vendors like SAP and Microsoft say embedding interactive business intelligence reports and ad hoc query capabilities into collaboration software will increase the speed of decision making and make the decision-making process itself more transparent. Employees will be able to share that information easily and quickly in different departments and divisions.

"We really think collaborative software can take business intelligence to the next level," said Mani Gill, vice president of SAP's Business Objects OnDemand division. SAP last week announced an OEM partnership with Jive Software in which Jive customers will have the ability to embed SAP Business Objects interactive reports, dashboards, and search capabilities in their Jive collaboration portal.

These interoperable functions are no longer "nice to have" but need to be part of how your enterprise looks at BI and its overall infrastructure. The more globally dispersed you are as an organization and the more you deal on a global basis, the greater the need for speed. Of late, I have had a lot of requests to work with individuals and clients in Asia and the Pacific.

The vast time differences make it a challenge, to say the least. If I am working late, I can have live chats with my cohorts far away, and there is always the ubiquitous email capability. Both sides in this equation are learning how to be more effective in communicating information more rapidly. A 24-hour turnaround is too long for many of the project items we have in play.

Summary

You cannot separate your web and portal and collaboration and BI infrastructures. What you ought to be doing, if you aren't already, is taking a long, hard look at the advantages you obtain with the marriage of the new web-based technologies in relation to BI and set some goals in place.

If you are headed for a course where there will potentially be vast separation among these major elements of your corporate infrastructure, some hard decisions have to be made. What does the future hold for you if others have embraced the modern, exciting collaborative features and functions while you are still attaching reports to email? Maybe your environment is set up in such a way that you realize that it would take too much effort and too many resources to make desired changes and that the way you operate actually works well despite some limitations. We all have to face reality.

However, if you have not considered the ramifications of portals, mashups, and similar technologies within your enterprise BI strategy, it's time to do so. Communication is an art form, and in the corporate world, it requires tact, a joint purpose, and an urgent need to remain on top or try to outdo those who are above you. It also requires a willingness to act as a mature individual and be ready to accept bad news with grace.

The colossal misunderstanding of our time is the assumption that insight will work with people who are unmotivated to change. Communication does not depend on syntax, or eloquence, or rhetoric, or articulation but on the emotional context in which the message is being heard. People can only hear you when they are moving toward you, and they are not likely to when your words are pursuing them. Even the choicest words lose their power when they are used to overpower. Attitudes are the real figures of speech.

—Edwin H. Friedman

17

An End User Survival Guide

I started this chapter as a white paper and thought that some parts of it might be good for the pure end users who have purchased this book. Please keep in mind this is a pragmatic view for end users and not one of telling the user how wonderful it is going to be. I would call it a more somber approach rather than pessimistic. The user should be very excited about getting involved in such ventures as learning a new BI tool or creating a new business solution. It is not helpful, however, to just assume any level of ease of use or lack of complexity going in. I hammer away at setting realistic expectations of the skills you will have to develop and will reinforce this throughout.

If you have previous experience with any BI tool then most of this chapter will not be a surprise. If you are not a technical end user it is intended to provoke some thought but not to be a discouraging chapter. The worst experiences I have had in BI are those where the end user expectations were so high going into the project and later had their hopes dashed on the rocks of technology because they were not properly prepared to take on the project.

Remember your first encounters with any user tools such as a spreadsheet or even a word processor? Simple, straight forward tasks were easy to learn and to apply. More complex operations such as calculations or formatting values took more time to learn and to use. I would encourage you to please take a deep breath, sit down with someone who has some exposure to the tool(s) if possible, and get some insight into the work you are about to undertake.

BI Basics

The siren song of being able to do your own BI with little or no assistance from IT continues to be played on the world's stage. The attractiveness of BI is due to the huge potential it offers in being more informed and more connected, and of outracing the competition. The frustrating side is that despite the promise of ease of use and self-service query, reporting, and so on, it remains just out of reach for many who would find it to be a game-changing offering.

Business Intelligence efforts require skills, tenacity, a willingness to experiment, and time...often lots of time. Time is one commodity that we can never renew, so it is imperative we use it wisely and productively. The single greatest shortfall in the majority of BI environments is the end user with great plans and dreams but little or no skill and inadequate time to invest.

If you are a potential user of any BI tool, I ask you to *please* be painfully honest with yourself and very carefully assess the time and energy you have available to spend with any tool. In particular, if you are not a particularly technically savvy individual, your honest evaluation of what you are willing to invest in BI will be critical. The typical fallback when someone can't handle BI and its nuances is to blame the tool. Blaming the IT department comes a close second, followed by the vendor. You are dealing with corporate data and computers; it isn't like working with an email system or a video game, and it often takes work.

In particular, if your enterprise is about to embark upon a journey with new BI technology, you may not want to be among the early adopters of the technology. If you have an urgent or specific BI requirement and cannot wait, this section may help you engage in a manner that will make you more productive, faster.

We have seen a swing away from "fat" workstation-based tools to a more streamlined thin client infrastructure, where all that is required is a browser and the proper connectivity to the network. In this new technology era, the end user must rely more and more upon an IT staff that is competent and sensitive to their needs.

To create a simple report, the user must invoke the browser interface, log in to the appropriate network, log in to their BI environment, access data that has been authorized for their use, create a query based upon values provided to them, view their results (assuming success here), format and mark up their report, and finally run the report. The interactions may vary from tool to tool, but this is pretty much what occurs.

What if you attempt to log in and are denied access? What if the data you expected to be there just isn't visible? What if the response from your query is very, very slow? What if the report fails right in the middle of making some changes? What if the network is simply unavailable for access?

In the steps just mentioned, I didn't touch on the network traffic and "chatter" involved in such a scenario. There is simply a myriad of elements involved in today's BI world compared to the past. In the "old days," you could get a BI tool installed on your workstation and, if given access to the data on the back end, you could do a number of BI activities with far less assistance and complexity.

Ease of Use, Leprechauns, and the Yeti

I have listed three myths in the preceding heading. Why do I place ease of use in the list of myths? I pulled this from an old customer request form. The author and actual customer is long lost to posterity:

> *Wanted: A Business Intelligence tool that is intuitively easy to use; it can access all my data efficiently, and requires little or no training. It must interoperate with Excel as well as run on all platforms supported within our enterprise. It must also integrate within our corporate portal, ERP system(s), and our CRM system(s), and allow us to use our office systems to collaborate among users both internal and external.*

Does such a product exist? Well, in theory, there are several solutions out there that fulfill this wish list. There are, however, words within the paragraph that are wide open to interpretation. Terms such as "easy to use" and "interoperate" convey different things to different people. What may be easy for you to use may cause me to take my laptop and try to set a new world's record for technology flinging. What most people want is a BI tool analogous to the "Easy" button you see in some television commercials.

Given this enigmatic scenario of ease of use versus rich, deep function, what can end users do besides take their best shot at selecting a tool or set of tools that may deliver the value they believe to be at the heart of BI solutions? If you had any experience with BI technology and were less than satisfied by this encounter, you might want to take up a chant based upon a popular song by The Who: "We won't get fooled again!"

Any BI tool will prove to be valuable given the proper amount of skill and accurate input data. As a guitarist and sometimes guitar instructor, I have found that BI is a lot like playing the guitar. Everyone wants to be like Eddie Van Halen without putting in the time.

Interacting with BI Tools and Features

The overwhelming majority of functions used in BI have to do with query, reporting, and business charting. This has not changed much from the earliest days of end user computing. Why? Business users have wanted to produce their own information and results for years. The age of waiting for someone to write a COBOL program to deliver results are long gone. You'll often hear the term "self-service" reporting used.

The dilemma in delivering self-serving BI output lies with the underlying data, the options available within the report writer and charting software, and the complexity of the business problem. Any modern reporting solution offers a view of the user data (often referred to as metadata) and a palette upon which to drag and drop values. Let's look at a simple query and reporting request using a fictitious BI tool.

The user wants to create a summary of sales and costs for each department in the business. The BI tool and interface looks something like what is shown in Figure 17-1.

Figure 17-1 depicts a simple query and reporting interface that is quite facile for an end user. The screen area on the left shows the data elements that are available to drag onto the palette and the area at the top contains BI functions (typically mini-icons) to apply against the results. One of these would usually be an option to summarize and group values such as creating a summary of sales and costs for each department. Most people can deal with BI at this level.

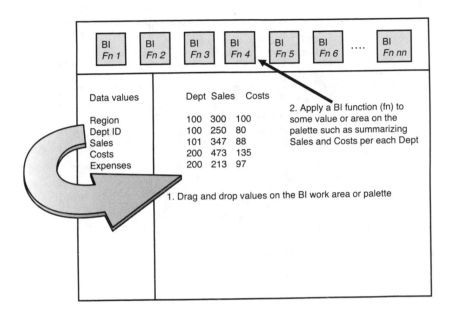

Figure 17-1   The BI tool interface

Now let's expand the business problem just a bit. One dimension of most queries is that of time. Comparative operations are the nature of most BI efforts, and they will almost always involve time. The typical BI analytic will require some contrast between or among values based upon time, such as this month versus last month or this period compared to the last. Then there is the added concern of "What if?" on top of comparative analysis such as, "What if we increased a value by xx%?" or some similar query.

In our simple query scenario, we are just querying data and performing a simple operation. What if the request were more of the type where the request is to show which departments have exceeded sales by at least 15% by month the past year, yet have kept costs at no greater than some standard percentage?

When you get to such a scenario, there are no mini-icons available to specify several of the conditions. If there were, they would fill the screen, and the work area would be the size of a postage stamp, as depicted in Figure 17-2.

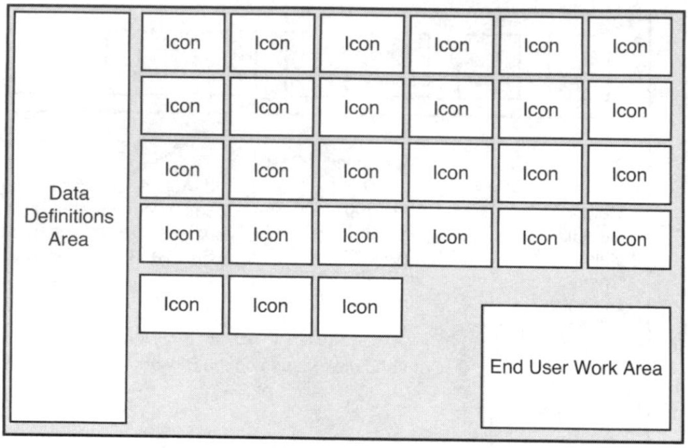

Figure 17-2   The "ideal" user interface

Figure 17-2 illustrates the "ideal" user interface where all features and functions are visible. Obviously I am being a bit facetious here, but not too much so. BI vendors have had to pile on extensions to their wares to keep up with others. The more you add, the more the users have to wade through.

So, one question from end users that comes up eternally in a sales cycle is, "Does it do _____?" The BI vendor inevitably will say, "Yes it does." The question then becomes, "How do you actually perform this feat?"

You will not see the term "easy to use" in definitions of BI outside of a vendor's materials. Wikipedia does not use this term in its definition of BI. Sellers are not being dishonest; they are just not going to tell the user they might have to actually learn some deeper skills to perform this magic unless asked. Refer to Chapter 12, "Intelligent Responses to an RFI/RFP and Setting Up a Proof of Concept/Technology," regarding RFI/RFP scenarios and PoC/PoT projects if you want to stay out of trouble.

NOTE

For a little eye opener on this, go to Google and type in "Business Intelligence ease of use." You will see that the major players in this space all pop up, touting ease of use. It is the brass ring all aspire to grab. It is a Herculean effort on the part of some. The simple fact is, Business Intelligence is just not easy due to the nature of the business problems it is attempting to address.

The manner in which a BI vendor opts to provide such functions varies widely. Some offer mini-icons, and some provide a right-click function; some provide pop-up options or pull-down menus. End users can sometimes be their own worst enemy when it comes to deciding the appropriate BI tool based upon how it performed a few functions. This becomes particularly endemic when a course has been set to replace Product A with Product B. No two products look and act the same, and you can spend a lot of time trying to get the new tool to look and act like the old tool.

The BI Skills Conundrum

One investment that will apply to all cases of BI tool usage and deployment is the need to develop the appropriate skills to get value from your investment. Let's explore the skills necessary to effectively use any vendor's BI tool.

In the selection and purchasing discussions, there has been a request for skills development for the end users. Skills learning can take many forms depending upon the offerings provided by the vendor. You may have classroom options, or computer-based training (CBT), or online tutorials. In cases where there is already some in-house expertise, peer-to-peer sessions may be offered. Any or all of these may be effective, or they may only serve to frustrate or alienate potential users.

CAUTION!

If you rely upon peers to provide education and skills, you could be at significant risk. It is most certain they mean well, but they have a bit of knowledge they have either acquired on their own or from someone else. There is no guarantee that this is the best practice for performing a specific task. I have seen numerous situations where a particular function being applied was far from the most efficient means that could be used. Once a stream of product knowledge begins to flow, the tendency is to perform something that way because it is the only way to do it. Quite often when new releases are made available, new functions or easier ways to perform a task are lost because "this is the way we do it" rules are applied. Climbing 20 flights of stairs is good for your heart, but it's a lot easier to ride the elevator.

So Who Are You?

I discussed BI roles in Chapter 6, "The Impact of Business Intelligence on Roles within the Enterprise." Remember that BI users come with a variety of needs, skills, and expertise. The first hard-core question you need to ask is, "Who am I really in the world and scope of BI within my organization?" Right at the start, you need to identify the type of user you are or would like to be. The technicians and heavy hitters in BI within your company have probably already been identified. Then there are those who have a desire to utilize BI tools to their advantage and are involved in the process out of desire or hoping they will benefit. You may even have been assigned to this with little choice. No matter, but in any case, you have some degree of expectation about what your experience will be.

To avoid therapy sessions and public humiliation, take a moment to write it down and ponder exactly what you believe your BI interactions and work will be. Is it something you would show to a peer or is it a bit of a wish list? Let's say for argument's sake that your foray into BI will be to use a new query and reporting tool to create some new information that would make your weekly planning a bit more orderly and allow you to predict some areas where trouble may lie ahead. A self-assessment might look like this:

- I am a business analyst with significant experience in my particular unit. I have had extensive experience with the creation and usage of spreadsheets in the past. I have had some interaction with databases and a couple of tools but mostly from a simple interaction perspective.

- I am not database literate. I do not really understand how our data is stored today other than I have seen some schematics of data in our enterprise and have a sense of what the names of the data elements are that we will be interacting with.

- My logic and mathematical skills are quite good, but I have never written a program unless you consider an Excel macro or formula to be a program. My BI goal is to produce some reports and charts we have needed for some time. It has been impossible to access the proper data using a known tool like Excel, so we have been involved in our new BI tool search.

■ I am absolutely swamped in my position, and even if I get access to a BI tool and produce this sorely needed output, I only have an hour per day, maybe, for a week or so to devote to learning the new tool. It is my expectation that the BI tool will not require extensive hands-on experience beyond the introductory training we have planned for.

Remember our discussion about ease of use? Here is where the majority of end users tend to get into trouble. The first mistake, and usually the biggest, is that assumptions are made about how easy a particular task will be given any BI tool. Remember, the right answer from any vendor addressing the ability of a product to perform a task is "yes." From the end user perspective, the key question you need to ask is "how?" The one you need to avoid is "why?"

Many end users have some familiarity with some tool, and invariably they want to launch a diatribe about, "Well, I worked with Product ABC, and all I had to do was ...." Then go buy ABC and justify it to your enterprise. Otherwise, keep in mind that the one now being used is NOT Product ABC, and there will be differences. Get over it!

What should be foremost in your mind is what the value may be in applying a particular tool to perform your work more easily and efficiently and how it will advance your career and your company's position in the market—period. If you get all glassy eyed about how much easier this new "thing" is going to be, you will be setting personal expectations that will not be met.

Think of all the new options available in many automobiles today. One we see more often is a built-in GPS device. I have not found a GPS system today that is so intuitive that you just hit the "easy button" and arrive at your destination. I have not found one that will drive my car for me to my destination. I have to apply some basic driving skills as well as open the manual to use a GPS most effectively. Yes, for the men out there, I am suggesting opening a user manual and that you ask for directions...go figure?

So, you want to be a BI user and abuser? Well, the first thing you have to do is assess your own skills and the time you have available to invest in learning enough to be dangerous. Swain Scheps wrote a book in 2008 called *Business Intelligence for Dummies* (Wiley Publishing, Inc.: Indianapolis, IN), which is 384 pages long. He segments the various elements of

BI in concise paragraphs and topics as most of the *For Dummies* books do. Think of reading 300+ pages as a "dummy"! BI is not simple; it may or may not be easy. Let's take a look at skills development and how to do so in an orderly fashion.

BI Skills Assessment

In Figure 17-3, we are making some quantitative assumptions about the time required to acquire skills based upon the type of BI function required for an individual whose responsibility will be to **create** results and objects with a BI tool (queries, reports, and so on).

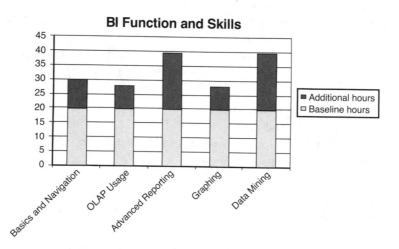

Figure 17-3 BI function and skills

Most BI tools provide a similar but slightly different UI for each major BI functional area. It may not take 20 hours of work on the baseline UI, but then again, to be a savvy navigator with a good grasp of the major functions, this is probably not an exaggeration. The area shaded for additional hours will be the time required to develop proficiency to the extent where experimentation within a functional area will feel "comfortable."

HINT

One function that is absolutely invaluable for any BI tool is the Undo operation. If the undo facility provides a "walk back" to a previous state for several changes, this is even better for the end user. Experimentation is encouraged when you can be "forgiven" for a previous action. In this manner, you can try something and walk back to where you were.

End users within a classroom environment often find it difficult to admit that they just do NOT get it when a topic has been covered, or they assume they'll pick it up later. The instant you use a function and do not understand what you did or why you did it and do not stop and clarify, you are paving the way to personal "BI Hades."

No one wants to appear to be the resident "dummy" in the group and will often remain silent while others seem to breeze through an exercise. Oh, the danger there! We are all different in so many ways, and we all learn differently. Things that may be inherently obvious to you may seem like rocket science to us. And the converse is also true.

In some situations, there will be an individual incessantly asking stupid questions. I have been involved in product training for many, many years and for many, many products. When facing a situation with someone who just cannot quite seem to get it, there is no easy way to tactfully address this. Either we have a real novice on our hands who has little or no technical skills, or we have one of those people who may have experience in something else and is one of those, "Why does it do this like this?" types. It's always tempting to give them a name tag that reads, "Hi! My name is _____ and I am a professional pain in the _____." But I digress....

If you are NOT a technical individual, your experience may be very frustrating at first. Even if you are technically oriented, you will probably encounter some areas where the BI tool seems quirky in how it performs some function.

Here is a checklist that may help in setting expectations for yourself and anyone who has deemed it necessary that you gain skills for a particular tool. For the sake of establishing a baseline, I have indicated whether a task is basic (rudimentary), time consuming but not too challenging, or difficult (typically skills intensive). Your involvement with any BI tool will be highly dependent upon your role within the organization:

- **BI tasks requiring rudimentary to moderate skills**
  - Basic query creation (no if-then-else logic)
  - Basic report creation (no additional logic required)
  - Business chart creation (no additional calculations required)
  - Interact with OLAP data sources provided (not create)
  - Personalize a portal page for self-use
  - Utilize data mining output
- **BI tasks requiring moderate to heavy skills**
  - Queries requiring if-then-else logic (beyond what can be dragged and dropped on the palette)
  - Advanced reporting with calculations
  - Advanced business charts (additional calculations and formatting)
  - Create data-mining scenarios
- **BI tasks requiring heavy to significant skills**
  - Data modeling
  - OLAP cube creation
  - ROLAP (Relational OLAP) cube creation
  - Complex data joining beyond what has been provided in the metadata models provided
  - Creating data mining algorithms/analytics

The list of skills and functions may be expanded exponentially, but you get the basic idea. It has been our experience that it takes around 20 hours of hands-on work with a BI tool to gain some degree of comfort where navigation and options are not a rude surprise or a mystery.

The additional deeper functions and features will require more work, and we highly recommend that you explore the classroom options available to you. A truly intelligent enterprise will make their users obtain this hands-on training on-site with data that is identical in definition and approximate value as the data they will actually work with. When a user encounters their actual data in form and format during training, the challenges they will face in providing meaningful BI output in-house will be dramatically reduced.

CAUTION!

Part of any meaningful BI quest within an enterprise should be to negotiate for education and skills building in-house. This is an area where the typical enterprise will cut corners and reduce their BI effectiveness dramatically. Keep in mind the 20-hour baseline of learning time to attain basic BI familiarity and semi-competence. Whether the learning experience is done by trial and error or formally, the 40-hour baseline would hold true. If the potential user's cost to the enterprise is $200/hr. (salary and internal costs), we see the 20-hour cost for skills development equals $4,000. Note that 20 hours of formal training and learning on your own are really not equal in value.

If you were to allow 10 individuals to "take a stab" at learning on their own, you are now looking at $40,000 of internal cost with no guarantee of success nor of having all 10 users wind up with equal skills. You can certainly budget for quality and consistent training for a reasonable amount of outlay and reap the benefits of your BI tool expenditure earlier.

HINT

Use the following to perform a Google search for end user skills: *how long to train Business Intelligence users.*

Do You Have a Standard for Naming BI Objects?

Let's say someone sends a report to you embedded within an email notice. It has been sent as a PDF document. Upon reviewing the report, there is something that captures your attention that warrants further investigation. Let's also assume you do not have access or authorization to run either the BI tool or the specific report.

The creator may have embedded information in the body of the report, such as the name of the report or creator. Or, they may have only sent a report that has excellent formatting, a title page, date created...and the information contained therein. A week later, the creator decides to pursue a career elsewhere. Now you have a dilemma:

- What was the actual report name?
- Where is it stored?
- Who else can run it, if anyone?
- What database(s) does it access?
- Are there significant BI calculations embedded?

Some enterprises are better than others at capturing and documenting metadata about their BI objects. In many cases, however, the creator will opt for producing a "pretty" report with the appropriate attributes for their end users. What about your Excel spreadsheet documentation?

In most installations, someone has enforced some standards about spreadsheet usage, such as creator, location, version, and so forth. We suggest that you do the same for each and every BI report created by any tool—the heck with beauty. Most BI tools enable you to create a header and footer section. In such cases, the footer section may be a great place to add this documentation. There are typically system variables that may be used, such as userid, date, or time (think Excel again). Make this part of your overall BI walkthrough process

It is stunning how many installations do not require a standard for naming objects that have been stored for reuse. It is not uncommon for someone in IT to wake up one day and decide the library of objects needs to be cleaned up. They have seen a large number of BI "things" lying dormant for quite some time that do not appear to be used anymore or used infrequently.

Sometimes BI objects remain in place for fear that removing them would cause someone grief, but no one is sure, so they are kept "just in case." If it was important enough that an enterprise acquire BI technology and use it, then it is important that there be a process of naming for reuse and possible retirement. This ought to be part of your contribution to the white board sessions. It will have an impact down the road for both you and IT.

White Board the Data Sources and Combinations

So, you either have data that is ready or data that may require some massaging. You may even have an intended data warehouse or data mart project proposed, but it is in the early stages of discussion. If you can, convene a working session where the data you believe is required or desired will be discussed.

I know it must sound as if I walk around with a white board and pen in my pockets, as I have emphasized this endlessly in previous chapters, but it works. If you do this at several stages along the way in your BI quest, you may save yourself and others huge amounts of time that might have been wasted.

As shown in Figure 17-4, have a discussion just about the data. Such sessions are intended to identify the existing sources being considered and whether it needs additional work, such as an ETL (Extract, Transform, and Load) routine or set of routines. You will be far more productive and far less frustrated if you do so.

Initial Project Scope, Skills Acquisition, and Actions

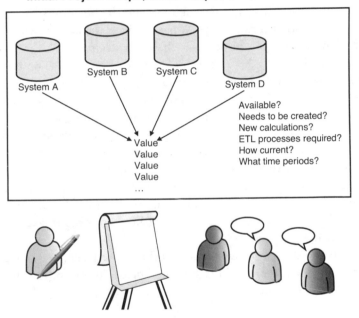

Figure 17-4 Initial project scope, skills acquisition, and actions

A reminder from our department of redundancy: One of the key elements of your BI infrastructure will be to determine how great a gap exists between the data values you will be provided and the number of calculations you and your peers may have to perform. If you discover a consistent pattern of a set of calculations, you need to discuss your source data with IT again. It is counterproductive and risky to have so much BI output dependent upon calculations being performed in Reports and so forth.

Summary

Your destiny with BI is in your hands; equip yourself with the understanding regarding ease of use, skills, and a realistic view of how you can deal with BI. Depending upon the degree of involvement you have had in the BI project, the end result will be that you are presented with a tool, its interface, and a means to access data that has been provided for you to try to produce BI output that is beneficial to your role within the organization. What if your first encounter with the combination of data and tool is less than rewarding? What if the data is not provided in a manner that enables you to perform the tasks desired?

Something is wrong here...the tool seems to be "ok." The user interface is such that you feel confident in being able to drag data onto the BI palette and perform some basic reporting. The moment you try to do just a wee bit more, the options and features become a blur, and after fiddling around a bit, you are stumped. Just when you began to feel like a BI dunce, you called a peer and found out that they too were struggling. Is it the BI tool, is it the data, or both? Every major BI provider works very hard to produce an offering that is efficient, robust, and appealing. Even if the vendor is also the provider of the database being accessed, they have little or no control of how your organization sets up the data for use.

With all the things thrown at you in these many chapters, would it be beneficial to provide a checklist for some of the more important BI elements? Please read on....

18

Checklists for BI Planning

Checklists are not intended for use as supreme sources of arbitration or definitive responses to BI activities, such as RFI/RFP responses, but are intended to itemize some of the more salient points and tasks necessary to properly set up and evaluate a project. I consider any BI work to be a project, even if it is only a single query and report. It is being produced for a reason and needs to have some business value associated with it.

I want to break up such lists into a variety of functional areas and levels within the enterprise from the top to a more granular approach. It has been my experience that you may overlook an item if it isn't on the list, but you won't when you have to put pen to paper.

As an additional comment and bit of advice, I would highly recommend that you develop and deliver your own checklists. I see many cases where one client will 'borrow' from another as they believe the other person has one that is more complete. It is more important that you develop one to your satisfaction and that it fits your specific business needs. Be sure you have agreement with the elements that are the most critically important to you and the business users.

Checklists should be created as a joint venture and should be reviewed from time to time by all parties. Every time a new BI venture is to take place, it is in everyone's best interests to review the list before starting. Chances are that someone has had an even more brilliant thought to add since the last time.

An Enterprise Checklist

At the enterprise level, I have discussed suitable approaches for RFP/RFI projects as well as PoC/PoT projects, so I want to keep this at the level where all interested parties would be able to reply "yes" or "no" and dig deeper later. These are areas that should be addressed at the enterprise level.

The purpose of providing checklists for any area is obviously to be able to make a case for your state of readiness and commitment to any of the items on the list. The goal is to have as many items checked off as "yes" as possible. If any are checked as "no," someone has to be involved to ask the hard questions about why we had to check the "no" box and what to do about it next.

- **BI mission overall**
  - Do we deem BI to be mission critical at the top levels of the enterprise?
  - Do we have a corporate BI vision statement and plan that is agreed to by all parties?
  - Do we have a corporate definition of BI that is agreed to by all parties?
  - Who are the primary units driving BI initiatives and who are their executive sponsors?
  - Do we have an approved vendors list with clear documentation as to why they have attained that status?
  - Do we have a formal process for RFI/RFP requests?
  - Do we have a formal process for PoC/PoT evaluations?
  - Do we have an enterprise BI support plan and infrastructure?

- **IT and business unit agreement**
  - Do we have buy-in from both sides?
  - Have they met and agreed to a specific plan, methodology, and implementation?

- Have both sides clearly agreed upon related costs and responsibilities?

- **BI tools standardization**
  - Have we settled on a single or reduced number of vendors?
  - Who are they?
  - What is the ROI?
  - Have we performed a cost/benefit analysis?
  - Do we have a justification document?
  - Have we identified all appropriate executive sponsors?
  - Do we have an implementation plan and roadmap?

- **Platform considerations**
  - Will we utilize internal or external resources?
  - If internal, do we have adequate staffing?
  - Have we identified and planned for an effective skills transfer set for all involved?
  - If external, do we clearly understand the costs and agility factors for our specific needs?

- **Server consolidation**
  - Have we weighed the pros and cons of mainframe versus distributed platform options?
  - Have we performed a thorough ROI study?
  - If we have opted for the mainframe, do we have a plan for measuring systems requirements and issues of scalability?
  - Have we weighed all cost factors, such as staffing, power consumption, and so on?

- **Data issues**
  - Have we settled on a set of DBMS vendors or a single vendor?
  - Have we validated their roadmap with our own plans (SOA, ECM, and so on)?
  - Do we clearly understand all business issues around periodicity of data refreshing, updates, and timely access?
  - Have the end users been scheduled for a white board evaluation?

- **BICC**
  - Are we committed to a BICC?
  - Have we defined and approved a budget?

- Does the BICC have a fully worked-out implementation and support plan?
- Do we have the proper staff or do we need to acquire one?
- Have we assigned management for the BICC?
- Do we have job descriptions for BICC staff documented, agreed to, and posted?
- Do we have unilateral buy-in for the BICC plan and associated responsibilities?

The Business Unit Level Checklist

At the business unit level, we enter the first areas where there will actually be some work accomplished. This level of involvement is really the make or break part of BI. The individual BI applications are targeted at supporting business units. Should they fail, then the rest of the BI infrastructure is a moot point.

- **BI mission overall**
  - Do we have an executive or management sponsor?
  - If an RFI/RFP is involved, do we clearly understand our role in it?
  - Are we actively engaged in PoC/PoT projects?
  - Do we have a unit definition of BI and the primary projects we believe will be of benefit?
  - Have we identified, validated, and documented our expected ROI?
  - Have we assigned individuals to elements of BI projects with a clear definition and understanding of their roles and responsibilities?
  - Do we have an approved budget for these projects?

- **BI tools usage**
  - What are the tools we will employ?
  - Who will use what tools and why?
  - Have we met with IT to discuss and map out data access strategies?
  - Have we defined how to liaise with the BICC, assuming we have one?
  - Have we committed to the proper education roadmap and timetable?

- Do we understand how support works with IT, the BICC, and the vendor?
- Do we have an implementation plan and roadmap?

- **Education and training**
  - Do we have a documented and agreed-upon education and skills acquisition plan?
  - Do we have a trained expert at out disposal (internal, partner, vendor, and so on)?
  - Do we clearly understand how the product(s) work that are involved, such as how data is accessed, what areas may be more difficult, which options may be slower, and so forth?

- **Data issues**
  - Do we know how to interface with our data?
  - Do we clearly understand the mapping between how the data is stored and the metadata definitions?
  - Do we clearly understand all business issues around periodicity of data refreshing, updates, and timely access?
  - Have we scheduled a white board evaluation with IT?

- **BICC**
  - Have we met with the BICC?
  - Do we have an agreed-upon implementation and support plan with the BICC?
  - Do we understand how to interact with the BICC?
  - Do we have documentation and project status reports as part of the plan?
  - Do we have a project database to store them in?

If a business unit is uncomfortable answering in the affirmative to any of these items, then someone better step way back and ask for a review of the BI plan. Not only do you lose the key users with a poor plan, but you will end up having many more people from multiple areas spinning their wheels for naught.

A BICC Checklist

As the BI professionals in the organization, you ought to have a comprehensive set of documented goals and processes. I will not delve into these here, as it is more important to look at how you can respond in relation to the rest of the enterprise and their evaluation of you.

If you are not confident in the perception others have of your efforts, it's time to get your executive sponsor and management team out prowling the hallways and making some calls. Sometimes the way a BICC is set up and promoted makes it appear to be a cost center instead of an innovation and profit center...big mistake.

- **BI mission overall**
  - Is the BICC included in the corporate BI vision statement?
  - Are you comfortable with the corporate perception of the BICC and its mission?
  - Do you have a fully worked-out implementation and support plan?
  - Do executives in other areas meet with the BICC management team regularly and provide positive feedback?
  - Are you and others comfortable with key measurements surrounding the BICC such as costs, revenue generated, productivity, and so on?
  - Are you the primary interface for BI tools in the enterprise and with BI vendors?
  - Are you adequately funded, and do you have a clear growth plan that is agreed upon?
  - What are the primary units driving BI initiatives and who are their executive sponsors?

- **BI tools**
  - Do you have highly skilled individuals for the tools you support?
  - Are they comfortable with their performance and growth plans?
  - Do you have adequate testing facilities for new releases?
  - Have you had a major hand in vendor selection and interaction?
  - Do you have the type of relationship with IT that nourishes cooperation and growth?

- Do you have well-documented and agreed-upon processes for introducing new projects and products?
- Are you satisfied with support from IT?
- Are you satisfied with support from the vendor(s)?
- Do we have an ongoing implementation plan and roadmap?

- **Platform considerations**
  - Do you have adequate BI platform skills?
  - Does IT have this as well?
  - Are you encouraged to provide education for platform-specific skills if needed?
  - Have you been forced to embrace a platform that you do not believe to be optimal for elements of your solutions?

- **Data issues**
  - Do you have the proper DBMS skills in the BICC?
  - Is it easy to interact with IT over data-related issues such as access to information?
  - Do you possess the correct authority levels and data access to serve the end users properly?
  - Are you involved in data issues to the extent that your opinions matter and are listened to?
  - Does your staff possess the skills necessary to work with IT and end users in data access and required output white board sessions?

- **Growth areas**
  - Do you feel the enterprise is committed to the BICC? Are we committed to a BICC?
  - Internally, are you considered
    - A cost center?
    - A revenue generator?
    - An innovation center?
    - The hub of enterprise BI?
    - An education and skills resource?
    - Only an evaluation group?
    - One of the "hot" new areas of the business?

An IT Checklist

So, you in IT are the ultimate arbitrators of much of the BI work that takes place. Sometimes IT involvement is far too heavy-handed to have a positive influence on the enterprise. Sometimes IT is held at arm's length, or they remain there on purpose, having been burned before. And sometimes the degree of involvement is just right. This reminds me of the fairy tale about the Three Bears!

Depending upon how you are structured, BI projects and coverage can be a real positive experience and can lead to reinvigorating your career with the opportunity to work in more business-related areas.

You know the technology side; there is no need to lay out all sorts of "geek" check items here. What is important from an IT perspective is to remember that you are dealing with people with horrendous differences in skills and interests. If you do not have a BICC, you will have to provide some support in areas that seem so obvious to you and so oblivious to the end users.

- **BI mission overall**
  - Do we deem BI to be mission critical at the top levels of IT?
  - Do we have a corporate BI vision statement and plan that is solid from an IT perspective?
  - Do we have a corporate definition of BI that includes IT's role?
  - Does IT have the proper level of support among the business user executives?
  - Do we have effective communications with the primary units driving BI initiatives and their executive sponsors?
  - Do we have an approved vendors list with clear documentation as to why they have attained that status?
  - Do we have a formal process for RFI/RFP requests?
  - Do we have a formal process for PoC/PoT evaluations?
  - Do we have an enterprise BI support plan and infrastructure?

- **BI tools standardization**
  - Do we have an approved vendors list with clear documentation as to why they have attained that status?
  - Have we documented why they deserve to retain this status?
  - Have we performed an impact analysis on our systems, the network, and other ancillary costs, such as power and staffing?

- Do we have an implementation plan and roadmap?
- Do we have documentation that describes how specific tools work?
- Do we know how to scale and secure our BI tools and usage?
- Do we have a tested and proven backup and recovery plan?

- **Platform considerations**
  - Are we adept in the platforms selected to support our BI infrastructure?
  - Do we have adequate staffing?
  - Have we identified and planned for an effective skills transfer set for all involved?

- **Server consolidation**
  - Have we weighed the pros and cons of mainframe versus distributed platform options?
  - Have we performed a thorough ROI study?
  - If we have opted for the mainframe, do we have a plan for measuring systems requirements and issues of scalability?
  - Have we weighed all cost factors, such as staffing and power consumption, with the platforms under consideration?

- **Data issues**
  - Are we comfortable with giving the access to data being requested?
  - Is the security of our data access audit-proof?
  - Have we validated the BI roadmap with our own plans (SOA, ECM, and so on)?
  - Do we clearly understand all business issues around periodicity of data refreshing, updates, and timely access?
  - Have the end users been scheduled for a white board evaluation with IT involvement?
  - Do we need to do anything new and different for data loading, refresh, backup, and so on?

- **BICC**
  - Are we effectively working with the BICC?
  - Do we have clearly identified mapping of product support for IT to provide the proper amount of assistance without getting swamped?
  - Do we meet regularly with the BICC?

- Do we provide product information updates to the BICC for elements such as the following:
  - Defects fixed?
  - New vendor information?
  - Bugs identified?
  - New release information?
  - Testing of new releases?
  - Performance and benchmark plans and schedules?
- **BI vendors**
  - Are we comfortable with the approved (or used) vendors?
  - Do we thoroughly understand how their products work?
  - Do we get quality support?
  - Do we feel we are provided best-practices guidelines?
  - Do we meet with our BI vendors on a regular basis?
  - Are we satisfied with the amount of interaction our vendors provide to our end users?
  - Do we feel we are getting the proper amount of value from our vendor's offerings?

Summary

As you can see from the checklist items, the emphasis here is upon elements of the bigger picture. I refer back to Chapter 12, "Intelligent Responses to an RFI/RFP and Setting Up a Proof of Concept/Technology," on the topics of RFI/RFP and PoC/PoC activities, where I have recommended tying the checklist items there to more expanded information, such as making sure there are specific user requests to match to a required function.

The checklists provided here are higher level in nature to encourage you to discuss them in depth with others and to come up with an honest, open assessment of where your organization and your area of BI coverage happen to be.

I was working with a customer at one of IBM's Briefing Centers where there was an opportunity to walk through some of the elements I listed previously with a couple of their key executives. It became slightly tense at times when we discovered many of the obviously important items were met with a negative response. One of the executives

broke the ice by finally just laughing and admitting that their position-
ing of BI as mission-critical rang a bit hollow in light of their loose
commitment to it.

Use these lists as a starting point. Any and all elements that you feel
need to be added or modified are welcome. Remember that the purpose
here is the honest assessment of where you really are with BI at the
enterprise level.

BI will continue to evolve and expand. What might we be looking at in
the future as far as features, functions, and new technologies? If you do not
have a solid BI plan and continue to approach it in piecemeal fashion, your BI
world will only get worse. Now is the time to carpe silica...seize the glass!

19

Speculation on the Future of Business Intelligence

If you are familiar with Johnny Carson of the *Tonight Show* on American television, he used to do skits on the air using various characters he had developed. My personal favorite was Carnac the Magnificent. Carnac would answer questions by first providing the answers and then opening an envelope that held the text of the questions.

In my 2003 book, *Business Intelligence for the Enterprise*, I predicted a lot more merger and acquisition activity, as well as greater platform integration and portal/collaboration work taking place in the BI space. Since then, we have seen a number of significant independent BI players absorbed by the mega-vendors. I have been tracking the portal/collaboration within the BI community, and all I can say is that it is hotter than ever.

I will use this final chapter to pull together thoughts and predictions from others I respect, as well as throw in my own feeble comments on the future of BI. There are several major trends evolving in this space, and they will all have an impact on your future involvement and success with BI.

Emerging BI Technologies

Kasper de Jonge posted on his BI blog on February 18, 2009 the following comments attributed to the Gartner group about BI in 2009 and beyond:

> *Gartner, Inc. has revealed its five predictions for business intelligence (BI) between the years of 2009–2012. Speaking ahead of the Gartner Business Intelligence Summit 2009 in The Hague, analysts' predictions ranged from the impact of business units exerting greater control over analytic applications to the effect of the economic crisis and how it will force a renewed focus on information trust and transparency to innovations such as collaborative decision making and trusted data providers.*

> 1. *Through 2012, more than 35 percent of the top 5,000 global companies will regularly fail to make insightful decisions about significant changes in their business and markets.*
> 2. *By 2012, business units will control at least 40 percent of the total budget for BI.*
> 3. *By 2010, 20 percent of organizations will have an industry-specific analytic application delivered via software as a service (SaaS) as a standard component of their BI portfolio.*
> 4. *In 2009, collaborative decision making will emerge as a new product category that combines social software with BI platform capabilities.*
> 5. *By 2012, one-third of analytic applications applied to business processes will be delivered through coarse-grained application mashup.*

This set of predictions certainly supports many of the topics and opinions covered in this book. One factor to note is the amount of total BI budget that will be held by the business units. This is primarily due to their driving need to apply BI to real business problems and not pay so much attention to the "geek" end of the spectrum.

I'd like to make this set of Top 12 predictions based upon what I hear from clients, as well as the many technology vendors I have worked with and had discussions with in recent months:

1. More enterprise uptake of DW and BI on System z as server consolidations and issues of scale and security increase in importance.

2. Greater uptake of Operational BI and supporting platforms due to requirements of real-time data access and driving BI down to more individuals in the enterprise.

3. Ever-tightening integration of metadata and data warehousing technologies with increased emphasis on BI-related functions by the mega-vendors.

4. A considerable number of new BI applications and usage revolving around the need to embed BI within composite applications.

5. Collaboration services held in equal esteem with BI analytics as the uptake of web-based BI suites increases.

6. Some acquisitions of the free-standing BI players occurring by ISVs who also own a DBMS of some sort.

7. More and more organizations continuing to invest in BI with SaaS applications or BI appliances if they do not have a solid enterprise BI strategy.

8. Web 2.0 technologies such as the use of avatars to do your bidding as part of search engines and provide a virtual person to search for relevant information

9. Unstructured data (XML) changing the face of BI and the data warehouse as we know it.

10. Information from multiple sources that is easier to access and analyze with a shift away from trying to move and locate all the information within a large, centralized data store. There is simply too much information in the world to do this and much of it need not be moved.

11. "Trendy" applications such as Facebook and Twitter slowly adopted into composite BI applications to enhance the global connectivity underway.

12. Excel remaining the primary user interface tool of choice. Advancements in its ability to scale to use greater amounts of data continuing to enable it to keep its dominance in the marketplace.

BI as we know it will change or be left in the dirt. More and more we see the interest and desire to use BI functionality dampened by the ongoing disparity of end user desire contrasted with ease of use.

Hugh J. Watson commented in *Business Intelligence Journal* (April 1, 2008):

It seems likely that future BI products will be more Google-like, providing a user-friendly approach for accessing structured and unstructured data. While BI professionals recognize that comprehensive decision support often requires access to both kinds of data, the reality in most organizations is that numerical data is organized in data warehouses and documents are maintained in content management systems, and there is little integration between the two.

What we are all waiting for is some radically new user interface to emerge that will take BI beyond its current state of usability. I mentioned the use of avatars as search drones for us within Web 2.0. I have been tracking audio query projects, hoping we will see the emergence of voice-activated BI query and usage. The dilemma with the voice-activated options is there is a heavy reliance upon local processing power in an age where everyone wants to "go thin."

There are wide disparities among BI players depending upon the level of usage and scale of their targeted client base. Stephen Swoyer wrote this on the TDWI website (December 9, 2009):

The influx of new players in the business intelligence (BI) and data warehousing (DW) segments has certainly made things interesting. Unfortunately, some analysts say, that's all these vendors have been good for. Once they're asked to show their cards, skeptics allege, they go bust—the vendors talk a good game, and they have promising technologies, but customer adoption (the yardstick of success) never takes off. Doubters like to point to would-be power-players-gone-bust such as LucidEra, Dataupia Inc., and (on the basis of fewer than half a dozen customers) DATAllegro Corp.

BI and DW upstarts are undeterred. For one thing, every BI or DW company worth its salt can point to a few customer success stories, and that hasn't always been the case. Half a decade ago, for example, DW pioneer Netezza Inc. was hard pressed to identify more than one or two named customers, while nascent rival DATAllegro couldn't produce so much as a single reference.

Furthermore, today's BI and DW entrepreneurs can point to customer success stories that purport to underscore the value—or the differentiation—they bring to the table. Their claim isn't just that their technologies add value but that their technologies add value by virtue of being differentiated from established offerings. Their offerings address needs, gaps, pain points, or cracks that established solutions ignore, address imperfectly (e.g., big square peg, not-so-big round hole), or simply omit, chiefly as a result of bloat or scope.

Take Lyza Soft, a BI newcomer that markets Lyza, an end-user-oriented analytic workbench. It's one of a handful of vendors that field "Workgroup BI" solutions (see http://esj.com/articles/2009/03/25/workgroup-bi-poised-for-a-comeback.aspx). According to CEO and founder Scott Davis, Lyza—like other end user-oriented BI offerings—targets the otherwise unaddressed requirements of real-world users. Davis has little patience for the hemming, hawing, or grousing of the data management (DM) establishment—the folks who tend to advocate a highly-centralized, single-version-of-the-truth-or-bust approach to BI and DW. In fact, such behavior has kept some kinds of users— particularly power users, analytic experts, and motivated self-starters—penned up and effectively constrained for far too long, Davis insists.

I submit that the main disparities among the BI players have to do with the fact that there are very few standards around the architectures, usage, objects, and the end user interfaces put forth by the major vendors. The common themes of master data management, metadata mapping, server-centric processing, and collaborative functions are first steps at creating a BI standard. IBM published a white paper in January 2009 based upon its Cognos segment and the initiative to create a BI standard in house. Other BI vendors will provide similar arguments and test cases.

As there is no industry standard for BI, we see a loose aggregation along interested party lines or competitive vendor lines. All BI vendors strive to keep abreast and pull ahead of their competition, and thus we have seen a number of parallel standardization plays.

My advice to you is to very carefully consider your options in light of your current infrastructure, as well as where you would like to be. There have been major innovations in BI with the emergence of in-memory analytics, rich reportlets (Flash, AJAX), advanced visualization, and predictive analytics, as well as the influence of Web 2.0 and social networking on business intelligence tools. At the end of the day, we are still creating queries, producing results, trying to predict things, and conveying our thoughts to others.

So, we see many innovations in BI, but are there some things that are missing? What are the "gaps" in BI, if any, given the current suite of vendors and offerings?

Technology Gaps

There is very little that I consider new in the BI space. There are very clever offerings and innovative technologies available that take some of the sting out of working with vast oceans of data and trying to make sense of it. However, there are some gaps in the BI space that I find irritating and inviting for those who see an opportunity to fill them.

The following gaps I list are in areas where clients have expressed a need, as well as a frustration given the lack of solution elements:

1. No universal BI standard. This leaves the market vulnerable to interpretation by any software vendor with a BI thought.
2. No new, hands-free query and output capability. Speech recognition or artificial intelligence software could make this possible.
3. Have we gone too thin with BI client? I believe there is a strong need for rich client technology that provides a deeper set of functions and allows a client to be disconnected from an application server and perform work.
4. Step-wise BI processes software. Some users like to approach a problem in stages and be able to reuse their steps. I want to run a query, have the software prompt me to see if I want to keep the intermediate results, and so on.
5. Mapping of BI metadata back to the database. Metadata flows from DBMS to BI layer relatively well, but if values are added at the BI layer they are not pushed back to the DBMS. Thus, there is a continued mismatch.
6. Universal exchange formats for BI objects. We all support XML, but why isn't there a standard format for query objects and so forth? Perhaps this is where open source solutions may emerge as key players.

And you may have others you can list. In a discussion with an ISV partner several years ago, they had a phenomenal idea of how to define BI standards such that a query from Product A could be dragged and dropped upon the report writer of Product B and so forth. The concept they put forth was extraordinary, but it also exposed the entire BI vendor community to the fact that they could not risk losing their market share. Plus, it would have opened up the market to a plethora of providers who might be able to create a better reporting engine and so on.

We will hopefully see better integration with MDM solutions and the metadata layer within all BI tools. The integrated suites we are seeing from BI vendors are improving, although there are vast differences in interoperability depending upon which vendor(s) you are talking to.

Another area that warrants close scrutiny is the disparity in platform support by some vendors. Despite the years of slow decline of the mainframe, it is returning with a vengeance and with innovative new technologies available for DW and BI. There aren't as many choices on the mainframe, yet but the portfolio is growing and having a wider choice of platforms should be a BI market driver.

Wayne Eckerson is a Director for TDWI Research. His keynote speech at one of their conferences is described as such:

> *"The future's so bright, I gotta wear shades," is a line from a popular 1980s song that could apply to business intelligence. When applied properly, BI functions as the senses and brains of an organization. It explains the past, informs the present, and directs the future. It plays a critical role in well-managed organizations.*

> *However, it's one thing to understand the value of BI and another to predict its future. Sure, we can rattle off a dozen technology trends that could emerge in the next three to five years, ranging from open source BI and software-as-a-service to real-time data delivery, decision automation, and predictive analytics. But to truly understand the future of BI, we must practice what we preach and understand business drivers first. To understand what will drive business in the next three to five years, and hence the kinds of questions executives and managers will ask of their data, we must first understand macroeconomic trends.*

> *This keynote will place BI in context of the changing global economy. It will also address how businesses may respond to new and changing economic and regulatory pressures. It will then identify the major themes that will drive the development of new BI solutions and the extension of existing BI applications. (Hint: more insights in less time at half the cost and double the return.)*

Mr. Eckerson's comments reflect several of the opinions expressed in this book. The greatest gap is the continued ignorance and overlooking of business drivers as a part of the BI process. BI vendors are constantly innovating and wringing their hands in frustration as they deliver new features and functions only to have their clients perform modest gains in users and usage. This is not the fault of the BI vendors; it is our collective fault for not demanding more of the industry and of ourselves.

Having been employed by large software development firms as well as having spent considerable time as a consultant, I can sympathize with the plight of the client as well as the vendor. If you want to see changes occur, then help drive them. If you have specific ideas on BI technology, then become an activist. There will always be gaps in technology, but they don't have to be the size of the Grand Canyon.

Trends to Monitor

Trends to monitor in BI are becoming more predictable. We have already covered most of them, but it might help to cover them once again at the macro level:

- **Integrated platforms by the mega-vendors: from data discovery to BI delivery:** There are a myriad of functions that need to be applied. Having an integrated suite is still the best option as long as the vendor's roadmap and stated directions are what you desire and they keep to their schedule.

- **Server consolidations:** We will see more movement back to platforms such as the mainframe now that they provide lower-cost options than supporting massive server farms.

- **BI tools consolidations:** Even if the economy is booming, it's time to pare down all those tools that are under-deployed and under-utilized. It is costly and inefficient, and lack of standardization keeps your environment.

- **Software as a Service:** SaaS is possibly the easiest way to implement BI, as you hand over the worries to a provider that has the skills, the resources, and the ability to scale. The dilemma is in being able to enact changes as rapidly as necessary, as well as the costs of working with a provider. These solutions are very good for limited and well-articulated BI projects.

- **BI appliances:** "BI in a Box" solutions work best if the data does not have to be critically up to date or the volumes aren't horrendous. If the data needs to be derived from multiple sources and requires substantial ETL, this may not be a suitable approach.

- **Cloud computing:** Subscription service BI may also be looked at as a form of SaaS. However, the newer BI clouds are more about rapid deployment that still provides a significant amount of independence for the end user. This is an area I find of particular interest, and in recent discussions with clients, there appears to be a substantial amount of interest in developing private clouds for BI.

- **Open source providers:** For those who don't see the need to have to work with a mega-vendor or are not concerned with the "iffy" aspects of dealing with open source code, there are many offerings to choose from. It is wise to consider these offerings a bit of a "wild west" in nature and not necessarily "cheap." You can still spend a lot of money on open source offerings and have far less control in the long run.

- **Web 2.0 mashups:** The cutting-edge aspects of Web 2.0, such as mashups and having avatars running amok in cyberspace doing your bidding, will be the most interesting trend of all. Some of the wild growth in this area has slowed a bit as the global economy took a downturn, but the payback in innovation and providing new value will keep this area moving forward.

- **Industry-oriented BI applications:** More and more, we see BI "bundles" where a vendor offers a self-contained solution that is oriented toward a specific business process. I foresee this as an offshoot of having fully integrated BI platforms, where the appropriate data warehouse and data delivery mechanisms are contained along with BI.

- **Unstructured data formats changing the traditional DW:** I have mentioned the many XML and beyond ramifications now that we have ways to define, identify, retrieve, and analyze new data outside the realm on the traditional structured warehouse. There are too many data warehouses built that house massive amounts of data that is never looked at. There will be a great deal of movement toward more on-demand and real-time data access beyond the scope of the traditional DW.

There are probably a few that you deem worthy that are not on this list. The ones I have listed are the ones I hear about most often, as well as the ones I hear about at conferences and for which I see announcements forthcoming. Trends are just that...trends. The only ones I take seriously are those where I see either enormous value or an inevitable move along that particular axis.

I often think of how client-server systems were all the rage and how the mainframe was going to be dead. So many grabbed onto this belief several years ago. Today, we see a shift toward thin client software and larger, more secure servers.

Responding to Trends

None of the trends or topics we've discussed amount to a hill of beans if they do not pertain to your environment or enterprise philosophy. As I've mentioned numerous times, you need to take a very careful inventory of what you have, what you like, what needs to be improved, and what needs to go.

If you have, for example, an environment where you have multiple BI tools and there is little you can do about it within the enterprise, you may not be able to do much to respond to trends. All efforts taken to standardize and pare down the tools have been met with failure, so the next best thing you can do is to make sure you have a competent BICC, where such products are well known and well supported.

If you have identified a clear vision for your BI futures and have narrowed down the technology paths you are interested in, you'll know which trends to track for your own success. One you cannot overlook is the overall trend toward thin client, service-oriented architectures, and embeddable BI options. These are common mega-trends with each BI vendor regardless of who they are or what their long-term intentions may be. Thin is in.

If you try to track all options and have no clear direction internally, you will drive yourself to the point of BI inertia. Regardless of how you implement BI, there are universal requirements you need to establish, such as how you will need to provide collaborative functions regardless of the BI technology.

Summary

I hope this book has been of value to you. This section on futures is nothing more than the toss of a dart in the end. I suggested several search criteria for some sections of this book. If you try to search for "BI trends" or "BI gaps in technology," you'll be disappointed in the resulting lists. You'll find a few who will venture forth to pontificate about the overall state of BI now and in the future.

The majority of futures articles will be those provided by vendors who have an obvious grasp on their own technologies, as well as where they want the market to go—sort of a self-fulfilling prophesy.

Now you have a destiny of your own to fulfill in the BI space. Either you have a solid plan or you don't. At this stage of BI within your enterprise, you do not have a massive amount of time to continue less-than-optimal efforts.

The volumes of data you will have to deal with will continue to grow exponentially. The pressure to compete as well as be concerned with what your competition may be using will increase. Features and functions will be added to existing BI tools, and platforms will continue to be enhanced.

Your critical moment for BI is now. To quote John M. Richardson Jr., "When it comes to the future, there are three kinds of people: those who let it happen, those who make it happen, and those who wonder what happened." In an earlier chapter, I asked you who you were in the scope of BI within your enterprise. In the terms of Mr. Richardson, "Which of the three types are you?"

Index

The New Era of Enterprise Business Intelligence

Using Analytics to Achieve a Global Competitive Advantage

Mike Biere

FREE Online Edition

Your purchase of *The New Era of Enterprise Business Intelligence* includes access to a free online edition for 45 days through the Safari Books Online subscription service. Nearly every IBM Press book is available online through Safari Books Online, along with more than 5,000 other technical books and videos from publishers such as Addison-Wesley Professional, Cisco Press, Exam Cram, O'Reilly, Prentice Hall, Que, and Sams.

SAFARI BOOKS ONLINE allows you to search for a specific answer, cut and paste code, download chapters, and stay current with emerging technologies.

Activate your FREE Online Edition at
www.informit.com/safarifree

> **STEP 1:** Enter the coupon code: LDRXAZG.

> **STEP 2:** New Safari users, complete the brief registration form. Safari subscribers, just log in.

If you have difficulty registering on Safari or accessing the online edition, please e-mail customer-service@safaribooksonline.com

Safari.
Books Online